# Dirty

# Dirty Leeds

Robert Endeacott

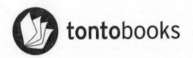

This edition published in 2009 by Tonto Books Limited
First published in 2009

British Library Cataloguing in Publication Data:
A catalogue record for this book is available from
the British Library

ISBN-13:
9781907183003

Printed & bound in Great Britain by CPI Mackays, Chatham ME5 8TD


www.tontobooks.co.uk

Dedicated to 'my girls' Sam and Sophie, who I met whilst writing this book and who made life that bit more complicated and wonderful.

# Chapter 1

## 1–1

Eamonn Andrews should have been a spy. How he manages to spring that bloody red book on his victims without them having a clue is like real *Callan* stuff. Big bloke he is too. I never realized.

Thirteen years and one month before, I'd been hanging around for ages waiting for Don Revie, freezing my small assets off. Thirteen years one month on, three or so miles away, I'm hanging around for ages for him all over again, but at least it's not cold tonight. And I've got proper trousers on this time.

My grandma always said Eamonn Andrews was dashing. Well, he was dashing tonight alright, all over the place, making sure it all went exactly to plan. Even I was on edge, and I had nothing at all to do with the programme or the sportsmen's dinner being held at the Queens Hotel. Yes, I'd been invited, but could I hell as like afford to hire a dinner jacket and chuffing bow tie. Ces didn't go either. John and Ray did, and John got on the television, right at the start of the programme, a big white smile underneath his big black Sean Connery moustache. He offered to pay for me to hire a suit and stuff, but I couldn't; I didn't like the sound of it all anyway, it was way too posh and snotty for me. Too many portly 'sportsmen' who'd never kicked a football in their lives. Counting money and chewing food's probably their only exercise. I'd have been right out of place, big style.

I stood around the hotel main entrance in City Square, thinking I'd definitely get my face on the telly. But I didn't. There was a kid already in prime position for the cameras. He got on the box alright, with his bloody parka and big autograph book, the little weirdo. Not that I really had anything against him for collecting autographs, I'd been exactly the same thirteen years ago, in 1961, when it all began. Up to March 1961 Leeds United were just a bad joke. I tell you, there were only a few of us who supported Leeds then, but we deserve a big bundle of credit for it.

Bored, I walked off for a cheap pint in the Scarbrough Taps round the corner. I was in a right mood, as dark as the streets around the Square: narked, feeling left out, lonely and a failure, nearly twenty-five years old, but knocking on sixty-five.

## 1–2

April, 1974. The Queens Hotel, Leeds. A special occasion organized by the chairman of the city's Variety Club, Marshall Bellow, to pay tribute to one of Yorkshire and England football's greatest achievers. It is a sportsmen's dinner, taking place in the vast dining room of the hotel. Famous names from sport, the media and the arts are here, with luminaries from the world of local business too. Some but not all of the men are in cahoots with Marshall Bellow in order to make the night an even grander event for their unsuspecting guest.

The Queens Hotel is white underneath its filthy, blackened coating. Connected to one of the country's busiest railway stations, it possesses a high reputation for the quality of its accommodation and restaurants. That reputation is preserved, despite the neglected exterior of the building. On the hotel steps stands television host Eamonn Andrews. A drone of motor traffic and a hum of voices indicate a busy Leeds City Square, though only a few members of the public are in camera range. One of those people, a teenage boy with lank hair, wearing a parka coat with a fur-edged hood, smiles at the camera and clutches a well-used autograph book. He has yet to get the Irish presenter's signature and will struggle to do for quite some time. And then Andrews receives a signal and it's time.

With microphone in his left hand, he talks to the camera – in a couple of nights his image will be addressing an audience of millions. His renowned brogue and those lilting tones, that most famous introduction, will charm and captivate the viewers of Great Britain and keep them in suspense for just a few minutes. Who is this week's famous victim?

'This is *This Is Your Life* ... Tonight we're in the north of England inside a hotel where a celebration dinner is about to begin. Although there are many famous faces, the man I'm after is only just about to arrive because he is the Guest of Honour of the Variety Club here at Leeds.

'Now, he's so respected and so well known that stars from many fields have come here to pay tribute ... There's "Man at the Top" Kenneth Haigh, soccer manager Joe Mercer, television personality Michael Parkinson, playwright and actor Colin Welland, that great character of showjumping Harvey Smith, and others ...'

Cricketer Freddie Trueman, footballer Derek Dougan, the 'Super Leeds United' team, wrestler-cum-actor Paul Luty ...

'But there's an extra guest – me, and this.' He indicates his microphone. 'I've got to move very quickly because he's on his way in now, and make sure I'm right behind him and his host Marshall Bellow as he's welcomed into that dining room.'

The oak double doors swing open on cue.

Inside the room, another camera pans over the seated, dinner-suited guests. It is packed. No spare seats tonight, folks. Long, white-clothed tables are lined up like in a canteen, with hundreds of men dressed to the nines seated around them. Others mill around on foot, anxious to find their places. Dinner jackets, bow ties, frilled and plain shirts, white and coloured collars, cuffs. Long hair, sideburns, moustaches, beards. Balding heads, some with hair combed over.

On each side of a tiny area at the front of the room are two small rows of cream, chic chairs for the *This Is Your Life* subject and his surprise guests.

Loud applause and boisterous cheering fills the room as the principal guest approaches. Eamonn Andrews is nowhere to be seen. Hiding. Quietly, unassumingly, Don Revie OBE enters, Marshall Bellow at his side. They pause at the door. Revie – wearing a dark blue dinner suit, yellow silk handkerchief peeking out of the breast pocket, big black bow tie over a proud frilled shirt – is momentarily wide-eyed with pleasant surprise at such a fervent welcome. The press cameramen request their shots. The television cameras don't perturb him – as the manager of one of the most successful football teams in the world, he is used to having them around. He is, though, rather embarrassed at all the fuss, though the enthusiastic applause continues regardless.

Behind him, a tall Dubliner enters the room, practically unnoticed. And to Revie's right, another dinner-suited man, uncannily like England footballer Bobby Moore, hands a new microphone to Andrews. Gesturing to the crowd to be quiet, he begins to speak into it.

'Gentlemen, gentlemen ... I know that you've arranged a very special night for your Guest of Honour ...'

Revie, until now oblivious, realizes an official is making an announcement. The voice sounds strangely familiar. His pleased expression turns to a mild frown, then to one of worry. Andrews now stands at Revie's side. Revie turns to look at him, and grins when he sees who it is, but the grin freezes as his eyes are drawn to a large, red book. He looks petrified.

Unperturbed, Andrews carries on. He's in full flow.

'... but I have your chairman's permission to add one extra touch and say ... Don Revie, tonight, this is your life!'

## 1–3

It was sometime in March 1961 and I was off school. I must have been waiting over two hours and my knees were tingling big time. In fact I think I'd lost all feeling there, I'd been in the cold that bloody long. I was hoping it'd snow to warm it up. It didn't. And I was the only one there.

Then it's *clack clack clack*, and it's about time too: the Leeds players and coaches after their training session on the Fullerton Park pitches. Slicked-back hair, black muck, dark looks, brown marks, no smiles. I had my little pale blue autograph book with me, nice and full of signatures. Too many to count: Freddie Goodwin's, Grenville Hair's, big Jack's, little Billy's, black Gerry Francis's. The backroom staff and all: Jack Taylor's, Syd 'IOU' Owen's, Les 'The Shocker' Cocker's, 'Smiling' Bob English's, 'Warm Face' Cyril Partridge's, Maurice 'The Gent' Lindley's.

And all the time I used to be thinking, non-stop, hoping and planning – *One day people will be asking for my autograph. Mine, one day, when I'm a Leeds player ...*

The rubbish you think when you're nearly eleven.

*Clack clack clack.* The best autograph in my collection was King John's, the greatest player ever to play for Leeds, for any

Yorkshire team most likely. My grandma took me all the way up to his house in Middleton to get it, it must have been 1957 or thereabouts. It was the furthest I'd ever walked – that hill was a right pain for my little legs and feet. 'Charlesy', *the* John Charles, actually came to his front door to see us and have a chat with us, smiling, ruffling my hair, stuff like that. He even gave me a banana. And the thing I remember the most, clear as day, is that he was a giant, massive, lengthways and across as well.

He signed my book *To Jimmy, Best Wishes John Charles*, and it's always been like a piece of treasure to me. I had other old, important Leeds players' too – Wilbur Cush, Georgie Meek and the nicest Jock footballer I ever met, Jimmy Dunn, who lived near us, just up the street opposite the Elland Road gates in the Heaths, lovely, big semi-detached houses with front *and* back gardens and sheds and garages and indoor toilets. The Heaths are like palaces compared to the Hoxtons where me and my grandma were. All the houses around there were redbrick. The Hoxtons bricks were more black and brown than red, because of the traffic and the factories.

There was one Leeds player's autograph I didn't have. Don Revie's. I'd never even had the chance to get it before.

*Clack clack clack.* The studs of twenty or so Leeds players' boots, down the crumbly steps from the Fullerton pitches. The team was doing rubbish and had just given manager Jack Taylor the push. Halfway down Division Two, we had no chance of promotion, but the way we'd been performing there was definitely chance we'd get out of the division – by relegation to the Third. There weren't many Leeds supporters any more, that's a fact, and this lot of players probably didn't deserve them anyway.

*Clack clack clack*, down from the pitches on to the black shale. I'd watched them train from behind the wire fencing at the top of the embankment. Any stray balls that came over, I was their unofficial ballboy, running up and down the hillock, whacking them back over the fence. I'd been fagging balls nearly all morning. Sodding sodden wet balls with the laces loosening, not in good nick at all, and weighing a ton, especially for a kid like me, a weed. And did anyone say thank you? Did they bollocks.

As the players made their way down the steps, I skidded down towards them. Crunch time for me. Them buggers didn't even look slightly cold, because they had layers of wool on over their training gear. It made them look like fishermen. Syd and Les had silly wool hats on and all, making them look a bit simple, in my opinion. Not that I'd ever let on: you didn't cross the Leeds coaches, I learnt that early on. They were right hard taskmasters and it wasn't worth upsetting them. Unless you were like Jack Charlton maybe, hating being told what to do and liking a quarrel or two.

The Leeds players, caked in cold, wet mud, training bottoms dark brown more than blue. And then I see him, Don Revie, and even he's got himself dirty. He must have slipped or been clattered or something because getting stuck in was never his style, he couldn't tackle for toffee. I homed in on him, my book poised, snaking my way through the others, dodging them like I was a sparring boxer.

'Don, Don … can I have your autograph?'

He didn't hear me, he was too busy talking to Jack Charlton. Or maybe he was ignoring me because I was being a bit impolite.

'Mister Revie, will you sign us this?'

He still didn't seem to hear me, they were still talking, arguing, in fact. Everyone always said that Jack could start an argument in a Trappist monks' monastery, or cause a fight in an empty room. He was cussing at Don Revie, dead angry, nearly shouting, on about not having a chip on his shoulder and Revie not being able to drop him from the team.

'You're not the bloody manager, so what the hell!' he said, and then peered down at me. For a split second he looked quite sheepish, but then just walked off, big giraffe strides towards the changing rooms.

I switched my attention to Don Revie again. 'Don … Mister Revie … can you sign us this?'

His face was red, and I realized it probably wasn't the best time of asking.

And then he says, right snotty, 'It's Mister Revie, pronounced Ree-vie.'

Everyone I knew had always pronounced it 'Revvie', not 'Ree-vie' – my grandma, Ces, John, Mr Hatfield, the radio. How was I to know? Maybe he was pulling my leg or putting an act on. Or maybe he was a weird split personality type. Or maybe he was just being contrary, depending on the weather or who he was talking to. I was confused – I often was – and a couple of the other players laughed, making me feel more embarrassed.

I only wanted his autograph for God's sake, so I asked again, right deliberate like, 'Can I have your autograph then, Mister Ree-vie?'

He didn't like that, it was obvious. 'No you can't,' he said, 'Come back when you've learnt some respect and better manners.'

And off he walked. Don bloody Revie or Revvie or however you bloody well pronounced it, miserable sod. He'd put me in my place, but it wasn't right, and I couldn't just let it finish like that.

I blurted out, 'I don't want it anyway – you're past it!'

He stopped walking. He turned around, gave me a right rotten stare. There was no one else around now and I'm suddenly worried I'm in big trouble.

'What did you say?' He didn't shout, but he was angry.

It was his fault I was annoyed, and I couldn't let go. I couldn't stop myself. 'Even my grandma says so, you're past it. *And* she's quicker than you!' Then I scarpered by him like a proper little coward, belting off up through the rusty gates, on to Elland Road. That had shown him. Well, not really. Not at all, in fact.

A hundred yards' sprint, by the petrol station and garage and the Old Peacock car park, past the terrace houses, across Wesley Street, round the corner into Hoxton Street where we lived. Washing lines were strung across the street, sheets and clothes wafting in the breeze, looking like an armada. Some hung their washing out most days, whatever the weather. Not my grandma though: wash day at our house was always a Monday, after work.

The smoke and fumes made me cough, as usual, and my throat and lungs throbbed from the cold air. I felt like I'd won a race but I had a chill churning in my stomach at the same time, like I was ashamed, like I'd done something very bad and which I'd live to regret. I was half worried Revie would try to find out where we lived. He'd know his way about our streets. Jack Charlton for one had lived here some time ago. Revie would be sure to tell my grandma so's she'd be able to bollock me as well.

### 1–4

As the *This Is Your Life* theme blares out, Eamonn Andrews leads Don Revie to his seat and into the spotlight. Revie feels more akin to a prisoner being led to the dock. He sits down and crosses his legs, leaning forward like a man awaiting excruciating dental treatment.

Andrews: 'We caught you on the hop Don, I think?'

Revie: 'Very much so.'

Andrews: 'Well Don Revie, this is your life, and tonight these distinguished guests are paying tribute to your tremendous career, which began in Bell Street, Middlesbrough, where you were born. Your first soccer pitch was right outside your own back gate on a cobbled alley where you played as a boy with a pair of Wellington boots as football boots and a ball made of rags. But that humble beginning was to put you on the road to lasting fame. And tonight, this audience is honouring your achievements. They're all men, but behind your success has been a woman, and I know she's your number-one fan – your wife Elsie.'

Elsie Revie emerges from behind the curtains, greeted with loud applause and the customary music. Her reddish hair immaculate, she is wearing a glorious green, white and violet patterned dress and a broad smile on her face, relieved that the harmless conspiracy has all gone according to plan. Husband Don would be proud of the meticulous planning and organization. Still in a state of mild shock, however, he looks at his wife with a trace of annoyance in his eyes ... he has been tricked and he does not like surprises.

Andrews: 'And, of course, with her, two more members of the Revie family – nineteen-year-old Duncan and fourteen-year-old Kim.'

More loud applause and music. Again, Don Revie appears rather unimpressed: they've been involved in the scheming too.

Elsie tells the audience about her husband's career and achievements. Another landmark is approaching – their silver wedding anniversary in October. Elsie, her gentle Scottish accent noticeable, jokes that she is hoping to be invited to that celebration. Football, she explains, brought them together in the late 1940s, through her dad Johnny ('Jocky') Duncan and uncle Tommy Duncan's connections with Leicester City, Don's first professional club.

Duncan Revie, studying Law at Cambridge University, tells of his dad watching him play football for his school team on one occasion. Dad's analysis? 'Fair skill but I could turn a double-decker bus quicker.'

Kim reveals that they are all ardent Leeds fans. Her father, meanwhile, looks like he wishes he was anywhere but here. He looks humble and sad, as if he is being criticized rather than praised. But at mention of his older twin sisters, Joyce and Jean, he brightens up, jumping to his feet to greet them. These are the sisters who helped to look after him when he was twelve, and fill the void left by the death of their mother in 1939. Jean tells how fourteen-year-old Don missed her wedding to play for Middlesbrough Swifts.

The next surprise guest is Bill Sanderson, Revie's first official manager at Middlesbrough Swifts. A recording of his voice describes Revie as a boy, sneaking into the Swifts manager's house to hear and watch his team talk. While Revie had later been involved in various record transfer fees, Sanderson's Swifts were the first club to pay a fee for his services.

Sanderson: 'Probably for an all-time low, Eamonn – five bob. In cash.'

Andrews: 'Don, it was while playing with Middlesbrough Swifts that your dreams come true with an invitation to join Leicester City as a part-time professional. At sixteen you pack your bags and leave home for the first time. How did you feel then?'

Revie: 'Er ... very, very lonely because I'd never been there before ... erm ... only as far as Redcar on a day out.'

March 1961. Military coups and brutal revolutions cause bloodshed the world over, countries are ripped apart by power, corruption and greed, while plans for a wall which will divide more than just a nation and its people are afoot in central Europe. Nazi trials still take place while the main victors of World War Two endure more hardship than the defeated. Spies defect, spies are jailed, spies are tortured, executed, murdered. There is the Pill, and Ban the Bomb, and the science fiction of rockets and satellites and animals in space. Maybe men will fly in space one day too. There are riots in London and other cities in the name of peace, while for months the Bay of Pigs has simmered, Kennedy, Khrushchev and Castro posturing and sparring.

March 1961. Don Revie is dropped from the Leeds first team. At thirty-three, the stamina and fitness were waning. The superstitious Revie should have known that his Leeds career was doomed – his conviction that birds brought bad luck was bolstered by the Leeds coat of arms' three owls and the club's nickname, the Peacocks.

A player of his calibre – England international, cup and award winner – in the reserves, having to prove himself all over again! Or maybe the truth was colder. Maybe Leeds didn't want him to prove himself, maybe they didn't want him at all, maybe they were trying to force him out of the club. Never mind a thinner pay packet, there was a distinct possibility of no pay packet at all.

Football was Revie's livelihood. He needed football and he was confident football needed him, even if it wasn't at Leeds. Lousy player discipline, lousy training methods, lousy facilities, lousy attitudes from unprofessional professionals, lousy performances, lousy results ... Revie knew it was time to leave. Leeds was a run-down, no-hope, Second Division, second-rate club, manned by players who didn't seem to care and run by men who hadn't a clue how to repair the situation. The club was on the slide.

Leave behind all the stress, the unclean south Leeds air, the polluted Elland Road atmosphere. It was time for a fresh start, a fresh challenge, fresh fields. Fresh air. Revie would escape the melancholic cloud that hung over the city. That was the Don Revie way: get out before you're forced out. Besides, Leeds United didn't deserve him any longer.

Football management was his aspiration. Had been for some years now, and Bournemouth & Boscombe Athletic had invited him to apply for the job of player–manager. Chester City and Tranmere Rovers were interested too. Even a club in Sydney was keen, though it was only a part-time position. The Australians had offered to fly the family out, find them a new home, help Elsie get a teaching job, look after the kids, make them all very comfortable. But England was where his home and heart belonged. He wanted the Bournemouth job. In his mind he'd already accepted it and was planning the move to the south coast.

Harry Reynolds, club director with an eye on the chairmanship, could be forthright and tough, but as a self-made millionaire he'd probably earned the right. 'Mr Leeds United' had the wealth and power, but he was trustworthy. But if you crossed him, it could cost you an ally for life.

He'd agreed to a meeting. Revie had expected to see a reference letter he'd requested from Reynolds, for the Bournemouth job. Revie had assumed that the meeting would be brief, ending with a firm handshake and the sincere best wishes of all at the club as he departed for the south coast.

Reynolds, genial and uncomplicated, had written the reference letter but had torn it up. Don Revie, he declared, would not be allowed to leave Leeds United, at least not without a fight. That 'fight', chairman Sam Bolton and the directors had agreed, would be a £6,000 fee for Bournemouth to pay. Revie was exasperated, and perplexed. Why were they trying to ruin such a good opportunity for him? He'd served them well; they didn't want him there any more.

Realizing that there was a serious misunderstanding brewing, Reynolds explained that they wanted Don Revie to be player–manager – Leeds' player–manager. He was ideal for the job. Revie lacked Reynolds' confidence: the job would be too big; there were too many wrongs at the club needing putting right. Reynolds casually dismissed Revie's concerns. He, they, would not take no for an answer. By the close of the meeting, Don Revie was the new and not particularly well paid Leeds player–manager.

The local press there to report on the hiring of a new boss, it was all smiles in the Leeds players' changing room before the morning's training session. From now on, Revie announced, they

17

should call him 'Gaffer', 'Boss' or 'Mister Revie'. Preferably 'Gaffer', and definitely not 'Don'. Conditions at the club would improve, there would be better, varied, more enjoyable and innovative training methods, and any man not working hard enough in training would be awarded with a yellow jersey with a wooden spoon sewn into it. 'If everybody is Leeds United minded and pulls together, from the directors right down to the ladies who do the cleaning and the washing, then the club will get somewhere,' he announced.

There were words of warning too: anyone talking about the Gaffer or his methods behind his back would be sacked, as Revie did not intend allowing the morale of the club to be destroyed by niggling, petty jealousies. They needed to be in it together – side before self. The team would start afresh on Saturday, away at Portsmouth. There would be few changes made to the team for now. It was too late in the season for that. He'd later make the Leeds formation 4–2–4, 4–4–2 when defence was needed, occasionally 4–3–3. But changes off the pitch began straight away: he instructed his secretary to rid his new office of all purples and greens – unlucky colours – plus any pictures of birds were to be thrown out. He was well aware that people scoffed at his superstitions, but those opinions never bothered him. His idiosyncrasies would only increase as time went on.

As the new manager, Revie retained the services of the coaching personnel. To a man, they backed him from the start, all committed to dragging the club out of the quicksand depression it had found itself in. On the 'home' room wall, the sign KEEP FIGHTING would appear.

Les Cocker and Syd Owen would train and coach the first team squad. Cocker was regarded as Revie's main right-hand man as well as physio for the first team during matches. Owen, the thinker, focused more on the tactics and set-piece plays, of the opposition too.

Chief scout Maurice Lindley would be assistant to Revie with everyday management work. Bob English and Cyril Partridge would coach and train the Leeds reserves, juniors and youth players, and all the coaches would help with the sessions of massage and physiotherapy.

The new appointment received scant mention in the national press. No comments, quotes, good wishes ... a small-time, second-rate, Second Division club in the gloomy north didn't merit it. Don Revie and Leeds United weren't important. The first match received about as much attention. A 3–1 defeat. Portsmouth, fighting hard against relegation, scrapped for every ball. For Leeds, relegation wasn't that likely, but it wasn't impossible. Eight games remained. Leeds were mid-table, with 32 points from 34 games played. Two teams would go down, eight games left ... Revie believed that 37 points should do it. That should see him safe.

## 1–5

I'd never get his autograph now, I just knew it. Me cheeking him off was one thing, now they'd only gone and made him the flipping manager! I'd probably get banned from watching the team training and all.

Served me right, according to my grandma. She'd laughed when I'd told her what I'd said about Don Revie being slower than her. It wasn't a long laugh, mind, and the next thing she was telling me off about being too cheeky for my own good, just like my father, and asking for a belt. I couldn't work her out sometimes. Truth is, my 'father' pissed off to God knows where when I was born, when my mum died, Rest In Peace. I didn't get how I could take after him. I was a good runner, maybe that's what she meant.

I'd decided to try and make up for being cheeky, even though he'd asked for it. I'd go, say sorry, and hope he'd accept it. Maybe he'd just been in a bad mood. Leeds were doing abysmally, he'd been out injured, and he'd been getting his ear chewed off by big Jack. Anyway, I needed his autograph: my collection was incomplete without it.

But my main reason for getting in his good books was because I wanted to be an apprentice player for Leeds when I was old enough. Apprenticeships started at fifteen, so I had about four years to wait. 'Forever' in my grandma's book. Mine was all just a little *Billy Liar* dream, and football wasn't important anyway, she'd say, between coughs, even though everyone else was always saying how good I was at it. I'd show her.

She wasn't that mean, I should own up. It was more to do with her worrying about me failing at school. Football wouldn't get me paid work, which is really what life is all about when you think about it. I understood that. But Mr Hatfield at school was always telling me that I could succeed as long as I tried my hardest and never gave in.

'Keep working hard, keep trying your best, keep at it. Win that ball, it's yours for the winning – win it, keep possession, use it wisely. Always be in a position to help your team-mates. Never hide. Football is for the eleven, not for you ...'

He knew what he was on about: he'd been sports teacher at school for years. He taught Paul Madeley a while back so he knew when he saw a good player. All I wanted was to follow in the path of Paul Madeley. Simple as that. Leeds scouts had kept their eye on him, signed him from Farsley Celtic. I could be as good, Mr Hatfield said.

It was early and I'd been running. Not long before Don Revie became boss, I'd begun a morning routine to get myself properly fit. My grandma, with her morning cough, would get me up at seven and out I'd go, rain or shine, dark or light.

It was better at that time of a morning, the air felt clearer and cooler, even though it often felt like a cold blade going right down my throat and into my chest, like it was punching my lungs and purifying them at the same time. Painful, but a good sensation. My legs always ached a bit – running downhill more than up, I never rightly understood that.

It was fine by me that hardly anyone was around early mornings to see me running. That way they couldn't be thinking I was barmy or up to no good, out burgling or something. Course, if anyone ever heard me singing at the same time as I ran they might have been on to the asylum straight away. I wasn't singing pop singles or anything. I just made up songs or lines to spur me on. I suppose it was like reciting multiplication tables at school, except I was using Leeds players' names.

I'd step out of our house, right foot first every time, for luck, saying to myself 'To Achieve Personal Greatness' ... A couple of stretches and bends on the pavement to warm up, then I'd be trotting up our street and round the corner on to the little patch of waste ground to do some star jumps, and then properly off. Once I was warmed up I'd be back down on to Elland Road in seconds, well on my way. And once I got into a comfortable breathing rhythm then I'd start with the 'song', in short breaths, in time with my paces. Like I was chanting, but really quietly. It was more mumbling than anything, to drive me on up hills and keep my brain from thinking it was all hurting too much. Daft stuff that wouldn't make sense to normal people because it didn't really make sense to me either. Little rhymes with players' names in. '*Hunger of Younger, There like Hair, Good as Goodwin, High as Jack, Read it like Revie, Earn it like Eric, Make it like Madeley, A king like John.*' And when I wanted to pick up the speed or make it more punishing, I'd change it around a bit, forcing the words out, sounding like a wild animal, growling, barking, grunting, '*BETTER than Younger! BETTER than Hair! BETTER than Bremner!*' I wouldn't care by then if I looked like a maniac. It helped me and it did me good, body and mind. To Achieve Personal Greatness ...

This one particular morning my route was Elland Road, past the Scratching Shed end of the stadium, the stretch of little shops and houses, the training pitches, more houses, the giant Greyhound Stadium stand, the workshops and factories and under the railway bridge. Advertising hoardings as big as the screen at the Rex. All the way along Elland Road until it rose into the hill up to Churwell, under another railway bridge, looking out for the Morley Milestone, like it was an old friend. If ever I didn't finish the run, I decided to stop myself having breakfast as a punishment. So I made sure I always finished. I'd plod right round the New Inn, careful of any stray beer bottles at the back, and head back down Churwell Hill, back under the railway bridge and the great big billboard sign again. Water always trickled down the sides of that tunnel, even in summer, and moss crept up the massive black bricks. I'd pass the little beck at the bottom of the hill again, which usually whiffed of chemicals or sewage.

All the way back down I'd go, on to level ground. Past all the fields and Cottingley Cemetery again, past the Drysalters. All the factories and workshops again, the shops and houses and the huge grey and black buildings dwarfing me but making me feel safe too. Then by Turners the Boilermakers' row of buildings and into the open again and the United training pitches. And then, nearly always, I'd see the light blue Ford Zephyr's indicators blink as it turned right to go down through the gates. That meant it was eight o'clock, dead on near enough. Don Revie was a real stickler for punctuality.

This time, right on cue, he was there, signalling. I slowed down to walking-fast rate, sweating but not done in or anything. I got my breath back easy enough, walking briskly and sucking in the air the way I'd been taught, through my nostrils and with my mouth shut. Inflating the lungs and then breathing out the 'bad air' through my mouth.

Through the gates, just a few yards off now. Don Revie was getting out of his Zephyr, parked snug inbetween the white lines. He was dead well dressed. His was the only motor there. Right down in the bottom corner at the back of the West Stand I saw Ces Burroughs, the boss groundsman, pushing a wooden cart alongside John Reynolds, his assistant. I always felt like calling Ces 'uncle' because he was always good to me, like I was one of his family. Even when he was telling me off or swearing he meant only the best for me. John was a great bloke too; he'd do anything for you.

Ces saw me and waved but they were both off sharpish before I could wave back, behind the Kop end. Don Revie had a shiny red–brown leather briefcase and he was smoothing down his shiny dark brown hair. His hairstyle was nearly like a Teddy boy's, side-parted but with a bit of a quiff at the front. Me, I had hair like a chimney sweep's brush and I looked like a tramp's neglected offspring, only muckier. I stood there watching, waiting, but he didn't see me, he was walking towards the little railings and fancy paved bit in front of the club reception doors.

Me being a bit shy, plus my throat was dry, I croaked at first. 'Excuse me, Don … Mister Revie …'

He looked preoccupied, so I coughed. He stopped, and looked at me. I bet he was thinking I was going to ask him for a shilling or some bread crusts or something. I couldn't have blamed him if he had.

'Yes?'

'Er, I just wanted to … to congratulate you on being made new manager.'

'Right, thank you …'

'And to say I hope you do well for us …'

'That's nice of you, son …' and now he was looking at me odd like.

'… and to say sorry for being cheeky to you the other week.'

And he'd just remembered who I was. He planted his briefcase on the ground. He marched over to me. I was going to get a whack for my troubles any second now, it didn't seem fair.

'Ah yes, the little so and so with a sprinter for a grandma.'

I felt like I was glowing red, and I couldn't tell if he was joking or not. 'I just wanted you to sign my autograph book and I'd been waiting ages and you told me to clear off.'

He thought for a second. 'That's not exactly what happened, now, is it?' he said, but his voice wasn't angry. In fact, he was smiling. Miserable Don Revie was actually smiling. There and then, in that very second, I decided never to call him names ever again. I'd been wrong. He was alright.

'What's your name?'

'Jimmy … er, James. James O'Rourke.'

'Irish, eh?'

'No.'

'Only asking lad, no need to get indignant.'

I wasn't sure what indignant meant, and I think he lost interest in talking to me. 'Apology accepted then, Jimmy.' He picked his briefcase up and walked off, through the glass doors, leaving me on my own like a dunce, not knowing what to do, whether to stay or just bugger off. But then a few seconds later he came back out, with a piece of paper in his hand.

'Here you go, add this to your collection.'

A sheet of paper with the Leeds United Association Football Club coat of arms on, and he's written *To Jimmy, Regards Don Revie*.

'Thank you!'

'That's alright. It's good to see you've learnt some manners.'

'I'm good at football, Don!' I call.

He just smiled and carried on walking, like he'd heard it all before. He probably had, thinking about it.

'No, I am, really! And I've just run five mile!'

He stopped again, turned to me. 'Have you really?'

I nodded. 'Nearly every morning.'

'What do your parents think about you doing that, then?'

'I haven't got any parents, just my grandma.'

'Oh, I see. How old are you?'

'I'm ten, nearly eleven. I play for my school, Cross Flatts, on the Park. Saturday mornings, ten o'clock kick off.'

'Well,' he said, 'if you're that good, maybe we'll meet up again.' Then he was away, inside the reception, and gone again, properly this time.

He didn't hear me shouting that I went to the same school as what Paul Madeley had or that the teachers reckoned I could be as good as Paul. So I walked back up. I had to get home and get ready for school. There was so much I forgot to tell him, like how dedicated I was to being an apprentice and about Ces letting me into the ground on Sundays so's I could practise my dribbling and shooting against the wall in the car park with the goal posts painted on, and Ces letting me into matches so I could watch and learn from professionals. But then I thought it was a good job I didn't say half of that, I didn't want to get anyone into bother, least of all Ces.

And then I bloody realized that we were playing away that Saturday.

### 1–6

'Don, you turned to one man for advice. That man was then Britain's most famous manager.'

The music rises again. Tonight, explains Andrews, Britain's most famous manager of 1961 has managed to make a 200-mile dash from London to attend this event. Great applause from the gathered audience greets Sir Matt Busby, former Manchester United manager.

24

On the morning of March 24, 1961, Revie drove over the Pennines. He had lived and worked in Manchester. He knew that the downpours of rain were not constant. Manchester did have dry, less bitingly cold days. This was not one of them. It had thrown it down all night and all morning. But the Zephyr was reliable and resilient; it would take him safely into the depths of Lancashire.

Matt Busby was a great success on and off the football field, one of the best, if not the best, bosses. Possibly his greatest ever achievement, though, was recovering from the terrible injuries suffered in the deadly Munich air crash, after which he went on to rebuild Manchester United.

Revie parked his trusty Ford yards away from the various Jaguars, Aston Martins, Mercedes, Humbers. Preparation, he believed, was everything. He would be ready to take on the mighty tasks ahead. He wasn't naive – if it all went badly, too badly, he knew he would be out on his ear.

Be brave and audacious, counselled Busby. Instill in your players a family spirit, an ethic of teamwork on and off the pitch, and a hatred of losing. And Revie, just for good measure, called on Tottenham manager Bill Nicholson for advice, too.

But next day Leeds' torturous season continued: a home 2–1 defeat to Sheffield United. Less than 14,000 had watched the match, Don Revie's home managerial debut. A pitiful, embarrassing attendance. Next, Luton Town, Saturday April 1. A Billy Bremner strike earned Leeds their first point under Revie in a 1–1 draw. Although still mid-table, things were looking up.

Small stature, big talent, a quiet and gentle man: South African winger Albert Johanneson's arrival brought potent outside-left creativity and pace to the squad. Finally, some glamour in the team. But Revie knew little of Johanneson's distressed Johannesburg childhood and turbulent background, or the violent bigotry he had faced, bigotry which didn't end with his move to Leeds.

25

Although he would be immensely popular at Leeds, terrible prejudice would be heard on the terraces at some grounds. Living away from the friends and family of his youth, Albert Johanneson would suffer from loneliness, insecurity and a profound lack of self-belief, much of it brought on by the appalling ignorance demonstrated by opposing fans.

Scunthorpe United, two days after Luton. Despite two goals from Jack Charlton, it was another defeat. But a tired Leeds benefitted from other teams' results. Relegation looked virtually impossible. They were six points above the relegation zone, with five games left to play. Not even a devoted pessimist could think the worst.

### 1–7

Up on my bedroom wall it went, written in big letters on the back of an old roll of wallpaper, covering a bit of the present pig-ugly pink roses decor.

### Season 1960–61

**Division One winners**: Spurs. Runners up: Sheffield Wednesday.
**Division Two winners**: Ipswich Town. Runners up: Sheffield United.
**FA Cup winners**: Spurs. Runners up: Leicester City.
**League Cup winners**: Aston Villa. Runners up: Rotherham.
**European Cup winners**: Benfica. Runners up: Barcelona.
**European Cup Winners' Cup winners**: Fiorentina. Runners up: Rangers.
**Inter-Cities Fairs Cup winners**: Roma. Runners up: Birmingham City.
**Football Player of the Year**: Danny Blanchflower, Spurs.
**European Footballer of the Year**: Omar Sivori, Juventus.
**Sweet Bugger All winners**: Leeds United.
**Leeds crowd average, home games**: 13,440.

Don Revie was made Leeds boss late in the season – there'd been only nine games left. For us to have been relegated would have needed a major disaster, but half the time the team looked like they were doing their best to achieve it. We scored over seventy goals but let in eighty-three. That worked out at just less than two a game – my own team let in less than that and we were schoolboys! Only a couple of teams in Division Two let in more goals than Leeds.

It did get a bit better straight after Don Revie took over, and the players definitely worked harder. The fellas around me at home matches said that as well. Whenever I got bored watching a match, I'd earwig those fellas talking. There was always at least one of them nattering away so there was always something to listen to. I didn't have a clue who they were or what their names were but those blokes felt like old friends I saw them that often. It was weird, but it was right, what those fellas said. At least the team still had something to play for – to beat relegation. Fighting to stay in the division was a genuine target for a small club.

My grandma was a Leeds supporter, on the quiet. Only a few women ever went to the matches, as far as I could tell, but it was my grandma who took me to my first Leeds game, for my eighth birthday. It was all her fault, me being obsessed with Leeds and with football. We'd stood near the front of the Lowfields Road terrace, near the wall. I must admit I wasn't that keen on watching, I'd have preferred to play footie in our street. I'd been pretty bored up until some fella near us shouted 'Give the blooming ball to Gerry, you mugs!' Anyhow, when Gerry, Gerry Francis, heard the bloke shout, he looked over at the terrace, right where me and my grandma were, and he smiled and put his hand up to wave, sort of saluting. Straight at us, and because he was black, that smile of his shone out like a star at night, and I was hooked.

It was Gerry Francis who had a hand in Don Revie's first signing, Albert Johanneson. He was brilliant. Albert wasn't like Gerry Francis, he was left-footed for one thing, and faster. Not that Gerry was a slouch or anything. The supporters gave Albert nicknames: the Black Flash, AJ and Go-Go Jo-Jo. I mostly just called him Albert, me.

# Chapter 2

## 2–1

In the twenty-plus minutes of *This Is Your Life*, Eamonn Andrews will tell the world of Don Revie's glorious achievements as a footballer and manager. There's nowhere near enough time, though, to describe every significant event (good and bad), the influential people (good and bad) and the important decisions (yes, good and bad) to have affected his life. No word will be made of how bleak and stressful those early months of Revie's Leeds reign were. There were precious few notable or rousing achievements in those early days.

As a player, Revie had always put on his left boot first; as manager a new pre-match ritual was walking at Les Cocker's left side, never his right. And maybe it worked – with 38 points, Leeds finished the 1960–61 season fourteenth in Division Two. Revie bade good riddance to the whole sorry campaign and began planning for the next. 1961–62 would be his responsibility. With the Leeds directors' support he'd be able to spend a little more money, as well as widen the scouting network. Investment in youth was crucial. But with debts of well over £100,000, there'd be no expensive new signings.

## 2–2

Most people loved summer. I never did. There was never any football to watch and all the other kids wanted to play cricket. Even the girls played, if the lads let them. Football didn't matter any more. They even took the goal posts down on the Park. I wasn't very good at cricket, football was my business.

I was lucky though, because Ces and John let me play on the shale between the Fullerton pitches and the West Stand. No one ever seemed to take much notice of me whacking the ball against the wall at the side of the Elland Road gates, with the goal posts painted on it. It's how Bobby Charlton used to practise his shooting. So, most school holidays I was on my own, my only companion being a football. My grandma was out at work in town. Ces'd let me borrow balls and even use the equipment in the gymnasium if no one else was around. Occasionally, if I was really lucky, John would have a kickabout with me and give me a bit of coaching.

## 2–3

A football manager's preparation involves the buying and selling of players – negotiating, bartering, haggling – and making tough decisions. Who to sell, who to release, who to buy, which youth players' dreams to ruin ... Revie detested this aspect of the job, but it was the way of the football world. Over the summer John McCole and Gerry Francis were sold to Bradford and York City. Revie had to look to the future, search for youth to invest in. New blood.

September 1961. Six months on from his appointment. Revie's plans had barely begun to pay off. The club was in deeper trouble, on the pitch at least. Match results had been poor, so had the attendances. Many Loiners remained true to rugby league, seemingly unwilling to indulge in two teams. Worse, the directors were negotiating the sale of Leeds' best asset, Billy Bremner, to Everton or Arsenal.

To Revie, selling Bremner was unacceptable: he announced to the board that if Bremner were to leave then they should start looking for a new manager too. The gamble paid off, the board backed down, and Revie won the day.

A filthy December night, 1961, and Leeds United's AGM is scheduled at the Queens Hotel. Revie had held on to his post, Bremner was still a Leeds player, and Harry Reynolds was to succeed Sam Bolton as chairman. Alderman Percy Woodward would continue as vice-chairman, while wealthy local business-men Manny Cussins and Albert Morris were made new directors. John Bromley and Sidney Simon were also recruited to the board, and successful entrepreneur Bob Roberts returned after ill-health. Lifelong Leeds fan the Earl of Harewood was elected as the first president of the club.

The 1961–62 season saw numerous changes. The Revie Revolu-tion was happening, slowly and surely. He retired as a player to focus on management. But there were still frustrations. Yes, some new youngsters had been brought in; a few low-priced more experienced players too: Ian Lawson, £20,000 from Burnley, and safe, wily defender Cliff Mason, £10,000 from Sheffield United. But the first team's quality still wasn't good enough, and Leeds were languishing in the depths of Division Two. Six new players were needed, Revie reckoned, for the team to avoid relegation. He was offered enough money for two, maybe three. The challenge: to convince a Division One footballer to join lowly Leeds United.

Merseyside. Everton Football Club. Revie, Reynolds and Cus-sins had travelled to Goodison Park to speak to one of boss Harry Catterick's players, controversially dropped from the first team: Bobby Collins. Thirty-one-year-old Collins, well known and highly rated, was loyal to Everton. Revie, though, desperately wanted the 'Pocket Napoleon' to join Leeds. Collins listened, thanked the Leeds contingent for their interest, but declined. He didn't want to join a club with one foot in the Third Division. Besides, he had everything he needed at Everton. Everything but a first team place and secure future, argued Leeds, and so Collins agreed to consider the offer.

# 2–4

I'd just done my five-mile Churwell Hill run and was out of breath. Not, though, out of things to say, especially this particular morning. Scraping off a bit of mud on the doorstep, I burst into the house.

'You'll never guess who we've bought!' I shouted, and then realized that my grandma was only four feet away, in the scullery. After coughing and muttering something unholy and retrieving her cig from the sink, she replied.

'Go on then, who?'

'Bobby Collins – from Everton! Can you believe it?'

'This isn't one of your little jokes is it?'

'Course not. It was the first thing Don Revie told Ces when he turned up for work. Ces was waiting to tell me specially. £25,000. Brilliant, isn't it?'

'How on earth can they afford him, and why would he want to come to Leeds? Everton's a good team.'

'Ces reckons that Don and Harry Reynolds went to talk to Bobby Collins at Everton's ground and later on at his house. And they wouldn't take no for an answer. Didn't get back till after three o'clock this morning.'

She bought the *Evening News* later, specially, to get the facts. It wasn't that she thought I was telling lies, just that it was all too good to believe. Or so she said. Everyone said that Bobby was a brilliant player, just what we needed in the team. We were having a rotten season, even grimmer than the last one. Buying Bobby Collins would give us new hope.

We'd started well and all – two wins out of two and decent performances. But then we got trounced 5–0 at Liverpool. Afterwards, Don Revie said he hoped to do at Leeds what Bill Shankly was doing at Liverpool – it'd taken Shankly about three years to build the Reds up and now they were looking dead certs for promotion to Division One.

Bobby Collins. £25,000 worked out at £390 per inch, so the paper said. He'd be making his debut against Swansea Town, wearing the number 8 shirt. Used to be Revie's.

I couldn't concentrate in lessons. I got a right bollocking in Geography for daydreaming. I was thinking about my running as well – I'd got quicker up that hill since the Bobby Collins news.

My grandma started asking me how I'd played in my matches for school, like she was interested all of a sudden. Then she measured my height and marked it on the kitchen wall in pencil. I was just less than five foot, still a bit shorter than most lads in my school year, but I was doing alright. Plus I was getting heavier; the tops of my legs were getting like tree trunks, even though I had no fat on me. Trouble was, I had calves like pipe-cleaners.

There were a lot more people at the Leeds–Swansea match than normal for home games. Even my grandma went, she paid us both in. She'd insisted I went with her. People were only interested in Bobby Collins. He had this sort of presence about him, an aura, is how my grandma put it.

He was everywhere on that pitch, hardly missed a tackle, never gave the ball away, played it simple, nothing fancy, but always accurate passing. He never stopped working, shouting, ordering players about. No one argued, they just did what they were told.

'Side before self,' I heard someone say.

He scored our first goal, beating a couple of defenders and then hitting a cracker from outside the area, high to the Swansea goalie's left. A *beauty*. Made hairs on the back of my neck stand on end, it really did. Even my grandma got a bit excited. We had to stop Swansea scoring, and the Leeds players grafted like their lives depended on it. Second half, Swansea were much more up for a game, they came close three times, but we tackled like demons. And we even got a second goal to finish it off. Billy McAdams in a goal-mouth scramble.

The week after, we were away at Southampton. It wouldn't be easy, they were doing a lot better than we were, and going for promotion.

It said on the radio that due to Tommy Younger getting tonsillitis Leeds didn't have a goalkeeper for the Southampton game. Second keeper Alan Humphreys was already injured and third-choice Terry Carling wouldn't have been able to get to the airport in time, they said, so Leeds hired a private plane specially to fly junior goalie Gary Sprake down on Saturday morning. A Leeds debut at sixteen: he'd be the youngest ever player for us.

I'd have been happy if Leeds had drawn at Southampton, but the radio said they looked like they were 'playing uphill'. Southampton walloped them 4–1. We were played off the park. Nine games left and we were still in the bottom two, still peering into Division Three. We'd played badly. I didn't think that would happen after we'd bought Bobby Collins. Maybe he was over-rated. Maybe Don Revie and Harry Reynolds had got it all wrong.

**2–5**

The writers of the Don Revie *This Is Your Life* didn't include the name of Bobby Collins once in the programme's script. Yet his 1962 arrival dramatically boosted Leeds' morale, and proved to be the club's as well as the manager's turning point. Had it not been for Collins, there probably would have been no Don Revie *This is Your Life* episode.

The script writers had so much material to use but too little time to use it all. Revie may have had a 'dazzling decade', as Andrews put it, at Leeds, but for a long time his life there was grim. His first full season was disastrous.

Easter 1962. Leeds lay perilously low in Division Two. Four hugely important matches that could decide the team's, the players' and the manager's future lay ahead. Four crucial games in just nine days; three of them within five days of each other; two of them were against Bury.

Bury. A hard team to beat. Real battlers. Took no prisoners. All the games were tough though, played on overused, weather-scarred, quagmire pitches; gruelling, painful, energy-sapping melees. Start saying your prayers, Revie warned his players.

Friday April 20, 1962. Bury versus Leeds, Gigg Lane. The lower half of the Second Division is tight, few points separate the bottom teams from those midway. Bury look to be safe, unlike Leeds.

34

There's only about 16,000 in the whole world who can say the same as me. I saw Grenville Hair score a league goal for Leeds United! Someone reckoned he'd only ever scored once before, in the FA Cup. But Leeds versus Middlesbrough, April 7, 1962, 2–0, Grenville scored, and I was there.

Two days after, we got a good 1–1 draw at Preston North End, moved up two places in the table and out of the relegation zone for the first time in ages. The following week we earned another point in a decent 1–1 draw at Walsall. Albert Johanneson for Leeds. Then we beat Luton 2–1, Billy Bremner got both, and after that we got a great point in a 0–0 draw at Leyton Orient, second top while we were second bottom. 'Don't count your chickens,' my grandma said, but I was sure we'd beat relegation. And it'd be mostly down to Bobby Collins.

I seemed to have more running energy the better Leeds were doing. Mr Hatfield told me to try and get my upper half stronger, so when I was running I started to box at the same time too, like Paul Newman in *Someone Up There Likes Me*. Before bed I'd do a hundred sit-ups as well, and when I got up in the morning. My stomach was solid as a board and my arms were getting a lot stronger.

Good Friday. Don Revie said in the paper that he thought four points from our last four games would see us safe. We had Bury twice, plus Derby inbetween, then away at Newcastle United. Bury games were always hard. I reckoned we'd beat Derby easily enough. And the Geordies weren't up to much, and they had nothing to play for at either end of the table.

1–1 away at Bury. Charlton, in the sixty-second minute, from a Collins free kick. A great result, we couldn't really expect better than a point away from home. The match report said both teams looked like they wanted to kick each other all afternoon rather than the ball, but I didn't care – it was another point.

Derby, at home. We played like a set of nervous cart-horses. But so did Derby. Another 0–0 draw, another point.

Bury. At home. Our third game in five days. A dull game, rough, tough and stormy, like the weather. Bury looked quicker and fitter than us, but another draw, another point.

The bottom of Division Two, April 24, 1962:

| 19 | Leeds | Played 41, | Points 34 |
| 20 | Swansea | Played 40, | Points 33 |
| 21 | Bristol Rovers | Played 41, | Points 33 |
| 22 | Brighton | Played 41, | Points 31 |

If we lost at Newcastle and Bristol Rovers won well at Luton, only then was there any chance of us getting relegated. It wouldn't happen. I was convinced of it.

A 3–0 win. McAdams, Johanneson and an own goal. We finished nineteenth in Division Two, with Swansea just below us and Brighton and Bristol Rovers the bottom two. Thank Bobby.

### 2–7

As the summer of 1962 approached, a business transaction was ready to be completed. More than thirty football clubs had tried to persuade the fifteen-year-old prodigy Peter Lorimer to sign for them. Talent scout John Quinn, in the employ of Leeds, was one interested party, and the Lorimer family (distant relatives of Elsie Revie) always looked forward to his visits.

Peter Lorimer had visited Elland Road before and liked what he'd seen. What the club lacked in financial clout, Quinn made up for with his persuasive and affable manner, and there was little doubt that Revie and Leeds would ensure the lad was brought up well. In addition to the excellent coaching set-up, the club had a doctor (Dr Adams), a padre (Reverend John Jackson), ex-headmaster Jeffrey Sanders to help the boys' academic needs, plus the one and only Les Cocker to give talks on sex education. Janet Lorimer would have the last word on where her son's footballing future lay, and she promised that Peter would sign for Revie's side.

The night before Peter Lorimer finished school forever, Revie and Maurice Lindley set off for Scotland, fearing they'd miss out on signing him. Other clubs were prowling around, Manchester United especially, and they had already offered a welcome gift of £5,000 for Peter to sign for them. That amount of money could buy the entire Lorimer street. And other clubs would be knocking hard at the Lorimer front door very early the next day. Even though Revie had assurances that Peter would be joining Leeds, he was still anxious to get the deal signed and sealed.

# Chapter 3

## 3–1

The poster on my wall wasn't exactly pretty reading, but Jesus it could have been a lot worse.

### Season 1961–62

**Division One winners**: Ipswich. Runners up: Burnley.
**Division Two winners**: Liverpool. Runners up: Leyton Orient.
**FA Cup winners**: Tottenham Hotspur. Runners up: Burnley.
**League Cup winners**: Norwich City. Runners up: Rochdale.
**European Cup winners**: Benfica. Runners up: Real Madrid.
**European Cup Winners' Cup winners**: Athletico Madrid. Runners up: Fiorentina.
**Inter-Cities Fairs Cup winners**: Valencia. Runners up: Barcelona.
**World Cup winners**: Brazil. Runners-up: Czechoslovakia.
**Football Player of the Year**: Jimmy Adamson, Burnley.
**European Footballer of the Year**: Josef Masopust, Dukla Prague.
**Leeds United crowd average, home games:** 13,594.

The arse-end of Division Two had finished like this ...

| | | |
|---|---|---|
| 18 | Bury | 39 points |
| 19 | Leeds | 36 points |
| 20 | Swansea | 36 points |
| 21 | Bristol Rovers | 33 points |
| 22 | Brighton | 31 points |

It had been a busy summer over the road. If I hadn't seen him, I wouldn't have believed it. I was only looking at the return of the King!

Big John Charles had come back from Juventus, for more than £50,000. Fantastic news, and it proved that Harry Reynolds and Don Revie were dead set on taking Leeds places. Charles's signing also meant that we had *two* new strikers because Jim Storrie, from Airdrie, signed in June for £16,000. The *Evening News* called him 'Diamond Jim', a non-stop bustling Scot and another discovery by the United scouts in Scotland. He joined a month after we signed Peter Lorimer. Around the same time another young player officially signed too, though Ces said he'd been with us a while, in fact: speedy right-half Jimmy Greenhoff, born in Barnsley. When young players moved here as apprentices they were usually put up in houses in south Leeds, Beeston mainly, with families. My grandma said that Jack Charlton lived in our street when I was a baby, before moving to a house on Beeston Hill next to Cross Flatts Park. The players paid board and lodgings, none of it was free, but I bet they had it nice and cosy. Maybe my grandma should have offered to be a landlady, to get a few more pennies in on top of her office job.

The best news I heard was that Paul Madeley signed professional forms for Leeds. He'd played well for the juniors in the Northern Intermediate League and Cyril Partridge reckoned he was going to become a right player, especially in defensive midfield.

### 3–2

Television airtime severely restricted the time allowed for guest appearances and the number of 'special mentions' of individuals who had contributed to the success of the *This Is Your Life* subject. As well as Bobby Collins, by the close of 1962 it was clear that other men would play or had already played a major part in the career and achievements of Don Revie. Men such as Les Cocker, Syd Owen, Maurice Lindley, Bob English, Cyril Partridge. And of course, most notably, Harry Reynolds, being the man responsible for persuading Revie to venture into management.

40

Although Revie told the press differently, in August 1962 he had high hopes for Leeds in the imminent new season. During pre-season he had worked tirelessly at improving the team. Out would go players he regarded as not good enough or who he could get useful transfer fees for. Players like attackers Derek Mayers and Billy McAdams, wing-half Peter McConnell who had joined Leeds from school in the previous decade, and right-back Alf Jones. Revie had spent more money than most managers in the entire Football League, and throughout, chairman Harry Reynolds and the Leeds board had supported him, believing his decisions to be risk free. However, the club's purchase of John Charles was an expensive gamble that nearly bankrupted it.

Normal player signings saw transfer fees paid in instalments. But the return of John Charles to Leeds from Juventus was not a normal transfer – deals with Italian clubs generally involved 'cash on delivery' terms and the Leeds board did not have the £50,000-plus readily available. Therefore, urgent arrangements were needed for them to raise the funding. If they wanted the return of the King, they'd have to pay for it royally. Hence ticket price increases, which didn't please many Leeds fans.

Revie told the local media that he was not one for building castles in the air and so would be happy with finishing in the top half of Division Two. Considering their scrape with relegation the previous season, it was a sensible remark to make, but with his team containing such balance of youth and experience, pace and stamina, flair and grit, rough and smooth, the club's aspirations were undoubtedly higher. A team that hated losing, containing fighters of the ilk of Goodwin, Charlton, Bremner, Bell and of course Collins, was going to be hard to beat and should be involved in the final promotion reckonings. Combined with the match-winning potential of men such as Charles, Albert Johanne-son and Jim Storrie, going up as Second Division champions could not be dismissed either.

41

The new campaign started promisingly with a win at Stoke City, a decent team performance in front of nearly 30,000. Charles's 're-debut' was a reasonable if not outstanding display. With only 14,119 in attendance, Wednesday August 22 saw a home 4–3 loss for Leeds to Rotherham, followed by a Saturday home win over Sunderland, attendance 17,753. Rotherham did the double over Leeds the next Tuesday, 2–1, and then Leeds travelled the short distance to Huddersfield Town to pick up a 1–1 draw. So, two wins, two defeats and a draw in the first five matches. Respectable progress, except it was identical to the start of last season's lousy campaign, and the team displays this time around weren't much better. Come a midweek home defeat to Bob Stokoe's Bury, in front of an impressive but soon depressed crowd of 28,000, Revie's patience was worn thin. For the next match, at Swansea Town, changes to the team-sheet had to be made anyway: Jim Storrie, with a broken finger, and John Charles, back strain, were late casualties, and already out injured were captain Freddie Goodwin, forward Ian Lawson and left-half Willie Bell.

'Some of our senior players have not struck top form yet,' Revie said, as he dropped goalkeeper Tommy Younger and, perhaps most surprisingly, full-back Grenville Hair too, replacing them with youngsters. Making their first team debuts would be Norman Hunter and Paul Reaney in defence and Rod Johnson up front with Noel Peyton returning also. Cliff Mason at left-back would captain the side. All brave, sweeping changes by the Leeds manager, seen as drastic by some.

Courageous in another sense too was allowing Jack Charlton to organize the defence 'his way', meaning that out went man-to-man marking and in came a zonal system of defending. He would organize the back four, and instruct the young lads where to go, when to mark, when to cover and how to pick up positions. The development delighted Charlton, relieved to be in Revie's plans still after he had smashed a teacup too close to the boss's head at half-time in the home defeat to Rotherham.

Twenty-year-old Billy Bremner, despite being only slightly older than the new lads, had played many more first team matches and was much more experienced. He helped them develop as players, coaxing and encouraging them, almost like a watchful elder brother. Nonetheless, he was still unhappy at Leeds and persisted in bugging Don Revie for a transfer as he wanted to be with girlfriend Vicky back home in Stirling.

Leeds were marginally lower than Swansea in the division and were expected to lose this tie. With pleasant weather and a soft pitch, though, the Leeds players, in all blue, went out determined to show their true mettle and enjoy themselves. Swansea did have an early goal disallowed, but Leeds grew in strength and confidence to outfight and outmanoeuvre the hosts. In goal, Gary Sprake, and in front of him Jack Charlton, gave storybook performances while Leeds' aggressive, hard-pressing style and impressive pace threatened the opposition with each attack. Collins, Bremner, Smith, Johanneson and Storrie dominated the play and early goals in each half by first Johnson and then Bremner gained an inspiring 2–0 win, just their third victory of the season.

The following weekend, two goals from Albert Johanneson brought an excellent home win against high-fliers Chelsea – and another good clean sheet with it – in front of over 27,000 spectators. They had won nine points out of a possible sixteen, things were now looking better. Until, that is, a midweek 3–1 defeat, at Stokoe's Bury again, which began a chain of five Leeds league games without a win.

During games and training matches in the 1950s, Jack Charlton often saw trails of human carnage left behind by the great John Charles and scoffed at the Welshman's nickname, 'Gentle Giant'. Charles would run with his arms and elbows high, powerful enough to pummel his way through and damage opponents' defences. He never deliberately hurt a player in his professional life, but that did not lessen the pain he often inflicted on the opposition. In 1962, however, the return of the heavier and slower John Charles brought precious few reminders of his glorious reputation.

Despite good pay and a splendid new home in Wetherby, Charles was unhappy and frustrated, and troubled by lack of sleep and minor injuries. He wasn't able to train well as a result and it was apparent to those at the club that he had lost enthusiasm for the game, and his level of fitness. His spark had gone and he missed Italy. By November Charles had played eleven games and scored just three goals. Leeds had failed to win the three games in which he'd scored.

Revie would not publicly criticize John Charles, instead he tried to help and encourage him. But he was very unhappy with the situation, too – it just wasn't working out. Plus when only 15,000 Leeds people out of a population of half a million were willing to pay a bit more cash to see a true great, something was wrong. Fortunately, an Italian club had emerged with a possible solution to the problem. They contacted the Football League's Alan Hardaker and tabled a bid to Leeds to recruit John Charles' services. Harry Reynolds called a board meeting and after two hours announced that Leeds were selling him to AS Roma. On November 2 1962, the deal was sealed, and Charles was on his way back to Italian soccer, for £70,000. He had been at Leeds again for just ninety-one days.

Charles said that it had been a mistake to come back to England and Leeds, and that leaving Juventus was his biggest misjudgement. He felt wracked with guilt for failing and disappointing so many Leeds people who genuinely cared for him. The Leeds board, also feeling embarrassed with the situation as they had profited nicely from it, offered refunds on season tickets and discounts on future home games. Harry Reynolds went to the extent of issuing an apology to the Leeds public for any offence the transfer might have caused in the first place.

For the personnel and supporters of Leeds United, and John Charles's friends and team-mates, it had been frustrating to see one of the world's finest players toiling. He was nowhere near the footballer they used to know, and he was unable to perform anywhere near as well as he had in the past.

I wasn't Catholic, so if I ever went to church as a kid it was St Mary's on Beeston Road (though I did go to Midnight Mass at St Anthony's one Christmas Eve when I was older, and drunk). I never had a clue what the difference was between religions, and I didn't really care either. Church and faith weren't topics of conversation in our house, mainly because my grandma wasn't interested. I knew her attitude was to do with my granddad getting killed in France in the war.

A young bloke called Passy, from a local church side, came to our house one evening when I was thirteen to ask me to play for Beeston St Anthony's. He was player–manager of the Sunday team, which I thought was a bit odd, a church team playing on Sundays. St Anthony's was a good club and well known in Leeds. They even had their own changing room and baths. My grandma had said it was up to me who I played for but when I was on the stairs I heard her asking Passy if I was old enough to look after myself in a men's league. He told her he'd seen me play and that I'd definitely be alright because I was quite quick and fit enough. Just in case, he promised that the fellas in the team would always make sure I was okay. So I signed their forms and he said he'd make sure they paid my shilling registration fee and my subs each week. Training was on Tuesday nights and they went in the Peacock afterwards, which was just about perfect for me, right next door, near enough. I'd never been in a pub at that stage; it wouldn't be so long before you'd have trouble getting me out of them. I was chuffed to bits to be asked and couldn't wait to get going even though I was dead nervous with it – a men's team in an adult league. It was a big step up from school football for me.

Maybe I was being soft, but I was upset when John Charles left to go back to Italy, even though it was definitely the right thing. Staying at Leeds wouldn't have helped him, he seemed miserable. In September we lost Eric Smith as well, with a broken leg. Poor bloke. And it wasn't the first time he'd done it either. It was one of those horrible incidents that probably meant we'd never see him in a Leeds shirt again. Our season had looked dead promising at the start, now it was looking like it could just die off with a whimper.

Once Charlesy had gone, Jim Storrie surprised a lot of people at how well he did. It was like he'd been given a new lease of life, and he scored a right rake of goals. And because he always ran his heart out, Leeds fans loved him. He never gave in, even when he'd been clattered by opposing defenders – plenty of the fans fell out with Charlesy for being just about the exact opposite. Daft thing was though, Diamond Jim missed more than he scored, and them that he did score were often harder chances than the ones he missed. But we all loved to watch a grafter. There was no such thing as a lost cause to Jim. You could be as gifted as King John, but if your heart wasn't in it, you weren't any good for the team.

Storrie created loads of goals just by harrying defenders and goalkeepers. He tried to enjoy himself, having a laugh with players on both sides and taking the mick out of opposing goalkeepers. He was one of the most popular Leeds players at the time, along with Bobby, Gary, Albert and Jack. Billy sort of split opinions; Leeds supporters either loved him or loathed him. Like this season, he went off the boil and didn't seem to like playing out wide, so he started slacking. He missed nearly half the games because he was either injured, dropped or suspended. Even then he scored ten goals in the League. He'd played around a hundred games already, but his discipline let him down. But then you could hardly blame him when defenders kicked lumps out of him and tried to get him into trouble with the referees.

We signed Don Weston from Rotherham with some of the Charles cash, a very nippy type who only went and scored a hat trick on his debut. Don Revie gave more young lads debuts too. There was Mike Addy, Barrie Wright and Tommy Henderson, a mate of Billy Bremner's, who all debuted, plus Jimmy Greenhoff late in the season, but none of them did that well. Even Peter Lorimer, 'The Cannonball Kid', hadn't been any great shakes in his first game, against Southampton. Maybe it was too early to blood him, him being the youngest ever Leeds first team player. And then he broke his leg in a junior game soon after, rotten luck I wouldn't wish on my worst enemy.

Just after Christmas and right up to March 1963 the country was gripped with a lousy big freeze. The year before's winter had been bad enough with gale force winds half the time, and now it was freezing weather, proper blizzards and snowdrifts all over the place. It was bad enough up here but they had it worse down south. Folk even died from the cold, and parts of the sea froze over and people went ice skating on the River Thames. Our house was perishing, and there were loads of times when I even had ice on the inside of my bedroom window.

Hardly a proper League game was played for three months. Even in our Sunday League we had to postpone loads of matches. Most didn't mind, it meant they could have more ale on a Saturday night and not have to fret about Passy dropping them from the team in the morning. Me, I got really frustrated because I couldn't stand not playing so I'd go sprinting on grass in my studded boots or I'd kick the ball up in the air and practise trapping it, stuff like that, hour after hour till it got dark. Frozen or snow-covered grass was usually a lovely surface to play on, soft and crushy and not risky.

When Walter Winterbottom left the England job, there were reports that the Football Association wanted Don Revie to replace him. We weren't even top of Division Two at the time, it sounded like someone had made it up. Anyway, he said in the papers it was a ridiculous idea and that he was determined to stay at Leeds and put them on the soccer map proper. I wonder what would have happened had they offered him the England job, though. Soon after, Harry Reynolds and the board offered Don a new and improved contract, to be manager until 1967. I know I felt relieved when he signed it, it didn't take a genius to see how much better the club was since he took over, even if it had taken a while.

That season, Don did what he said he'd do – he put Leeds on the soccer map. Unfortunately, we still missed out on promotion. Losing three games in a row late on in the season didn't help. We ended up finishing fifth in the end, a grand effort and a near miracle compared to last season, but still, when it boiled down to it, it was pretty disappointing.

# Chapter 4

The Profumo scandal. The Great Train Robbery. 'I have a dream.' The 1963–64 season. Leeds versus Rotherham. A difficult but deserved home win. Revie, desperate for a good start to the season, considered his team's performance 'satisfactory'. Billy Bremner had moved into the centre of midfield at right-half. In his place on the right flank came in Don Weston, who struck the only goal of the tie. Revie worried Weston was not the solution for Leeds' lack of ammunition on the right; he was quick and skilful but inconsistent. The forward line would benefit from a bit. of muscle and height. Collins and Bremner, in midfield, looked an excellent combination. Bremner made the position his own, yet his name remained on the transfer list. Clubs would come in with enquiries and offers, which Revie would purportedly consider and then casually dismiss as too low.

August 29 1963. A deal was done, papers signed and hands firmly shaken. In the papers, Revie looked like that cat with the cream. £33,000 to Matt Busby's Manchester United for Johnny Giles, a quiet, earnest young Dubliner. Revie was in no doubt that he was crucial to Leeds' chances of success.

John Giles. A technically gifted player, steady temperament, good fitness levels. He'd suffered a badly broken leg, which would have ended many a career. Not Giles's: it toughened him up. Not that he had been a soft touch before.

A newspaper-wrapped bundle Giles had placed on Revie's desk went unnoticed by the manager. He was in full flow. It was difficult not to be impressed by his motivational talk. John Giles had never felt so important before.

Revie stops talking. 'What's that?'

'My boots, Boss.'

'Get them off! Quick! Don't you know it's unlucky to put shoes on a table?'

## 4–2

Season 1962–63. It had the usual, bleak Leeds-less look about it, but everyone was optimistic about the next season.

**Division One winners**: Everton. Runners up: Spurs.
**Division Two winners**: Stoke City. Runners up: Chelsea.
**FA Cup winners**: Manchester United. Runners up: Leicester.
**League Cup winners**: Birmingham City. Runners up: Aston Villa.
**European Cup winners**: AC Milan. Runners up: Benfica.
**European Cup Winners' Cup**: Spurs. Runners up: Athletico Madrid.
**Inter-Cities Fairs Cup winners**: Valencia. Runners up: Dynamo Zagreb.
**Football Player of the Year**: Stanley Matthews.
**European Footballer of the Year**: Lev Yashin, Dynamo Moscow.
**Leeds United crowd average, home games**: 20,215.

As a boy, nothing ever came around quickly enough. Birthdays, Christmas, the new football season, the pining for Leeds to win promotion. It felt like torture, lifelong torture. It was an obsession. Morning, noon and night, I couldn't get Leeds out of my head.

When your team's in Division Two you don't expect headlines, barring a rare big signing. But then 1963–64 came along. Leeds looked like they could beat anyone in the division. Promotion was only a matter of time.

1963–64 was the start of something big for me too. I wasn't fourteen yet but I was playing in the St Anthony's first team and there were club reps watching me, so I heard. I knew I was playing well, and we were always in the running for our league title, and local and West Yorkshire cups. The only scouts I wanted watching me were Leeds scouts.

I watched every home game that season. The team looked like they knew promotion was coming. They had a swagger about them and the all-white kit made them look bigger and stronger than everyone else. We were on the up. I don't think we were ever out of the top four all season. Don Revie had opposing teams watched and he prepared a plan for each match. 'The Don' had all the Leeds players organized the way he wanted. The juniors, the reserves, the first team: they all played the same system or pattern, so when one player had to drop out he'd be replaced by someone who knew exactly what he was supposed to do and was good enough to do it. It worked a bloody treat nearly every single time. Home attendances went up to nearly 30,000. Quite rubbish when you looked at how many people lived in Leeds, but still.

I reckon once Leeds started doing well something about Don Revie changed. Whenever he talked to the papers or on the radio it was like he was a different person, as if he'd rehearsed what he was going to say.

John Giles from Manchester United was a great signing. Not the fastest wing man, but he was consistent and had the ability to swing in great crosses when it mattered. We even got past the FA Cup third round. We lost at Everton in the fourth round replay, after drawing 1–1 at home, but 48,000 turned up to watch, the biggest crowd I'd ever seen.

There were some bad moments in that season too: Leeds were away at Cardiff in the Cup and Freddie Goodwin was marking John Charles, who'd signed for them for £25,000. After a collision between them, Freddie suffered a broken leg. In three places. My grandma made me laugh about it, she didn't quite get it. 'Surely he must have been in one place, how could he have been in three different places?' she'd said. Jim Storrie got injured quite badly too, but Ian Lawson worked his clogs off in his place and scored some important goals. Jack Charlton was out injured for nearly half the league games, too. But others' bad luck meant someone else's good luck. Our Paul Madeley for one, he made his debut, in defence, in January 1964 versus Man City.

Harry's cheque book signed England centre-forward Alan Peacock from Middlesbrough for over £50,000. Leeds meant business. We were battling with clubs like Sunderland, Preston North End, Charlton Athletic and Manchester City for a top-two position.

51

Me, it seemed I was getting bigger and taller every day. The taller I got the more my grandma got hacked off. I cost her more cash all the time in food and clothes.

## 4–3

Revie had arranged a special gathering in the Astoria Ballroom in the north of Leeds. A party to celebrate the team's promotion. Promotion had been won two weeks before the season's end, 3–0 away at Swansea Town, Sunderland being runners up in the league. Harry Reynolds had sent the Wearside club a telegram to congratulate them. The Leeds players' celebratory meal on the coach journey back from Swansea's Vetch Field was fish and chips, wrapped in newspaper, and champagne drunk from anything available.

# Chapter 5

They did it, God bless them, they bloody well did it, and with the highest number of points ever too. We were back in the First Division, where we belonged. St Ant's were doing great too.

## 1963–64 Football Honours

**Division One winners**: Liverpool. Runners up: Manchester United.
**Division Two winners**: Leeds United. Runners up: Sunderland.
**FA Cup winners**: West Ham. Runners up: Preston.
**League Cup winners**: Leicester. Runners up: Stoke.
**European Cup winners**: Inter Milan. Runners up: Real Madrid.
**European Cup Winners' Cup winners**: Sporting Lisbon. Runners up: MTK (Budapest).
**Inter-Cities Fairs Cup winners**: Real Zaragosa. Runners up: Valencia.
**Football Player of the Year**: Bobby Moore, West Ham.
**European Footballer of the Year**: Denis Law, Manchester United.
**Leeds crowd average, home games**: 29,950.

All the newspapers said Sunderland would do better than us in Division One. In fact, according to them we were going straight back down again. But the 1964–65 season would be when Don Revie and co proved what everyone involved with Leeds already knew. I wrote myself a little dossier on the Leeds players.

**Gary Sprake**
Age: 19
From: Wales
Good points: the best young goalkeeper around. Brave, agile, hard working. Wales international.

Bad points: needs to communicate more with the defence. Suspect temperament. Needs to stop punching opponents or will get sent off or chinned, or both. Nervous before games, vomits before nearly every match.

Likes: pop music and golf.

### Paul Reaney

Age: 19

From: born Fulham, bred Leeds

Good points: strong, fast, reliable, quick to tackle, never gives up. Likes to attack down the right wing. Should play for England.

Bad points: could be better at crossing.

Other: Billy Bremner's nickname for Reaney, Sprake and Hunter is 'Snap, Crackle and Pop' because they're inseparable.

### Willie Bell

Age: 26

From: Scotland (hewn from Scottish granite)

Good points: very consistent, can play at left-back or left-half or across the defence. Fit and experienced. Good leader for the younger players. Has the sweetest left foot in the business.

Bad points: not the fastest.

### Billy Bremner

Age: 21

From: Scotland. Will play for Scotland, no doubt about it.

Good points: can do just about anything but needs to stop arguing. Never gives up.

Bad points: Fighting. Smoking in secret.

Likes: fighting, arguing, golf, family drives, bacon and eggs for breakfast, and salads. Smoking in secret.

### Jack Charlton

Age: 29

From: Ashington

Good points: lynchpin of defence, superb header of the ball, good leader of the back four. Useful in attack at corners and free kicks.

Likes: hunting, fishing and smoking (also in secret) and letting Billy take the blame when caught.

### Norman Hunter
Age: 20
From: Eighton Banks
Good points: tackles like a demon, good striker of ball. Left footed but right handed. Solid partnership with Charlton.
Bad points: not very strong in the air.

### Johnny Giles
Age: 24
From: Dublin
Good points: Eire international. Highly intelligent player, excellent crosser and passer of the ball, and penalty taker. Good with both feet so can play on right or left. Makes playing football look easy, can look after himself.

### Don Weston
Age: 28
From: Mansfield
Good points: good reserve right winger or attacker, joint top scorer last season.
Bad points: needs to get stuck in more.

### Alan Peacock
Age: 26
From: Middlesbrough
Bad points: not a good injury record.
Good points: but has scored crucial goals for us and set plenty more up. Great header of the ball.

### Bobby Collins
Age: 33
From: Glasgow
Good points: brilliant leader, superb footballer, a perfect captain, incredible will to win. Tackles harder than anyone, brilliant passer and shooter. Should be playing for the Scotland, I don't care how old he is.

### Terry Cooper
Age: 20
From: Brotherton

Good points: left-footed, fast, keen tackler, great crosser. Could be used to replace Willie Bell or Albert Johanneson.

### Jim Storrie
Age: 24
From: Scotland
Good points: excellent work rate and enthusiasm. If he scored as many chances as he creates, he'd deserve to be in Scotland team too.
Bad points: last season ruined by injury, the team missed him and his goals.
Other: nicknames 'Diamond Jim' or the 'Laughing Cavalier'.

### Albert Johanneson
Age: 24
From: South Africa
Good points: excellent season, joint leading scorer, top goals-creator. Would be near unbeatable if had as much confidence as he had ability.
Bad points: needs to toughen up, couldn't tackle my grandma.

### Ian Lawson
Age: 25
From: Ormston
Good points: good worker, skilful, a good back-up forward, decent scoring record. Scored some important goals to help promotion.

### Jimmy Greenhoff
Age: 19
From: Barnsley
Good points: quick, very promising right-sided forward. Not seen much of this player yet though.

### Paul Madeley
Age: 19
From: Leeds!
Good points: looks useful anywhere in defence. Excellent worker, good with both feet. Should play for England. Recently called up by the England Youth team.

**Peter Lorimer**
Age: 17
From: Broughty Ferry, Scotland
Good points: right-sided forward or midfield player, the finest striker of a football at the club. Youngest-ever Leeds first teamer. Should play for Scotland.

**Jimmy O'Rourke**
Age: just gone 14
From: Leeds
Good points: very promising. Quick minded, very fit and an excellent passer of the ball. Good tackler. Potential captain. Will play for Leeds and then England if there's any justice in the world. Bad points: not the fastest.

Football looks like an easy game to play – put more goals in your opponent's net than they put in yours and you win. It can be as complicated as chess, though. Each player has his job to do and has his own skills or moves. Plus every single man involved can win the match.

I played at right-back for St Anthony's. I don't remember missing one game in the first couple of seasons because I worked my socks off, learnt from the other three in our back four about how to mark and defend properly and hardly let any goals past me.

East End Park Working Men's Club in east Leeds had its own football ground. It had changing rooms for the players and officials, a tiny wooden dug out for each team at opposite sides of the pitch and even a little concrete terrace for spectators. In March 1964 it even hosted a youth international game, Elland Road being waterlogged. I got to play on the East End Park pitch two months after that international match, in May. St Anthony's got to the final of the West Yorkshire District Cup. My first ever final, against West Yorkshire Amateurs FC. We weren't expected to win, as they were in a higher and better league than us, but we were going to give it a bloody good go.

The West Yorkshire District Cup was silver and nearly as big as me. We didn't get our hands on it, in fact we were well beaten. 3–0. It hurt at the time. But we tried our hardest. After we'd been given our Losers' medals, our gaffer, Passy, got us all in a circle, thanked us all one by one, shook our hands and told us how proud he was to be player–manager of such a fine team of lads. I was flushing hot with pride and I had a lump in my throat the size of a cue ball. It was at that moment I promised myself to never leave that team unless I had to.

My ambition, though, was still to play for Leeds. Ces gave me the best tips, all in a list that he wrote for me that summer. 'Read these, learn them off by heart and you can't go wrong,' he said.

### The Leeds United 10 Commandments

1    Push back the opposition and play your football in the opposing two thirds of the field.
2    Failure is no crime provided you have spent your last breath trying to avoid defeat.
3    Expect to win every 50/50 ball in a tackle and mean to win every 60/40 ball.
4    Never be afraid of shooting in the box.
5    Never get caught in possession.
6    Always look for a team-mate to pass to before looking for an opponent to beat.
7    Every pass that leads to a goal rates equal merit with the goal itself.
8    In a tight situation don't pass the buck by passing the ball to a team-mate no better placed than yourself.
9    When you make a foolish mistake don't look for an excuse, look for a way to retrieve the situation.
10   When things are going badly for you, don't hide.

I read them over and over. And things got better. I got a letter from the club, inviting me to trials there in July.

### 5–2

Two of the main guests on *This Is Your Life* were, especially during the 1964–65 season, Revie's greatest rivals in football. The three managers were embroiled in numerous battles for superiority over the years. There would be disagreements between them, the greatest of rivalries, but they'd hold one another in the highest regard.

Revie wanted to see his players expand their game and play a faster, more direct, more attacking style of football. But August 1964's edition of the *FA News* hurt Leeds' and Revie's cause. The editorial of the newsletter, which went to every club in the Football League, mentioned that the Disciplinary Committee had considered the list of clubs whose players had been cautioned by referees, suspended, censured or fined during the previous season: 'Ipswich Town and Sheffield United had the best record, and Leeds United the worst.'

Furious, Don Revie felt compelled to protest: 'We did not have a single first team player sent off last season and we had only one suspended, Billy Bremner, after a series of cautions, which is a lot more than many clubs can say. The majority of our offences were committed by junior, second team players or boys.'

Everton, a league match at Goodison Park, on Saturday November 7. The match started off badly. Everton's Sandy Brown was sent off in the fourth minute for swinging a punch John Giles' way after a heavy challenge. Gary Sprake was pelted with coins; the rest of the team had other missiles aimed at them. A few minutes before half-time, an accidental collision between Willie Bell and Derek Temple ended with both players laid out on the turf. Bell was carried off the pitch by Les Cocker and Giles, while Temple had to be stretchered off. Both teams' trainers, as well as the referee, Ken Stokes, and one of his linesmen, were struck by more objects from the crowd. Fearing an invasion, they left the pitch. The teams followed minutes later. An announcement over the tannoy said that the game would be restarted in five minutes but if objects continued to be thrown on to the pitch it would be officially abandoned. It was a serious promise. The players' withdrawal was said to be the first ever in English football history.

Objects did continue to land on the pitch, frequent fouls and heated arguments flowed freely, but the game was eventually played in full. Amidst 'Dirty Leeds' chants from the crowd, Leeds forced a 1–0 victory with a well-taken Willie Bell header.

After the match, the Leeds team and officials made a swift getaway. The unfortunate referee and linesmen were holed up in their room for a few hours. Revie was indignant and felt that the team's tagging as a hard, dirty side by the press and the FA wasn't a fair judgement. In the November of 1964 the FA and the Football League set up a special committee to investigate any misbehaviour by players and spectators.

But a win was a win, and the two points gained took Leeds to an impressive third in the table. On December 9 Sandy Brown was banned for two weeks and Everton fined £250 for their supporters' misbehaviour. Leeds received no punishment whatsoever.

League Division One table, up to November 7 1964:

| 1 | Manchester Utd | Played 17, | Points 26 |
|---|---|---|---|
| 2 | Chelsea | Played 17, | Points 25 |
| 3 | Leeds Utd | Played 16, | Points 22 |
| 4 | Nottingham Forest | Played 17, | Points 22 |

Leeds had been drawn to face Manchester United in the FA Cup semi-final in late March. The Peacocks were the real big success of the season. They'd shaken up the 'big boys', they had made their mark, and were in the running for honours. Chelsea faltered, and the title chase became a two-horse race.

Hillsborough, March 27 1965. Yorkshire–Lancashire derbies being rivalrous occasions, the football world should have known to expect a bad-tempered match, especially since Leeds had won the last encounter 1–0. Then, after the teams had lined up to take to the field, George Best felt a sharp pain in his right calf. Someone had kicked him, and not playfully or gently. Bobby Collins. 'And that's just for starters, Bestie,' he said.

This time there'd be no need for melodramatic press reporting. And true to form, the match was ugly, mundane and hostile. There were no goals, few scoring chances, many fouls, two bookings, a couple of injuries and no shortage of bitterness.

Reporters criticized the referee for being too soft with the players and complained that both sets of players had been more intent on kicking each other than the football. 0–0. A replay would be needed. It would take place on the following Wednesday at Nottingham Forest's ground.

5–3

I had to watch the replay on the Peacock's TV set, which was miles better than ours. I'd been desperate to go to Sheffield and then the midweek replay in Nottingham, but my grandma wouldn't let me. It wasn't just about the cost: she didn't think it'd be safe as there had been some trouble on and off the pitch at Hillsborough. I'd never been to an away game before and hadn't seen any real trouble myself. She knew I was dead disappointed and promised to let me go to Wembley if we got there.

According to the papers the first semi-final had been a boring nil-niller and more like a street fight than a match. But I had a good feeling about the replay, I thought we'd beat them, especially if Paul Reaney could keep George Best shackled again. The FA Cup loves an underdog.

Inside the pub it was standing room only. I found a spot on a window ledge. It was so crowded that the frosted windows were steamed up and condensation ran down the glass into the dust. The weather at Forest was a lot drier, so the pitch was in much better nick. We were more up against it due to Albert being out injured. Terry Cooper came in as left wing-half in his place. Most of the first half was Man United on the attack, but our defence stood solid and Gary Sprake worked hard for his pay, making good saves from Law, Herd, Best and Bobby Charlton. Our back five really did look like a wall, hard as rock to break through. Jack hit the Reds' crossbar with a header; Alan Peacock went close a couple of times for us as well. Half-time, 0–0.

The second half was dead tight and cagey, like two boxers probing, sussing each other out, looking for the best point to attack. Each team searched for weaknesses in the opponent's defence to exploit. But neither team looked like it had any real weaknesses. It looked like the game could go on forever.

61

With about twenty minutes to go, an old chap watching said to me, 'Don Revie's done summat, look, look how he's told John Giles to move into the middle and take Billy Bremner's place. Jim Storrie's switched from inside-forward to Giles' place on the right wing so Bremner's playing up front now, in Jim's place. That'll confuse the Manchester defenders, you just watch, kid.'

He was right and all: we did most of the attacking now, as the final whistle got closer. We had five corners in a row in the last few minutes. You could hear the Man United fans whistling because they were so worried. The Reds managed to defend all the corners though, so it stayed 0–0. It was real nerve-racking stuff. It looked like there'd be another half-hour extra time, maybe another replay as well. But then Nobby Stiles gave away a free kick for obstruction on Johnny Giles, just inside the centre circle.

There couldn't have been much more than a minute left. The Manchester crowd's whistling got even louder as Giles got ready to take the kick. I couldn't hear the TV, so I made up my own commentary.

Giles sets himself to take the kick; he's over forty yards away from the goal. Steps back, away from the ball, five, six, seven steps, eyes fixed on the penalty area. He's scanning, he's planning. Looks like he's trying to tell a team-mate where he's aiming. He takes a step and then a funny little skip towards the ball, but then stops, like he's changed his mind. And then it's back on again, and with a swift, sharp right-footed strike the ball launches into the air towards the crowded penalty area. It looks like he's overhit it; the goalkeeper thinks the same, that it will bounce once and then out. The players agree. Except for one. He keeps moving, keeps watching and keeps calculating. He tracks and anticipates the ball as it drops, drops, drops towards the six-yard box. Nearly there now, it's six, five, four feet off the ground.

Three.

Three, and Bremner launches himself, twisting his body in mid-air, stretching, straining to meet the ball. With his back to the goal, his body near horizontal, he connects to head the ball, firmly, with his left temple. Goalkeeper Dunne moves, but he's too late. The ball veers towards the goal and under the crossbar.

The Manchester defenders wave their hands to protest that Bremner was offside, but no one takes any notice. Bremner sprints towards the left corner, where the closest Leeds crowd is. Nearly all of his team-mates follow him, and a couple of young supporters climb over the wall to join in the celebrations too. Further down the touchline, nearer the television cameraman, sheepskin coat-clad Don Revie grabs sidekick Les Cocker in a tight embrace. They laugh and shout with triumphant glee, almost disbelieving – they've finally done it, they're in the FA Cup final!

I'm standing on the window ledge, fists clenched, arms up in the air, tears running down my face.

## 5–4

Prior to their first ever FA Cup final in May 1965, Leeds had the small matter of the League Championship title to settle. Leeds and Manchester United were still vying for first place. Chelsea had faded.

Monday April 26, and Leeds' last league game was away to already relegated Birmingham City. Manchester, with a game in hand and a superior goal average, were just one point behind Leeds and were at home to Arsenal, while two nights later their final game would be away to Aston Villa. Leeds would have to beat Birmingham and hope that Manchester United would drop points in their last two games. The chances were slim.

Leeds' title hopes had waned with defeats to Manchester United and Sheffield Wednesday in mid-April. The Birmingham match saw their challenge all but killed off with a 3–3 draw. Manchester beat Arsenal 3–1. Leeds could only finish top if Aston Villa beat Manchester United by a phenomenal scoreline on the Wednesday night. Top of the table:

| 1 | Man Utd | Played 41, | Points 61 | GA 2.38 |
|---|---------|-----------|-----------|---------|
| 2 | Leeds Utd | Played 42, | Points 61 | GA 1.60 |

And so Revie contacted Matt Busby after the Monday games to congratulate Manchester on being worthy League Champions.

The FA Cup final was on May 1. Leeds versus Liverpool. Instead of being allowed home for a couple of days' relaxation, though, the lads spent the week at the team hotel in Selsdon Park near Croydon. They weren't impressed with the idea of spending so much time together, even with Revie's friend Herbert Warner – the club's unofficial court jester - on hand to try and keep spirits high. There was dissention in the Leeds ranks. Bingo, dominoes, cards, carpet bowls, indoor golf, billiards and snooker couldn't keep them entertained for long.


## 5–5


I couldn't get a ticket for the final. They cost too much. I didn't want my grandma paying more than she could afford, it wouldn't be right. The papers said that tickets that were usually a couple of quid at the most were going for fifteen times that on the black market. Two quid was more than enough as it was. Maybe it was best I didn't go, I said ... I'd stay here to watch it on TV.

I didn't go running that day – I didn't want to miss anything. Dead early, even from my bedroom, I could hear the coach and car engines at Elland Road, ready for the drive to Wembley. I was sick with jealousy. My grandma made us steak and kidney pie specially, for dinner. She came to the pub to watch the match with me. Aitch had saved us two seats near the TV.

You could hardly hear the commentators the crowd at the match was so noisy. There was a deafening buzz as the teams came out of the tunnel. Hairs were sticking up on the back of my neck.

The Don led Leeds out. He's in a sharp dark suit and tie and white shirt. The Leeds players look immaculate in the white shorts and socks and white tracksuit jackets. Bill Shankly has a lighter suit on, his players in all red.

Don Revie, walking in front. Smiling proudly for the camera. Then captain Bobby Collins, small and tough, wearing his 'lucky' socks, which were more a white gone off now; blond keeper Gary Sprake, tall and broad; black-haired Paul Reaney; slim and tall Alan Peacock, lean Norman Hunter; Albert, Johnny Giles, both as small as Bobby; gritty Willie Bell and Jim Storrie; then Billy Bremner, bouncing an orange football on his head likes he's just

64

got it for Christmas; finally, at the back, as always, big, fair-haired Jack – serious, determined, cool. Every one of them looks deadly sombre, as if they're walking into a gladiatorial arena.

This was Leeds' first ever FA Cup final appearance but Liverpool's third. Lucky third time around for them, too, as they beat us 2–1, after extra time. But, in our first season back in Division One, we'd come second in the league and second in the FA Cup. Not bad for a team of alleged cloggers tipped for immediate relegation.

Liverpool were the better team on the day. They were composed, more confident and better organized than us, and their tactics for the match worked better. We just couldn't seem to turn it on, our performance was tired, frustrating, and most of the players just didn't play well enough, Albert Johanneson especially. I thought he looked scared to death, not that that was his fault: hordes of Scouse pigs pretending to be proper football supporters were to blame. They weren't supporters, they were just scum: every time Albert got the ball, they'd boo, jeer, whistle him, and some even made gorilla noises at him. They were branding *him* an animal. Bastards.

We deserved to lose, that's the hard truth. Billy was crying at the end. He just stood there on the pitch, swiping tears off his face while The Don consoled him. But what the Leeds players had achieved that season was bloody amazing. They were heroes, each and every one of them.

### 5–6

Soon after their astonishing 1964–65 season, Revie dispensed with the services of forwards Ian Lawson and Tommy Henderson, to Crystal Palace and Bury respectively. Both had served him well, especially Lawson, with twenty-one goals in fifty-one Leeds appearances, but Revie was looking to the future and believed he had better, more dynamic players in the reserves.

In September 1964, Leeds had visited Bloomfield Road, home of Blackpool FC, in the league. In spite of Syd Owen's detailed dossier on the Blackpool team, Leeds were annihilated 4–0. A small, cocky, ginger-haired nineteen year old had inflicted much of the damage. Alan Ball. He had good pace and agility, spirit, stamina and creativity. Revie wanted him for Leeds.

# Chapter 6

## 6–1

The 1964–65 Honours didn't look embarrassing any more:

**Division One winners**: Man United. Runners up: Leeds United.
**FA Cup winners**: Liverpool. Runners up: Leeds United.
**League Cup winners**: Chelsea. Runners up: Leicester.
**European Cup winners**: Inter Milan. Runners up: Benfica.
**European Cup Winners' Cup winners**: West Ham. Runners up: TSV 1860 Munich.
**Inter-Cities Fairs Cup winners**: Ferencvaros. Runners up: Juventus.
**Football Player of the Year**: Bobby Collins, Leeds United.
**European Footballer of the Year**: Eusebio, Benfica.
**Average home gate**: 37,484. Many Leeds people had rediscovered the use of their legs.

We had won bugger all. But at least there was credit for the team's efforts, plus really good crowds, and Bobby Collins getting the recognition he deserved. Actually, for finishing second in the league we qualified for the Inter-Cities Fairs Cup. So in a way we did win something.

Fullerton Park training pitches. Twenty lads in all sorts of football kit and a few men in clean, bright blue Leeds tracksuits. Coaches Cyril Partridge and Bob English are running things. It's like an army sports day. They're telling us where to stand, what stretches and exercises to do, while giving us a green bib or a yellow bib each. This is serious business. I haven't slept well for days, one reason being that there's been a sparrow trapped in our chimney, making all sorts of racket at all hours. Probably dead by now.

There are red cones dotted all over the place, flags on all the pitch corners, net-bags with white leather footballs in as well as brown and orange ones, small-scale goal posts and big cloth soccer kit bags, and the huge grass-roller over at the side. Further in the distance, near the boiler-making factory side of Fullerton Park, a few of the junior players are knocking footballs around. Practising free kicks, whacking long passes, trying to outdo each other. Trapping the ball stone dead, expertly, with either foot or chest, then juggling it with their feet and head and shoulders. And I'm watching them as I stretch and warm up, thinking, knowing, that I can do just as well.

I'd lost count of the number of times I'd stood at the top of the little embankment, above the car park, watching the training and drills. And now I'm here, inside that fence, inside the heart of the club itself, about to try out to be one of the next generation of Leeds players. It's time for me To Achieve Personal Greatness. I'm nervous, scared even, but I try to turn it into a positive, as if it's a challenge. I'd shed blood for The Don and Leeds, I would.

I've been picked for midfield, where I prefer playing. Cyril and Bob make us do a couple more warm-up exercises and stretches, and then three laps around the pitch. I've seen a few of these lads down here before but most I've never set eyes on until this morning. Some had travelled from Wales to be here. I was raring to get started. The adrenaline was pumping big time. It was the middle of July, I'd just turned fifteen and school was no more. I was on the threshold of something brilliant.

The pitch was quite stiff and there wasn't much grass on it. Dried mud was rutted in the centre circle and in both penalty areas, but it wasn't sun-baked, liable to cripple you if you landed badly.

My team kicks off, one of the forwards taps the ball to another team-mate, then it's passed to me. I try to keep hold of it for longer than the others, to try and show I'm not nervous. I look up towards our attackers as if I'm going to hit a long pass, but then I side-foot it short, horizontally to our right-back, a yard in front of him – place the ball in front so he can run on to it and not have to alter his stride. Short, simple, *effective* passing.

Our performance definitely improved as the first half went on, and that's when I began to notice a few more spectators on the touchline. Maurice Lindley, Syd Owen and Bobby Collins. Ces, of course, and a couple of the other ground staff. Passy too, which I thought was great of him. There was no Don Revie though.

We were only 1–0 up at half-time, but the goal was a fluky deflection off a defender's shoulder. The result wasn't important: it was about how the team played. The passing, the communication and the linking up.

We were given water in plastic cups to drink, plus quarters of orange to chew and suck the juice out of. Cyril Partridge checked we were all okay and not injured, coaching us, encouraging us, telling us to keep focused and to carry on playing as we are. Bob English came over to us too and said that we were doing well and dominating the game, especially in the midfield area. On the other side of the pitch, the other team had Bobby Collins talking to them. I was so jealous, greener than Glasgow Celtic.

The other team played better in the second half, putting us under pressure and giving us less time on the ball. We started losing possession too easily and hardly put any good moves together at all. It needed some firing up. We got a free kick on the edge of our area. I called for it, received it and turned to run a short distance before passing it. But then I tripped, causing me to stumble slightly on the rutted mud. One of the Welsh lads from the other team comes tearing in to try and tackle me. But he misses the ball and he misses me: I've toe-poked the ball between his legs, fooling him. There's a cheer from a couple of the spectators. I say sorry to the lad and he grunts back, his face flushed and angry.

The match carries on and it's all a bit stale and ordinary, like everyone's just going through the motions. Then, with only a few minutes left, we get another free kick on the edge of our area, and our keeper decides to take the kick and pass it short to me. Except my back's turned away from him. I'm completely unawares. Realizing he's calling out to me, I stop and turn around. I hurry towards the ball. Then I get the weird feeling that something else is coming my way.

The Welsh lad from before has smelled a chance of an attack. He wants the ball, and he's got a few yards and seconds of start on me. He's sprinting full pelt. I get there first. I put my right foot on it, my body weight all on my left leg. And it's at this exact, precise, moment that the Welsh lad slams into me. The sole of his left foot lands on my left ankle while his right boot, studs first,

69

pummels into my left leg just below my knee. My ankle has given way and there's disgusting pain there, but the pain higher up is worse. I'm on the ground, I'm woozy, trembling, I'm nauseous and I'm out of it, I'm yelping, I can't move my legs or even breathe without pulverizing, stabbing screams searing through me. Any movement just makes it worse. Just being awake makes it worse.

I fainted. I woke up with Bob English trying to treat my wounds and trying to calm me down, Cyril Partridge and Ces and Passy looking down at me. Someone put a blanket over me. I couldn't stop shivering.

Real men don't cry. Real men don't let on they're hurt, real men don't faint, they black out, real men grin and bear it, real men take it on the chin, real men take it in their stride, real men get on with it. Real men don't bawl and wail like a baby. I wasn't a real man. I begged them not to move my leg, but they did, and I fainted again.

### 6–2

Nothing was said on *This Is Your Life* about Revie's and Leeds' first foray into European competition, which began in late September 1965. Playing in Europe was to boost the club's coffers as well as the reputations of the manager and players. But amongst the many highlights and triumphs they were to experience on their travels abroad, would come cruel tragedy.

In the summer of 1965, football experts in the media casually wrote off Leeds' chances of success for the forthcoming campaign. They'd be a 'one-season wonder'.

Leeds' compiling of dossiers on opposing teams was never a popular strategy, as if it were unethical or even a cheating ruse. Scant recognition of their qualities, individual and collective, came Leeds' way, while the team's bad reputation showed no signs of leaving just yet.

By the end of September, Leeds were joint top of Division One, with fourteen points. A decent start, with just two narrow defeats, at West Ham and Tottenham, and two draws with Sheffield United and Leicester. Good hard-earned wins over Sunderland, Aston Villa (twice), Nottingham Forest, Blackburn Rovers and Spurs indicated that Leeds would be strong runners again.

Before the start of each season, Revie prioritized the team's games. The 'lesser' games would give him the chance to utilize some of the younger or peripheral players at the club. Manager and coaches pushed the players hard. Complacency would not be a danger in 1965–66. Alan Peacock was recalled to the national squad. While call-ups were something to be proud of, Revie bemoaned how they upset his plans. Young 'hotshot' Peter Lorimer had recovered from a broken leg and returned to first team action in scorching form. Injuries to Willie Bell and Albert Johanneson meant chances for first team action for Paul Madeley and Terry Cooper, occasionally Rod Johnson, and young forward Jimmy Greenhoff appeared a number of times and proved himself a versatile and capable prospect. As the season wore on, other youngsters would play 'bit parts': Mick Bates, Terry Hibbitt, David Harvey, Nigel Davey, Rod Belfitt and Dennis Hawkins. The young Scot Edwin Gray had officially signed forms for the club too, a superstar in the making, according to Syd Owen. Left-footed boy Gray had it all, Owen said. Jimmy Lumsden, a promising, fair-haired inside-right, was signed from school, along with Gray.

Leeds' European debut came in 1965 in the Inter-Cities Fairs Cup, first round. Ties were played over two legs, home and away. Soon after the draw for round one had been made, Don Revie and Syd Owen travelled to Italy to analyze the opponents – Torino. The two spies returned carrying a hefty and detailed dossier.

The first game was the home leg. Leeds went into it fresh from a sound home victory against lowly Blackburn Rovers. Revie swapped around his players' shirt numbers in an attempt to confuse the visitors. But the Leeds midfield bossed the game throughout and the defence snuffed out every Torino threat comfortably. A shot by Bremner on twenty-five minutes was fumbled by the Torino keeper into his own net. Despite allowing

Torino to grab a breakaway goal with only a few minutes of the tie left, Leeds held on to win 2–1.

The Stadio Communale, Turin, October 6 1965, the night Brady and Hindley commit their final, appalling crime. Torino, in maroon shirts, white shorts and socks, played host to the all-white Leeds United. They welcomed back Gigi Meroni, 'the Italian George Best', to their line-up and were hoping to finish the tie quickly, believing an early goal would kill Leeds' spirit and make for a comparatively easy game. They had underestimated the strength and commitment of Revie's team, though, who played passionate and combative football. But, five minutes into the second half, one Leeds man's life would be changed forever.

Bobby Collins had collected the ball twenty or so yards outside the Torino penalty area. Torino left-back Fabrizio Poletti intended to stop him. Collins raced ahead into free space. Over a short distance, he was still one of the fastest players around, and it is possible that Poletti misjudged Collins' pace. Poletti careered towards his target, but changed neither speed nor his angle of approach. At full throttle, Poletti thuds into Collins, his knee thrusting into the Scot's right thigh.

The damage done to Bobby Collins is serious. Collins staying down means he is genuinely injured and in need of attention. The referee simply gesticulates that the player should be lifted off the pitch to allow play to continue. A couple of Torino players make to drag him over the nearest touchline. But the protective frame of Jack Charlton strides in to stand over and shield the motionless Leeds captain, like a bodyguard. The Torino players know what's best for their own safety and leave the scene, while the enraged, tearful and disgusted Billy Bremner promises to avenge the assault on his skipper Collins.

The referee, finally grasping the extent of the injury, signals for a stretcher to be brought on. Les Cocker races from the Leeds dugout to the stricken player. He frantically tries to comfort him but it's a lost cause, the injury is severe.

The ten men of Leeds continued to defend the contest, which ended in a 0–0 stalemate. But the victory was hollow, as for the Leeds players and officials the only concern was Collins' injury.

Torino players visited him in the local hospital, and Poletti showed sincere remorse.

Collins' splintered femur bone needed a fifteen-inch pin to graft the bone back together. He vowed to be back soon. Two weeks later, Collins returned to a hero's welcome at Yeadon Airport, greeted by a small but very appreciative crowd of supporters. Within those two weeks, Revie moved quickly to try and repair the damage to his team.

He switched Johnny Giles from the right flank to fill Bobby Collins' place, and in came a new player, the skilful Huddersfield Town right winger Mike O'Grady for £30,000.

## 6–3

In a matter of seconds, my dreams had been crushed. As had my leg. The pain was unbearable, it hurt so much that I cried many a time, I'm not ashamed to admit it. When you're awake and you've got a bad injury, you *know* that you've got a bad injury. With a broken leg and ankle, there's not exactly much chance of forgetting. But when you're asleep you're not in the real world. Lying there, you move and fidget and twitch, and if you're anything like me, you sometimes even try to run and kick as well. A thigh-length plaster of Paris boot stops you moving properly, but not completely. You can still move a leg a fraction, broken bones or not. Your body only needs a fraction of opportunity to remind you it's broken. The tiniest move of my leg made me yelp and curse. My crying out would wake my grandma up. Those nights made my life a misery.

The pain made good sleep impossible. Insane, evil little notions would pop up in my head and torment me. Not sure what was real and what was just imagined, I sometimes thought I'd have to have my leg amputated. Or I'd be thinking I could walk again but only on stilts.

I'd often nod off in the daytime to catch up on the lost sleep. Then I'd feel less tired the next night as a result, meaning I'd be more restless and wake up even more easily in the early hours again. It was a vicious circle.

I had to endure that filthy full-length pot for eight weeks, and I had two wooden crutches to help me get around. They rubbed my

73

armpits raw and caused infected sores under both arms. My grandma got me some cream from the chemist, which did work, but stunk something rancid.

One morning someone knocked on the door. It woke me up with a start, it was about eleven o'clock, and I was hot and worn out. Another knock. Whoever it was wasn't going away. It was Ces, come to see how I was coping. Or not coping, more like. He had a bottle of sherry with him, a fancy card wishing me a speedy recovery and a letter in a white Leeds United envelope addressed to my grandma. First thing he did was go to the window and let some light in, then he re-opened the door like he was letting the bad atmosphere out.

The card was signed by the coaches as well as 'on behalf of' Don Revie', probably by his secretary Jean, I suppose, plus some of the ground staff and Bobby Collins and Nigel Davey, who had seen what'd happened to me.

I was pleased to see Ces and hoped he wouldn't see me bawling. He was here on a mission. Of course, he, the physios and coaches had seen it all before. It was an injury, easily mended. The club said I could go in for treatment and weight training whenever I liked. My leg'd be in pot for weeks, but that shouldn't stop me from exercising my upper body. I couldn't think of anything less appealing, to be honest, I just wanted to rest and feel sorry for myself. Let nature take its course in repairing my leg, knitting the bones back together, and, with luck, not letting the muscles waste away that much. The hospital had said that my ankle should heal quite quickly and easily. The fibia fracture was the main concern; it would take weeks longer to recover.

Ces took me to the pub for dinner. The Peacock was only about two hundred yards away yet it took me nearly twenty minutes to get there, obviously not exactly adept with the crutches. Landlord Aitch stood behind the bar and clapped me when I finally crutched my way in, and then I noticed him wipe his eyes and nose. That got me nearly blubbing all over again, the big girl's blouse. They had it all worked out for me: they'd set out a little round table and put a stool and a cushion next to the seat for me to put my leg up. They'd picked the seat closest to the toilets, as well as near the pinball machine and the jukebox.

74

It was October. My playing season had been done for three months before, and my season watching Leeds hadn't been allowed to even start. My grandma said it wasn't safe for me to go to the matches while I was on crutches. Instead, I'd go to the Peacock most afternoons and get nice and cosy, courtesy of Aitch and any other generous souls who knew and felt sorry for the feckless invalid feeling sorry for himself that was me. On match days we'd put the radio on so we could keep up to date with the football news. We could usually hear how Leeds were doing just from the noise over the road. We hardly ever dropped points at home, and there were always over 30,000 for League games, even midweek. When Liverpool came the crowd was over 49,000. That was Christmas week, and it was only a day after we'd beaten them 1–0 at Anfield. Peter Lorimer got that one. Liverpool got their revenge by beating us in the second match, same scoreline. I never understood why the League would schedule two games in two days, especially involving the same two teams.

Two weeks after Christmas, Man United came, and the crowd was only a couple of hundred short of 50,000. The Mancs got a 1–1 draw, but they were never really in the title race this season. It was mostly us, Liverpool and Burnley in the running.

That Leeds–Man United game was on a freezing cold night, and the Saturday after Leeds were at home again, to Stoke. A week after that they were drawn to play Bury in the FA Cup at Elland Road. On its good days, the Elland Road pitch wasn't great, but it was reasonable – it soaked up water too easily, as it didn't have any decent drainage, but it wasn't bad. It was worse if there was frost or freezing fog, though: the pitch would be solid. There'd be dangerous little frozen ridges all over the place and you knew all about it if you landed on one. After the Man United game on the Wednesday, Ces and the ground staff, plus the apprentices, were up against it to keep the pitch in good enough condition for the Stoke match on Saturday January 15. The weather stayed bad, meaning that the pitch wouldn't improve, not by nature anyway: no sunshine, only freezing fog, sharp frosts and chill winds. Ces and co would really have their work cut out.

Friday January 14, a day I'd been looking forward to for ages. Six months, in fact. I was due to be freed from the pot on my left leg. Six horrible months. Today meant no more crutches, no more risking breaking more of my bones on cobbled streets or slippery pavement slabs. I caught a bus to the Infirmary and waited for the nurses to cut off the half-pot. My leg had got so skinny, especially below the knee. To build it up was a challenge, though. I was determined there'd be no more feeling sorry for myself, no more being a lazy-arse layabout. Each day's aim would be to get better and stronger – To Achieve Personal Greatness. I'd been so close before. The doctor said I'd have to be careful but I could start training again, slowly and surely, just with long walks at first. I couldn't wait to get going and I even walked from the Infirmary back to the Peacock, with the aid of a National Health walking stick. It still took me well over an hour, but I loved every minute of it. I was nearly normal again.

I had a couple of celebratory pints in the pub with Aitch and then decided I wanted to show Ces my skinny but 'new' leg. So off I hobbled to the stadium, slowly, carefully, happily. As I'm passing the club reception, Bobby Collins comes walking out of the glass doors. He seems to be faring okay after that horrible injury, and I'm dead pleased for him. I stop for a few seconds, standing there lamely with my stick at my side supporting me. Him being my all-time favourite player, I really want to say something to him, but I lose my nerve. I'm glad I did. He sees me and says a standard hello to me, and then he does a double-take as he's just remembered who I am. I can see from his eyes and the expression of near disgust on his face that he is far from impressed with me, with the crap condition I'd let myself get in.

### 6–4

Last season's losing finalists fell early in the next FA Cup. After impressively beating Bury 6–0 in the third round, the fourth round produced a much harder pairing for Leeds, at Chelsea, where they undeservedly went down 1–0. The Yorkshiremen outplayed the Blues for long periods of the game and their performance earned praise from the London press, with the *Times* for one describing aspects of United's attacking play as superb and mobile, cold-blooded but clean. Hardly a glowing term, 'cold-blooded but clean', or a fitting one for that matter, but it was, at least, an improvement.

In the match, Leeds could have won by three or four clear goals their dominance had been so strong. Could have – but bad luck, the lack of a clinical finisher in attack and the presence of Peter Bonetti in goal in brilliant form meant Leeds went out. The Leeds attack had been weakened by the loss of Alan Peacock in January with damaged knee ligaments. His season was finished and Leeds' age-old problem in attack had returned.

The League was the most important competition in English football, bringing with it the 'bread and butter' of the sport: regular revenue at the turnstiles. But the Leeds players, like most footballers, in certain respects preferred cup matches, as they had an edge over the League and were often more exciting and special occasions. Knockout matches in general were naturally more dramatic, too – fates were decided and heroes and villains made within a matter of minutes, whereas the League campaign normally lasted nine months. The Football League Cup, though, was still young and a very definite poor relation of the FA Cup, borne out by vastly inferior match attendances. It had first been introduced in the 1960–61 season, eventually won, over two legs, by Aston Villa against Rotherham United. But five years since its inception, some managers (Don Revie one of them) regarded the competition as minor and certainly the least important prize going, at least in those early years.

October 13 1965. Revie insisted his team selection for the League Cup third round tie at home to West Bromwich Albion had been entirely appropriate, even though his young Leeds side had lost the match 4–2. And the crowd of just 13,455 demonstrated how highly the paying public rated the competition. Nevertheless, criticism headed Revie's way for fielding a weakened team, and not for the last time.

Revie believed that to win the League title as well as other trophies using the same pool of eleven or twelve players, for what would probably involve more than sixty matches, was nigh-on impossible. And this season there were times even Mother Nature seemed to be against them – Leeds had games in hand over their rivals for much of this season due to weather-postponed matches. Games in hand did not signify points of course, but they nearly always did cause fixture pile-ups and player fatigue problems late in the season.

In the race for the title, Leeds had occupied top spot for a short while early in the season but gradually fallen behind, due to losing points in surprising, disappointing draws and defeats or just by having matches postponed. Although they would remain heavily involved in the League fight, the 1965–66 season seemed to be as much, if not more, about the Fairs Cup than domestic honours for Leeds. It had been their official introduction to European competition and they had taken to it remarkably well, despite the horrific injury to Bobby Collins in Torino.

In the Fairs Cup second round, Leeds had been paired with SC Leipzig of East Germany. The first leg was away, behind the so-called Iron Curtain, in late November. It had snowed heavily but the tie had never been in doubt as the Leipzig ground staff had worked hard to flatten and pack the snow, paint blue pitch markings on it and provide orange rather than white footballs for the game.

Leeds, through Lorimer and Bremner, only managed to score in the last ten minutes of the match and even then Leipzig pulled a goal back through Frenzell to make it a tight 2–1 Leeds win and all definitely still in the balance for the return leg.

It took place at Elland Road, on a cold 1 December night. Revie selected his strongest line-up, but the 32,111 crowd were not much entertained and instead had to endure a dour 0–0 draw. But at least Leeds advanced, drawn against Spanish side Valencia in round three. The first leg was scheduled for Elland Road, in February next year.

### 6–5

My grandma had told me she wanted a little chat with me, 'adult to adult'. I must admit, I'd been expecting another bollocking, or at least a more than mild ticking off, but she was great, like she knew exactly what was going on in my head and how I was feeling. She would help me any way she could to recover from the injuries.

And so, from late December, she'd get me up each morning again, seven or so o'clock, and pot free I'd go out for a brisk walk – running, even trotting, wasn't possible yet, my bones weren't anywhere near strong enough and I needed to build up my leg muscles as well.

I'd see people going to their various places of work, on buses or walking or in cars, and I'd ponder on the fact that I'd never done a proper day's work in my life. True, I'd trained hard, but most of the kids I was at school with would have been in new jobs or apprenticeships for months now. Printing, building, clerical, the copper-works, even in the forces or down one of the pits not too far away. Me, I'd set my stall out early on to be a professional footballer, everyone knew that, but all I'd got so far was agony from a snapped leg and ankle. For me To Achieve Personal Greatness or anything like it again wasn't going to be easy.

I'd missed a lot of Leeds games because I'd been laid up, so there were a load of arrivals and departures and debuts that had passed me by. Don Weston joined Huddersfield for £3,500 while Mike O'Grady arrived from there for £30,000. By all accounts O'Grady had done excellently since joining, scoring a few, setting up a load and giving Leeds a fresh threat on the right wing as Johnny Giles was moved into Bobby Collins' place in central midfield. Everyone was saying it looked as if the position had been made for Giles.

In the League, after Christmas we were hardly in the frame to win it. Liverpool were coasting. We'd been unlucky in the FA Cup, losing 1–0 away to Chelsea, and the League Cup finished early with West Brom beating us 4–2. So far I'd missed the debuts of Mick Bates, Eddie Gray, Dennis Hawkins, Nigel Davey, David Harvey in nets, Terry Hibbitt and of course O'Grady.

The League table, on January 29 1966, after we lost 2–0 at Sunderland:

1    Liverpool  Played 28,      Points 41

| 2 | Burnley | Played 27, | Points 36 |
| 3 | Man Utd | Played 27, | Points 34 |
| 4 | Leeds   | Played 25, | Points 33 |

It was obvious that Liverpool were doing really well, but the fight for the Championship wasn't over by a long chalk. We were looking the likeliest to battle it out with them but I was never that confident because having games in hand never equalled points on the table.

Even though he'd asked for a transfer, Jimmy Greenhoff lined up in a few games and played well. Paul Madeley had established himself in the first team and he'd even scored his first goal, last September. The Leeds coaches had high hopes for all the new lads, none more so than Eddie Gray.

## 6–6

February 2 1966, Elland Road. Valencia, twice winners and once losing finalists in the previous three years of the Inter-Cities Fairs Cup, wore all red, versus Leeds' all white, and took an early lead. For Leeds, young centre-forward Rod Belfitt was in attack on his European debut, practically on his own. Leeds deservedly equalized in the sixty-fourth minute through a sweet strike from Lorimer after a good low cross by John Giles. The match, though, was remembered more not for the quality of play but for its violence, which, according to the *Times*, was instigated by Valencia players, with Leeds giving as good as they got in response. The score stayed 1–1.

In Valencia, Leeds wore a seldom-seen kit of blue shirts with yellow shorts and socks. Gary Sprake was on great form. The Leeds plan was to absorb the Valencia pressure and reply on the break with counter-attacks. Jack Charlton was playing like a true stalwart, leading by example, and the whole team fought magnificently throughout, in front of a partisan 45,000 crowd.

In the seventy-fifth minute Leeds' resolve paid off as Mike O'Grady, receiving a good pass from Paul Madeley, ran on to the ball and beat the Valencia offside trap to strike a low, angled drive, which eluded goalkeeper Vito inside his near post. The goal quietened the home fans' whistles and jeers and finished Valencia's already wavering hopes of winning.

The same night as Leeds were negotiating their way past Valencia, Chelsea drew 3–3 on aggregate with AC Milan. To decide who went through, the toss of a disc was required. Chelsea called the toss correctly, meaning there were now two strong English sides in the last eight of a very tough competition. Chelsea were paired with 1860 Munich while next up for Leeds were highly rated Ujpest Dozsa, from communist Hungary. Receiving a bye in the first round and having beaten FC Cologne and Everton in consequent rounds, Ujpest were another side very confident of beating the young debutantes.

Ujpest Dozsa's typical plan for away ties in Europe was to defend en masse and hope to score breakaway goals. If their opponents did score, Ujpest possessed so much attacking flair within their ranks that they were always capable of hitting back quickly. So far in the competition they had lost by the odd goal in both their away ties but comfortably won their home ties by three or four goals. So Leeds would not represent much of a problem, being new to Europe, and Ujpest were deservedly one of the tournament favourites. Their odds, however, began to lengthen rapidly during early events of the first leg, at Elland Road on March 2 1966.

To the Hungarians' annoyance, the game went ahead despite heavy rainfall and the pitch being a 'gluepot', which meant the football would slow up and prevent quick and incisive passing and movement. Revie had had Ujpest watched three times and was well aware they were a fine team, with talent enough to beat any team around. He expected them to come to Elland Road to defend, in the hope of exploiting any gaps Leeds left at the back in their anxiety to score in front of their own fans. As 40,462 looked on, the Leeds players kicked off with instruction from Revie to attack as quickly and directly as possible.

Ujpest had not reckoned for such a swift onslaught. Leeds battered them from the start and scored their first goal in just the sixth minute, Terry Cooper netting from close range after a parried Willie Bell cross. The pressure from the home team was relentless and by half-time, with further goals from Bell and Jim Storrie (both headers) and Billy Bremner, who just about walked the ball into the net, it was already 4–0. Ujpest scored a consolation goal in the seventy-fourth minute but their quest for Inter-Cities glory was seriously damaged. Ujpest's manager described the Leeds team's performance as simply fantastic.

At the Szusza Ferenc Stadium, near Budapest, the first half of the return match was a vintage display of continental football, with Ujpest menacing Leeds' goal almost non-stop. But, met by a vintage display of English defending, Ujpest's efforts were frustrated. They hit the post three times though, as well as shooting narrowly over a couple of times too. But Gary Sprake was having another superb game, the sort most goalkeepers can only dream of.

The hosts did manage to score shortly before half-time, making it 2–4 on aggregate. With more than fifty minutes to go, more goals were very possible. Ujpest's immense pressure on Leeds continued, but they were unable to breach the Leeds blockade again. Late on, compounding the Hungarians' frustrations, by wrong-footing two defenders by craftily letting a pass from Mike O'Grady go through his legs, Peter Lorimer raced fifty yards with the ball before slotting it into the Ujpest net.

Leeds were now through to the last four of their first ever European crusade. Elsewhere in the Fairs Cup, Chelsea had managed to win through to the last four as well, by scraping a 3–2 victory over 1860 Munich. They were drawn to play Spanish giants Barcelona, while Leeds' semi-final would also be against Spanish opposition, the 1964 Fairs Cup winners Real Zaragosa.

6–7

After we played Everton at home, on April 16, we were definitely out of the League title race, even though we'd beaten the Toffees 4–1. The same day, Liverpool beat Stoke, while Burnley lost at Aston Villa, meaning Liverpool couldn't be caught at the top of the table and so were League Champions for the 1965–66 season. They deserved it, even though I reckon what The Don and the lads had achieved so far for Leeds was just as brilliant. And then there was little Burnley, still second, with us third: someone was working miracles there, just about.

So, the Inter-Cities Fairs Cup turned out to be Leeds' most realistic target for 1965–66. We'd been knocked out of the League Cup early, and the FA Cup in February, but in Europe we'd done fantastically well and reached the semi-final stage. After knocking Ujpest Dozsa out in March, we were paired with Real Zaragosa, in late April. The first game, away, Zaragosa won 1–0.

In the second leg at home we went close a few times in the first half, and Willie Bell hit the post with a header too. In the twenty-third minute Charlton headed on a lob from Johnny Giles, which Albert Johanneson managed to trundle into the net to level the tie. Zaragosa must have been looking forward to half-time; they were under that much Leeds pressure. It was still 1–0 to Leeds at the interval.

The second half was a different story. The Spaniards looked a lot more composed and confident, even though we had most of the possession still. We seemed to have lost impetus. And then, around the hour mark, Zaragosa scored with a cracking half-volley to make it 2–1 to them on aggregate. The Don pushed Jack Charlton up into attack to try and get Leeds back into the lead again. It worked a treat within minutes; Albert Johanneson ran like the wind to reach a ball on the wing before it went out of play, passing it back down the touchline to Norman Hunter, who crossed it in perfectly for Charlton to head it home. 2–1 to us on the night, 2–2 on aggregate. It must have been a great match to watch for the neutral, but horrible end-to-end stuff for fans, with both us and them going close. The score stayed the same. Leeds won the toss of a red and white disc to decide where the replay would be played: Elland Road in two weeks' time.

As if the Elland Road pitch wasn't in a bad enough state as it was, even in May, The Don only went and got the fire brigade to flood it for the replay. Having seen the Zaragosa players training on Fullerton Park, The Don apparently was worried that they would be too quick for Leeds on a dry surface. There were quite a few Spanish internationals in their side, plus some Brazilians, too. Their nickname wasn't 'Los Magnificos' for nothing, and their front line was nicknamed 'The Magnificent Five'. A boggy surface would, we hoped, slow them down and not be to their liking. But the whole plan backfired for us, big time.

No one could have expected such a start. Zaragosa were beating us 3–0 inside the first quarter of an hour. Fair enough, their second goal was a great strike, but the other two were just poor defending on our part. Leeds had played their first ever Fairs Cup tie last September, but tonight, around eight months later, was their first proper European football lesson. Jack Charlton pulled a late goal back, and we hit the post twice in the second half as well, but Leeds were soundly beaten.

# Chapter 7

It would have been an interesting series of questions for Eamonn Andrews to ask. Without the influence of Don Revie, would Jack Charlton really have developed into a world-class defender? Would coach and physio Les Cocker's reputation have flourished so well? And would Norman Hunter have even made it as a first-rate professional footballer?

On July 30 1966 England beat West Germany 4–2 in the World Cup final, after extra time. English and German players had shown remarkable levels of fitness and resilience to be able to last the whole game. Don Revie target Alan Ball played magnificently, while West Ham's Geoff Hurst got most of the acclaim for hitting a stunning hat trick. Regardless of the controversy that justifiably raged over the legitimacy of Hurst's second and his side's third goal, England deserved the victory. Many said that England had a Russian linesman to thank for the team lifting the World Cup. They didn't. The credit had to go to a single-minded, extremely professional manager together with his exceptional group of players.

At the time, FIFA maintained that substitutes were not needed in the tournament, even to replace injured players. Also strange was winners' medals being awarded only to the eleven England players who appeared in the final. No other players, the coaches or even the manager were rewarded for their efforts.

One sure sign of a football club's successes is the recognition of its players by their countries. Goalkeeper Gary Sprake was now just about a fixture in the Wales squad, and only twenty-one years old. Billy Bremner had recently been capped for Scotland

and Willie Bell would get the call-up too. Bobby Collins had made a Scotland comeback during Leeds' momentous return to Division One, until his nasty injury, while teenagers Peter Lorimer and Eddie Gray were already well known at Scotland youth levels. If they continued playing well for Leeds then they surely would not have long to wait for their call-ups to the full squad. When he joined Leeds, John Giles was already a seasoned international and now a near-permanent cornerstone for the Eire team, and he wasn't even twenty-six. Many Leeds players enjoyed international successes for England: Mike O'Grady, Alan Peacock, Norman Hunter and, most notably, Jack Charlton, had already played, and young Paul Madeley, making a name for himself as the 'play-anywhere Peacock', had appeared for the England Under 23s team. Hunter would be in the 1966 World Cup squad as deputy for captain Bobby Moore while Charlton would partner Moore throughout the entire tournament. And if apartheid hadn't meant suspension of a South Africa national team, it is highly likely that Albert Johanneson would have represented his country many, many times. Other members of the Leeds squad would have to wait for their national chances a while longer, but considering that it had been only five years since Revie took charge of the team, the progress of Leeds was astonishing. When he'd first taken the job, not one current international had been playing for the club.

In 1966 Leeds reported a profit and the club was completely debt free, supposedly for the first time ever. There were rumblings of dissatisfaction from the supporters, however: the trophy cabinet was still relatively bare and there were no apparent big-money signings being made. The public wanted to see new players, most importantly a proven, high-scoring centre-forward.

Revie, though, was prepared to wait patiently for the players he wanted and whom he considered right for the club. He believed that the time was right for players such as Paul Madeley, Eddie Gray and, more importantly, in attack, Jimmy Greenhoff and Rod Belfitt, to graduate to front of stage. Greenhoff and Belfitt he saw as potentially the ideal striker partnership. Greenhoff was graceful, creative and quick, while Belfitt was a more physical footballer who pressurized defenders. The main drawback was, at twenty and twenty-one years old respectively, both had too little experience.

Once the 1966–67 season started, supporter resentment about the lack of new signings seemed to intensify from game to game. Injuries to Albert Johanneson, Mike O'Grady and, especially, Alan Peacock had limited the Leeds team's attacking options. They were in dire need of a powerful target man. Belfitt would battle valiantly and try his damnedest, but whilst his time would come, he was not the immediate solution.

The season began badly for Leeds, with a 3–1 defeat at free-spending Tottenham: Spurs were buzzing and Leeds lost to a livelier and more attack-minded team. The week before, in a Hampden Park friendly against a Glasgow XI, Jack Charlton had sustained a hamstring injury, which would cause him to miss a third of Leeds' league games.

Although Leeds were beaten soundly by Tottenham, the man of the match was Leeds' returning captain Bobby Collins, showing skill, fitness and energy above that of most of the much younger players. This scintillating display from the 'veteran' Collins made his exclusion from the next Leeds game – a tight 2–1 win over West Bromwich Albion – due to an ankle injury all the more disappointing for the fans. Sadder still was the limited number of Leeds games he would later feature in. A perfect midfield replacement for Collins was Johnny Giles, but a thigh injury would cause the Irishman also to miss a third of the League season.

Injuries early in the season and to key players hindered any chances the Leeds team had of striking up a rhythm. By the end of 1966 and just past the half-way stage, they had drawn eight, lost five and won only ten of their league games. The good news, though, was that the season was proving to be a closely fought affair, especially at the top of the table, with as many as eight or nine teams in the Championship running.

By New Year's Eve, having played just over half of their League games, Leeds were sitting respectably in sixth place. They had a game in hand on leaders Manchester United, with whom they had drawn 0–0 that day, and were only five points behind.

The League Division One table (top), December 31 1966:

| | | |
|---|---|---|
| 1 Manchester Utd | Played 24, | Points 33 |
| 2 Liverpool | Played 23, | Points 31 |
| 3 Nottingham Forest | Played 24, | Points 30 |
| 4 Stoke City | Played 24, | Points 29 |
| 5 Chelsea | Played 24, | Points 28 |
| 6 Leeds Utd | Played 23, | Points 28 |

On the face of it, Leeds could still mount a serious challenge for the League title, but a humiliating 5–0 defeat at Anfield in November had cast serious doubts over their credentials as title contenders. An incredible 7–0 thrashing at Ron Greenwood's West Ham United less than two weeks earlier had put paid to their League Cup hopes too.

On Valentine's Day 1967 Bobby Collins' romance with Leeds finally ended as he left the club to join Bury. He had endured a tough time since his terrible injury in Torino, and his recovery and return to first team action at thirty-five years old was no mean feat in itself. But with Revie's fervent interest in signing Alan Ball, who had signed for Everton for £110,000 the previous August, as well as the flourishing partnership of Johnny Giles and Billy Bremner (Bremner was the new skipper, too), Collins knew that his Leeds playing days were limited. Collins left, with the best wishes of everyone at Elland Road and the eternal gratitude of Don Revie, on a free transfer.

In comparison to recent years, this season was an up-and-down time for Leeds, and with more downs than ups. However, with victories over DWS Amsterdam in the second round (including a Johanneson hat trick), Valencia and then Bologna, ending with a May semi-final aggregate win over Kilmarnock – thanks mainly to a hat trick from Rod Belfitt – Leeds had quietly, assuredly, progressed to the Inter-Cities Fairs Cup final, to be played at the beginning of the next season. And, by finishing fourth in Division One, they had qualified for the same competition again anyway.

7–2

Up on my wall, the 1965–66 Honours:

**League Champions**: Liverpool. Runners up: us, Leeds, second time in a row.
**FA Cup winners**: Everton. Runners up: Sheffield Wednesday.
**League Cup winners**: WBA. Runners up: West Ham.
**European Cup winners**: Real Madrid. Runners up: Partizan Belgrade.
**European Cup Winners' Cup winners**: Borussia Dortmund. Runners up: Liverpool.
**Inter-Cities Fairs Cup winners**: Barcelona. Runners up: Real Zaragosa.
**Football Player of the Year**: Bobby Charlton, Manchester United.
**European Footballer of the Year**: Bobby Charlton.
**Average Leeds home gate**: 35,773.

All over England kids would be playing football in the parks and playgrounds and streets, with jumpers or chalk on walls for goal posts, and they'd nab the name of Geoff Hurst or Bobby Charlton or Roger Hunt, Alan Ball, Bobby Moore, Martin Peters, or even Jack Charlton, George Cohen, Ray Wilson, Nobby Stiles. The goalkeeper, of course, would always be Gordon Banks. But not in Leeds, not even after 1966.

In Leeds, the kids would be Gary Sprake in goal, or Paul Reaney or Willie Bell or Billy Bremner or Jackie Charlton or Norman Hunter or Eddie Gray or Peter Lorimer, or even Terry

Cooper, Albert Johanneson, Paul Madeley, Jim Storrie, Alan Peacock, Jimmy Greenhoff or Mike O'Grady. And it was nothing to do with the kids in Leeds being all manner of nationality and not just English: it was because Leeds were making their mark on football, and shown on television a fair bit as well.

But my chances of playing football for Leeds weren't even a dream. They weren't anything, they didn't exist. Once the pot was off my leg, I soon discovered how badly I'd let myself go during those months in plaster, how unfit I'd become.

My belly had grown, my lungs felt like they'd shrunk, and my left leg had lost strength in a big way. I made some major changes to my life. I stopped drinking pints of beer through the day and only had sherry (with raw eggs) on a morning with my breakfast. But even though I wasn't running full pelt yet, just jogging, by July 1966 I'd got myself quite a lot fitter, rebuilding muscles that seemed to have gone flabby – or just gone – and strengthening my ankle by hopping on my left leg. Whenever it was cold or damp, more often than not I'd get this throbbing chill in my leg where the fibia bone had been broken. It still happens now, but the doctors said it was nothing to worry about: just in case, though, I was told to drink more milk to increase the calcium content in my body. Not just any old milk either, but full cream, handily available at the stadium. I hated it: it was like drinking snot, the milk was that thick.

Tuesday nights were training nights for St Anthony's – mainly shuttle running (which I also hated), a couple of laps round the Cross Flatts Park pitch and then a seven-a-side match. The first couple of times I just refereed the games rather than playing in them, but after a while I made a return. Passy and the lads wouldn't tackle hard in fear of hurting me, but I got back into the swing of things quite quickly. I planned to be back playing in the St Ant's eleven by spring 1967. By then I'd be seventeen or thereabouts, and would have missed nearly two full seasons, but you can't hurry recuperation from serious injury, no matter how desperate you are. Then, I hoped, I'd be fully fit again. Would I be confident enough, would I have the guts to tackle hard again, and to really give the ball a whack with my left foot?

Bobby Collins left, and Jim Storrie had moved on too: the business of football. I felt like I'd lost two friends, even though I hardly knew them. I'd never forget how much good they'd done for Leeds, especially Bobby. Without him we would have been a Division Three club by 1963, I was totally sure about that.

As substitute, I made my return for St Anthony's in early 1967, against some Working Men's Club team from Swarcliffe. Anyway, I only got on for the last twenty minutes and we were already winning 4–0, but it was so bloody good to be back. I'd been champing at the bit to get on, although I'd not slept well the night before for nerves. When I first went on to the pitch, it was one of the proudest moments of my life, it really was, as the referee and all the players, both sets, applauded me. How generous was that? I felt as proud as a peacock, but close to blubbing, too. Within seconds, though, I received a whack on my shin and a 'Welcome back, kid' from one of their players, to bring me right back down to earth.

There were no twinges, no after-effects, nothing – my leg and my ankle felt as good as new. Still, I had a secret weapon, a home-made shin pad I'd created out of the mouldable pot the hospital put on my leg underneath the half-length pot. I'd heated it up again, shaped it round my leg and cut it down to size with scissors. And like pilots in the war made a record of their kills, I marked in ink on the pot each St Anthony's game I played.

The ground staff at Leeds consisted of the full and part timers, led by Ces and John, plus loads of 'casuals' who helped out, especially when the weather was crap and when the games at Elland Road piled up. I was one of them. And a handful of us casuals were more like regulars and worked nearly on a daily basis, just not paid as much as the proper employees. I loved the job, and I was grateful the club knew I existed and all that. I felt part of a team, even if it wasn't one of the football teams just yet. Plus it got you into matches for free, and I started travelling as staff to away ones.

It was a three o'clock kick off but I knew before the whistle started the game that we'd lost the semi-final against those London ponces Chelsea. In fact, I knew at 1.25pm on Saturday April 29 1967.

'That's our bleedin' goose cooked then, good and proper,' Ces said, on sight of a group of big fellas in suits near the Villa officials' entrance, posturing like they owned the whole of Birmingham as well as Villa Park. Match referee Ken Burns was posing for photographs with twin brothers Reggie and Ronnie Kray, all shiny and black slicked-back hair, looking like they'd been dipped in Brylcreem. Other huge, well-dressed blokes hung around them, like guard dogs, watching and trying to menace anyone and everyone who went by. One thing was dead bloody sure, Ces said: that those two charmless Cockney crooks were famous for a lot of things, but being football fans or Chelsea supporters wasn't among them.

To be chosen to officiate an FA Cup semi-final was quite an honour for a referee. Ken Burns had obviously done something right in his career to be so well regarded. As far as I knew, the decision was based on a referee's superior ability to control a big game, not on who he knew or how much grubby money certain 'interested parties' were 'offering' him, or how much they threatened him to swing a game.

Leeds didn't lose the match, they had it stolen. Even without Jack Charlton, who had a broken toe, and Albert Johanneson, with a muscle strain, anyone in their right mind could see we were the better team but ended up getting cheated out of it. Leeds had supposedly been clear favourites to win the match.

Chelsea played well, especially in the first half when they were the better team and had a few good efforts on goal as well as scoring the one. Sprake made a truly great save from their defender McCreadie and we were under a lot of pressure. Typical of Sprake, though, to ruin it all, he only went and kicked their player Doyle in the head, knocking him out for a few seconds, early in the game. God alone knows why. We were lucky Sprake stayed on the pitch, because he deserved sending off for that, the idiot.

Chelsea led at half-time but we were easy the better team in the second half, especially in the last twenty minutes or so.

Revie had made a first team squad of thirteen available for the FA Cup semi-final. The Leeds men had played thirteen matches in thirty-three days and suffered some casualties along the way, with injuries to Mike O'Grady, Albert Johanneson and, most importantly, centre-half Jack Charlton, causing them to miss the Chelsea match. Nonetheless, their selection problems did not prevent the bookmakers from making Leeds clear favourites to beat Chelsea.

Soon before the end of the first half at Villa Park, Chelsea's number 7, Charlie Cooke, received the ball on the left touchline and ran twenty yards with it into the Leeds half. It was more thanks to his quick wittedness rather than his swift footwork that he eluded Belfitt, Bremner and then Gray to whip in a fine cross for centre-forward Tony Hateley. Hateley met the ball powerfully with a thrusting header before his marker Madeley got his challenge in. Sprake had no chance. 1–0 to Chelsea. Half-time arrives.

In the second half, Leeds ran the game, having the majority of possession and trying to break down the Chelsea defences. They had, though, not seriously threatened Chelsea's goal until, with less than ten minutes of the ninety to go, everything changed and the tempo of Leeds' advances increased dramatically. From the centre circle, Norman Hunter stroked a thirty-yard pass to Jimmy Greenhoff on the left wing. Greenhoff controlled the ball and quickly lobbed it towards Chelsea's penalty area. Billy Bremner, now in attack, jumped high for the ball to easily beat his marker, just outside the box, to flick the ball on.

A few feet in front of Bremner was young left winger Terry Cooper. He watched the ball narrowly elude Chelsea defenders' heads and drop to him. From just inside the penalty area, he trapped the ball expertly and took less than a second to strike a sweet, low shot towards goal. Chelsea keeper Bonetti dived quickly to his left but the velocity of the shot beat him and the ball landed in the corner of the net. The linesman, however, had raised his flag almost immediately when Cooper received the ball:

offside by the narrowest of margins. Understandably, the Leeds players disagreed, but the goal was correctly disallowed.

A few minutes later, Hunter made a foraying thirty-yard run into the Chelsea half before being fouled by Tamblyn. Given the horrendous challenge by Gary Sprake on Chelsea forward Doyle in the seventh minute, the Blues' aggression was not entirely surprising. Leeds were awarded a free kick thirty-five yards out. Number 7 John Giles placed the ball on the turf and waited for the referee's permission to take the kick.

So good a striker of the ball is Giles, Chelsea have formed a three-man defensive wall ten or so yards in front of him. Referee Burns is standing a few yards from the wall, almost parallel with it. Giles waits anxiously for him to give the signal, and the Chelsea men in the wall stay in position, albeit twitching nervously. Belfitt's substitute Peter Lorimer, probably an even better striker of the ball than Giles, stands a few yards square in-field to his team-mate. Lorimer wants the ball but Giles appears to ignore his pleas, nervously waving his left arm as if directing team-mates in the opposition's penalty area.

Giles looks at referee Burns. Referee Burns looks back at Giles and raises his whistle to his mouth. Giles takes the kick and it's a short pass to Lorimer, just as the whistle is being blown. Lorimer shoots, connecting so well that the ball rockets into Bonetti's top left corner of the net, despite the keeper's valiant attempt to stop it. Bonetti was clearly unaware, as were all the other players in the penalty area, that anything had been wrong with the free kick. To nearly everyone's shock, Referee Burns decided the free kick should be retaken. To the majority of people watching, Mr Burns appeared to wait until the ball had hit the Chelsea net before deciding to disallow the goal. Without doubt, to the neutral, and of course to everyone in the Leeds camp, the goal should have stood. But the referee ignored all Leeds' pleas and to add to the controversy ended the match prematurely too, blowing the final whistle a full two minutes early and thus inviting even more media criticism.

## 7–4

Burns blew the final whistle and Leeds were out of the FA Cup. Back to bloody West Yorkshire with nothing but a moral victory, a bad taste in our mouths and our tails between our legs again. The final whistle was early, not that that mattered: with two Leeds goals disallowed in the last few minutes, we could have played for a month of Sundays and still not had a goal given.

After the FA Cup exit, we still had the Inter-Cities Fairs Cup to go for, plus an outside chance (a very outside chance) of the League title with five games left, so it wasn't completely grim. We'd been drawn to play Kilmarnock in the Inter-Cities semi-finals so that shouldn't be too difficult a match, I thought.

# Chapter 8

Naturally, *This Is Your Life* focused on the positive aspects of Don Revie's career rather than the reported darker sides of his Leeds life. Nothing was said on the programme of the bad reputation Revie and the Leeds team had 'earned'. In the openly aggressive sport of professional football of the day, the Leeds players most certainly were no angels, but there were plenty of other First Division players who were equally as tough, who also gave as good as they got. But every play or pantomime needs a villain, and the Leeds team seemed to be the nation's favourite – encouraged by the press, of course – for that particular role.

May 3 1967, a Thursday, was Leeds United's first game since being controversially knocked out of the FA Cup. They were at home to Liverpool and a crowd of 36,547 watched as they won 2–1. Leeds fans were not in good spirits though, due to the semi-final defeat, and referees were not flavour of the month. Numerous violent incidents occurred on the terraces during the match whilst the referee, Jack Taylor, a highly regarded official, was even attacked by a spectator who ran on to the pitch. The trouble reached such a level that Harry Reynolds stood, armed with a microphone, on the pitch and announced that closure of the ground was being considered. Matters did calm down somewhat afterwards, but the *Yorkshire Evening Post* commented that Leeds 'has never seen worse conduct'.

On the final day of the 1966–67 season, Manchester United were crowned Division One champions with a 6–1 victory at West Ham. For many there, though, crowd trouble and rioting made it a far from enjoyable day, with some spectators needing hospital treatment afterwards.

In time for the 1967–68 season, the club had readied itself for fans trying to steal into Elland Road matches without paying. The previous season had seen chaos at a Leeds–Sunderland match, probably the result of so many gatecrashers, and on that occasion the club had been extremely fortunate that there were no fatalities. Now, to improve spectator safety, admission prices had been increased and the damaged terracing rebuilt, plus corrugated sheeting had been added to the wall behind the Spion Kop to make it eight feet high and thus less inviting for any illegal climbers in the vicinity. Other, more mysterious, changes had been made at the stadium too.

Revie had invited a well-known Blackpool fortune teller called Gypsy Rose Lee, possibly not her real name, to help the Leeds cause. This odd behaviour from the notoriously superstitious manager could easily have been viewed as a silly and cheap publicity stunt, but the Leeds manager was deadly serious, believing that the Elland Road ground had been cursed and that there were people with genuine powers capable of lifting such a curse. Revie regarded superstitions as relevant and important, not caring what scorn or ridicule he would attract. A Catholic, he often carried a small plastic figure of St John with him, as well as other lucky charms, which he considered no more bizarre or harmful as praying to God every night.

The rumour was that the site had been home for a community of gypsies early in the twentieth century. However, following a dispute with the council over land ownership, the gypsies had been forced to leave, and so they had put a curse on the land. Revie believed the story held credence, so the club hired the Blackpool lady to resolve matters. Once on site, she demanded that every door within the stadium be locked and that only she and Revie were to remain. She proceeded to scatter a collection of seeds in each corner of the ground and the centre of the pitch.

She also confided in Revie 'certain little secrets', all of which he considered as proof of the occult but which he would never publicly share.

More rituals had entered the Leeds dressing room before each match's kick off. Revie would rub Terry Cooper's back with Algipan, Billy Bremner would have a lukewarm bath, and Eddie Gray would ensure he was the first player changed into his kit. Bremner's shorts were always the last part of his kit to go on, and he would borrow Norman Hunter's comb before leading the team out, carrying a ball thrown to him to catch each time, a custom that had begun with Hunter throwing a ball to Bobby Collins a few seasons before. Hunter, after completing a game of head tennis with Jack Charlton, would be the last player to comb his hair before going out to the pitch. And Paul Reaney needed to kick a football against Don Revie's trouser leg at least once before every match.

The football director was a strange breed. Strange and rarely popular. Supporters distrusted them; footballers' opinions were rarely more favourable. In his autobiography *The Clown Prince of Soccer* Len Shackleton included a chapter called 'The Average Director's Knowledge of Football'. It consisted of one blank page.

Directors, though, were well aware of football supporters' short memories. Just five years ago, Leeds had been hovering over the chasm of Division Three, and their safety was only confirmed on the final day of the season. Now, late August 1967, three weeks into the new campaign, Leeds were due to play in the two-legged Inter-Cities Fairs Cup final. Yet supporters' complaints never seemed to let up. The Leeds directors had forked out a lot of their own money on behalf of the club but were rarely recognized or thanked for their efforts. Last season, Leeds had finished fourth in Division One, five points behind winners Manchester United, as well as being cruelly beaten in that FA Cup semi-final against Chelsea, two achievements hardly representing a poor season, even with the trophy cabinet still bare. And now, after beating Kilmarnock 4–2 on aggregate, Leeds were through to their first ever European final. But the public complained about ticket prices.

Leeds would meet the highly rated Yugoslavian team Dynamo Zagreb on August 30 and September 6, with the new English season already three games old. Unfortunately, this was United's worst start to a league season for years, with only one point out of a possible six earned and one solitary goal scored. The situation was not helped by injuries to John Giles, Albert Johanneson, Willie Bell and Paul Madeley.

Some felt the blame could only lie at Revie's door, for not buying proven players, especially a top-quality centre-forward. Greenhoff and Belfitt were still young and inexperienced. It wasn't the best-kept secret in football that Revie was on the lookout for a proven striker. The pair, though, remained part of his long-term plans.

Zagreb were renowned for their attacking football and ability to score goals aplenty, so it was always likely to be a tough game for the Peacocks. But as long as they didn't get thrashed, Leeds were expected to do what was necessary in the home soil return leg and thus win the trophy. The first leg result, 2–0 to Zagreb, wasn't a thrashing, despite the visitors only occasionally threatening the hosts' goal. By now, UEFA had introduced the away goals rule: if the teams were level after the two legs, any goals scored by the away team would count as double, so had they managed to score, a Leeds goal might have been invaluable. Alas, one never looked likely, as Zagreb coped comfortably with Leeds' attacks.

Leeds chairman Harry Reynolds was suffering from arthritis, so decided to tender his resignation as chairman. Chairmen rarely receive credit for their work at football clubs, but Harry Reynolds, the self-made Holbeck millionaire, a man who hated snobbery and who would always stand firm for what he believed in, was very possibly the most important man ever to be associated with the club. His money, his ambition and influence combined with business acumen were integral in wrenching the club from near collapse to a successful and highly respected organization of considerable note. He enjoyed the trappings of his hard-earned wealth, with expensive cruises, a new Mercedes, rich meals at Sheeky's in London and the like, and playing polo and hunting, but he remained unwaveringly working class in attitude and manner, preferring beer to wine and fish and chips to caviar.

Possibly the only serious professional disagreement between Reynolds and Revie was over the manager's pursuit of Blackpool FC's Alan Ball. Reynolds agreed all along that Ball was an excellent player but the board refused to match Everton's offer of £110,000 and were entirely against entering an auction for him. Revie, convinced Ball was the perfect player to complement Bremner and Giles in the Leeds midfield, was appalled to lose out on the player. Rumours circulated that Revie and Reynolds' dispute was irreconcilable, but rumours are all they were.

Albert Morris, a Leeds director since 1961, took over from Harry Reynolds. Although the choice of replacement was not surprising, with it came reports that Revie was unsettled at the club. Negative rumours like manager unrest were of no benefit to anyone, and Revie knew that as well as damaging club morale, his own reputation could suffer.

He acted quickly to scotch the gossip. 'I am very happy with United and I always have been,' he told the press. 'Since I became manager a family spirit has built up, which I should hate to leave. I've had most of my players since they left school, and while we have won nothing yet we have been very close – and I want to see the job through. I grew up as a football manager under Harry Reynolds and I am positive the club spirit which he did so much to build will continue to be as strong as ever under Mr Morris and the other directors.'

In the summer of 1967, ambitious Coventry City had hopes of luring Revie away, while Manchester United were on the lookout for an eventual successor to Matt Busby, who was considering retirement sooner rather than later. Allegedly, various big Italian clubs also made approaches for Revie's services. True or not, these reports must have made the Leeds board very aware of the value of their manager.

Also over the summer, Willie Bell was sold to Leicester for £45,000. He had played 260 times for Leeds, the vast majority of the appearances for Don Revie, scoring 18 goals in that time. The emergence of Terry Cooper, at first playing on the left wing or midfield but now a fine left-back, signified less opportunity for him. Down the years, Revie would single out certain players for their consistent professionalism, loyalty and commitment to his and the Leeds cause, and Willie Bell's name would almost always feature in that particular honours list. Revie held Willie Bell in similar regard to Grenville Hair, now in charge at Bradford City: high praise indeed.

## 8–2

The 1967–68 season was always going to be a poor one because we didn't have enough quality in the Leeds squad to build on. It started badly with a draw at home to Sunderland and defeats away at Man United and Wolves, and then we sold Willie Bell to Leicester for £45,000. Worse was Harry Reynolds packing it all in as chairman. There was often talk of Harry wanting to retire because of ill health but I never thought he'd actually do it. He was like a part of the furniture. No, he was more than that: he was a proper pillar of the football club. I remember when the supporters took the mick out of him when he'd gone on to the pitch at half-time to declare that Don Revie would take the club on to glory. Most people thought he'd lost his marbles. Thank God he was right. We had everything to thank Harry for, and I mean everything: the club would have gone to the dogs without him, no mistake.

This season, there were bad signs before a ball had been kicked. It looked like Johnny Giles might be out injured for a long time. We had last season's Inter-Cities Fairs Cup final to play, though, both legs of it, against Dynamo Zagreb.

In the first leg, we performed a lot better than we had in the three League games so far, though we didn't manage to score. We had a mountain to climb in the home leg, that was a definite.

102

If we'd had Alan Peacock in the side, fit, it could have been different, but big Al'd only played six league games the season before and it wasn't much of a secret that his knees were just about done for. I never wanted to criticize The Don for his tactics and team selections, but I had to say that I thought he made mistakes for the second leg against Dynamo. We were 2–0 down after all, plus we were lacking height and heading power in attack, it was clear as day. No matter how hard Rod Belfitt and Jimmy Greenhoff tried, neither of them was going to be as effective as Alan Peacock. I suppose beating Fulham 2–0 the previous Saturday in our first League win – with Belfitt getting both goals – must have given The Don something to think about, but still.

Alan Peacock left Leeds not long after the final, for Plymouth Argyle, which might have had something to do with it, I'm not sure. He'd been criticized at Leeds a fair bit and only played about sixty games for us in all, but he'd still managed a scoring rate of one goal in every two games nearly, plus set up a load as well.

That win over Fulham was one of those silver linings with a cloud weighing it down. Billy Bremner had been sent off for arguing with the referee. And swearing at him. Swearing at him a lot. Reports said there was some 'crowd trouble' on the terraces as well, but I didn't see anything, though it's obvious the sending off didn't go down well with our fans. Billy got a twenty-eight-day ban by the League, which meant he'd miss seven matches. Seven matches, just for arguing with the referee and using colourful language. The *Evening Post* reckoned it made a total of sixty-eight days he'd been suspended in his career, plus he'd been given £350 worth of fines in all. Jesus, he should learn to keep his mouth shut. His was an expensive bad habit. We were always a better team with him in, so it was costly in both respects.

Billy wasn't suspended for the Inter-Cities final, but with the team he picked, it looked like The Don showed too much respect for Zagreb. He picked Paul Reaney, not at right-back but on the right of midfield, which was just odd. Because of the away goals rule, if Zagreb scored one at our place then we'd need to score four. You could see his point, being defensive in his tactics, but not *that* defensive. As it turned out, we didn't play badly, but the problem was, neither did Zagreb. They defended really well, and even though we bombarded their penalty area with crosses and long-range shots, there weren't any real chances to score. The sad fact of the matter for us was that the team was too predictable and the Zagreb defenders had quite an easy time of it all night.

It was a 0–0 draw and so we were losing finalists, again. Overall, Dynamo Zagreb had deserved it, but there was no getting away from the feeling that we'd used the wrong tactics and let them off the hook.

So the Honours list 1966–67 was complete.

**Division One winners**: Man United. Runners up: Nottingham Forest.
**FA Cup winners**: Spurs. Runners up: Chelsea.
**League Cup winners**: QPR. Runners up: West Brom.
**European Cup winners**: Celtic. Runners up: Inter Milan.
**European Cup Winners' Cup winners**: Bayern Munich. Runners up: Rangers.
**Inter-Cities Fairs Cup winners**: Dynamo Zagreb. Runners up: Leeds United.
**Footballer of the Year**: Jack Charlton, Leeds United.
**European Footballer of the Year**: Florian Albert, Ferencvaros.
**Leeds crowd average**: 35,217.

With Leeds, I had this niggling, not-so-little worry that we'd gone as far as we could; we were destined to be also-rans rather than proper silverware winners. Worse, the team would decline, slowly but surely, and we'd return to being like our old selves. Our old, depressingly useless, selves. But I wasn't a pessimist at heart and, as if to show that my opinion was worth sweet FA, lo and behold, the team's performances and results began to improve almost straight away after the Fairs Cup final loss. There were close but still really good wins over Everton and Burnley and a draw away at Southampton. We beat Luton 3–1 in the League Cup second round as well, with Peter Lorimer smacking in a hat trick. He was proving himself as a real match winner and was on a right scoring run, like we suddenly didn't need a target man after all. Of course, we still did need one. Late in September 1967 Don Revie finally did it. He bought a top striker.

There had been Francis Lee of Bolton, who had a scoring ratio of better than one goal in every two games, but he wasn't anything special in the air, which is what we most needed. Then there was Hull City's Chris Chilton, who seemed perfect as a target man, but

Hull knocked us back, even after we'd offered Terry Cooper in part-exchange. I knew Cooper had asked to leave, but still, that seemed odd, especially as he'd really started to prove himself at left-back for Leeds this season. He wasn't on the transfer list for long anyway, which was good, even after Sunderland supposedly offered £40,000 for him. We had even enquired about Ray Crawford of Ipswich, Ces reckoned, but he was near thirty and therefore too old. There was mention of Tony Hateley, before Chelsea bought him.

In the end, we paid Sheffield United £100,000 for Mick Jones, two weeks after the Zagreb game. He made his debut against Leicester. Sheffield United supporters were supposed to be up in arms about selling him, but money has always talked loudly to certain clubs and directors. I could see the Blades fans' point of view: what a time to sell your best player, less than two months into the season.

Jones was only twenty-two, but he'd already played for England, twice. It turned out, or so Ces had it, that the transfer fee was in fact £99,999, though no one seemed able to say why it wasn't a full hundred thou.

8–3

Looking at his moderate scoring record for Sheffield United, Mick Jones' arrival at Elland Road might not have appeared too important, but for Revie it represented the final piece in his young Leeds United jigsaw. The team seemed to have revitalized itself after the Zagreb defeat by putting together a good run of results, totting up an impressive number of goals on the way.

He had waited patiently for months for Sheffield United to accept the bid for Jones' signature. Even though the player had plenty to learn – he needed to improve his close control, his shielding of the ball and keeping possession – he was the high-quality centre-forward Revie had yearned for.

Whilst it took seven games before Jones scored his first League goal for Leeds (against Wolves, two days before Christmas), his early displays were widely praised, with one newspaper describing him as the finest centre-forward to play for Leeds since the great John Charles. Jones had not wanted to leave Sheffield but the Leeds opportunity was too good to miss, and they were an ambitious, exciting young team.

Leeds had reported record profits for the second consecutive year but Revie wasn't free to spend what he wanted, even though he had a constant 'wants' list. He was required, not forced, to release players too, to help balance the books. And since its return to the top tier, the board of directors had drawn out their own plans for the club, away from player recruitment – primarily the improvement and expansion of the stadium and its facilities. Those plans didn't include Harry Reynolds' idea of repositioning the Leeds pitch and building a direct railway link to the north-west of the stadium. Reynolds believed that this would enable more supporters to get to matches and thus increase attendances and revenue. We would never know.

After a black August, Leeds seemed to have got their act together by the time of Jones' arrival. However, there were disappoint-ments away in the League, to West Bromwich Albion, Manchester City, Liverpool (including a freakish own goal from Gary Sprake) and, just as astonishingly, Sheffield United. Sheffield United had been without their goalkeeper for most of the game due to a dislocated finger injury, so winger Alan Woodward deputized in nets. For eighty or so minutes. The Blades still managed to keep Leeds out and went on to beat them with a second-half goal. But aside from that particular embarrassment, and a couple of substandard League and complacent Fairs Cup displays, Leeds' reputation as genuine contenders for honours was making a return.

By New Year's Day 1968 Leeds were sitting not exactly pretty but a relatively handsome third in Division One and in contention for all the trophies available to them, having racked up some memorable results along the way. In January, they started the year by slamming in ten goals in total, without reply, in the games against Fulham and Southampton, and they could have scored more. They had hit a Fairs Cup record-breaking 9–0 away win at Spora Luxembourg, plus the 7–0 home leg, as well as defeating much better opposition from Yugoslavia, Partizan Belgrade, in the following round. There was the amazing 7–0 win against Chelsea in the League, too. In addition, with sound wins against Luton, a Bobby Collins-led Bury, Sunderland and Stoke City, Leeds had stealthily progressed to the semi-finals of the League Cup, the furthest they had ever reached in the competition. European qualification for the trophy winners, and the final being held at Wembley, had given the League Cup much more appeal in the eyes of the top clubs. Fearing even heavier fixture congestion than usual, Everton, Liverpool and Chelsea had chosen not to compete in it.

Division One League table (top), January 13 1968:

| 1 | Manchester Utd | Played 25, | Points 37 |
| 2 | Leeds Utd | Played 26, | Points 35 |
| 3 | Liverpool | Played 25, | Points 34 |
| 4 | Manchester City | Played 25, | Points 32 |

Injuries and suspensions regularly provided opportunity for youth to step in and prove their worth to the team. This season saw fine performances from 'squad' players like Jimmy Greenhoff, Rod Belfitt, Terry Hibbitt, goalkeeper David Harvey and midfielder Mick Bates. Even though he was barely twenty, Mick Bates was proving himself as an ideal professional for Revie's Leeds. His best position was probably in central midfield, though, so his chances of playing would be limited to whenever Bremner or Giles were unavailable. From Armthorpe near Doncaster (as was a lad called Kevin Keegan), Mick Bates was proud and happy to be a part of the Leeds squad. And while the Leeds midfield was hard to break into, the defence was possibly even tougher.

From the beginning, Don Revie had built his team from the back, and such was the strength of the Leeds defence that when the back five of Sprake, Reaney, Charlton, Hunter and Cooper remained unchanged, consistently high-calibre performances could be generally relied upon. Leeds were lucky in the 1967–68 season that those five would miss only a few matches between then.

January 6 1968, saw Leeds against a struggling Fulham side at Craven Cottage, and aside from injuries to O'Grady and Johanneson the team was at full strength again. Jones, Giles and Bremner were back and the gaps left by the two wing-men were more than ably filled by Jimmy Greenhoff and Eddie Gray. An away win could hardly be classed as a major surprise, but nonetheless, games in the capital were rarely easy for Leeds. Today, though, was to prove different and by the half-hour mark Leeds were already leading 3–0, thanks to two goals from Greenhoff and a virtuoso effort from Mick Jones. He headed his second soon after the restart and Greenhoff went on to grab his hat trick not long after. 5–0 to Leeds in a performance Revie described as 'terrific' and the best in all his seven years as manager.

Leeds' fine form didn't last long. They met Hibernian in the Inter-Cities Fairs Cup third round, second leg. They played poorly and were blessed with more than a little good fortune, scraping through 2–1 on aggregate after being outplayed for much of the 1–1 draw.

In the domestic cups, Leeds were scheduled to play Division Two Derby in the two-legged League Cup semi-final as well as the FA Cup third round. All three ties were to be played within three weeks of January and February. Derby, managed by Brian Clough, were struggling in Division Two, looking more contenders for relegation to Division Three than promotion. The similarities between the early managerial careers of Clough and Revie were strong. Playing wise, Clough deserved better than just the two England caps he had won, and enforced retirement due to injury was cruel luck for a great talent. He was a record-breaking centre-forward but his career was effectively finished late in 1962 with knee ligament damage after a collision with the Bury goalkeeper. Clough returned to playing a whole two years later, but he had lost pace and suppleness, and managed only a few games more before retiring. It was a bitter end to an outstanding career in which he had scored a near goal-a-game ratio with hometown club Middlesbrough and then Sunderland.

Before Leeds and Derby played, Clough was interviewed by the *Yorkshire Post*. After mentioning their forthcoming games and describing Leeds as 'such a good side with a top class manager' he added, 'They can teach my lads a lot - how hard they have to work, how much effort and dedication is required. In short, a complete picture of what we have to aim for in the future. Leeds must be the envy of nearly every club in the country with their spirit and running power and large pool of good players. People tend to underestimate their individual ability, but make no mistake about it - these lads can play.'

Clough and Revie were both Middlesbrough born, yet they shared nothing like a good friendship. Before too long, whatever the extent of their relationship, it would markedly deteriorate. Four days before meeting Derby, Leeds swept aside Southampton 5–0 in the League, without Charlton, Bremner and Gray. Excellent teamwork combined with fine individual performances, notably from understudies Bates and Hibbitt, made it somewhat of a canter. Giles and Madeley in midfield and Cooper at left-back (the position which looked 'made' for him) helped wrap up the points before half-time, against a poor Southampton side who had just sold Martin Chivers for a record £125,000 to Spurs.

Wednesday January 17, League Cup semi-final, first leg, at Derby County's Baseball Ground. While Leeds' Elland Road pitch was similar in (low) quality to most British pitches, Derby's was commonly regarded as the worst in existence. Its main problem was rain water not being able to drain away. The pitch held it and wouldn't let go of it.

Leeds had scored ten goals without reply in their last two League games but anyone expecting an exciting goals-full semi-final was to be disappointed. Despite Derby's lowly position in Division Two, Revie knew it would be a tough affair and prepared his players accordingly. Derby would come at them from the kick off, and Leeds needed to be ready for a torrid opening. They were, and they defended in number for much of the game, returning the pressure on the County defence only sporadically, by counter-attacking.

Leeds played a classic 'away' performance, soaking up the pressure from their opponents and taking them on the break. Leeds-born Kevin Hector caused a few scares for United, but overall the visitors coped well and their gritty display was rewarded with a penalty after a foul in the County penalty area.

Johnny Giles rarely missed a spot-kick, and today was no exception. 1–0 to Leeds and the scoreline stayed that way. This semi-final first leg at Derby was watched by close to 32,000, the return leg at Elland Road by less than 30,000, whereas their FA Cup third round tie at Derby attracted well over 39,000. Testament to the everlasting glamour of the FA Cup, whereas it seems there was still had much work to do to improve the image of the League Cup.

## 8–4

Five days before Christmas 1967, I got a right surprise – Hibernian had me playing for them against Leeds. It was in the Inter-Cities Fairs Cup against Leeds, third round, home leg. Okay, it wasn't me, but a Jock player with my name. He played up front, 'the stockily built Jimmy O'Rourke, an instinctive goal scorer'. Stocky was a good description: his thighs were thicker than the whole of me.

Despite the decent reputation that Jimmy O'Rourke had, he didn't have a good game this night. Hibs' best player by a mile was Peter Cormack in midfield. He ran the show, even with Billy Bremner playing directly opposite him. Every attacking move seemed to come through Cormack.

Neither side played particularly well though, and it was all a bit boring after a bright start. It was bloody freezing as well and the pitch was rock hard – there wasn't much the groundsmen could do to improve it. If a pitch is frozen solid, you can't even fork it to give it more … give. There's not much good to be said about playing on frozen mud, it looks ugly, it feels ugly and by Christ if you land on it with a clatter, it hurts ugly as well, whatever level of football you play.

The Leeds colours were yet another variation tonight, we'd played in some odd strips in our time. I wished they'd stick to all white, that was Leeds United. This time it was more like England's kit – white shirts and socks but dark blue shorts. Hibs played in their normal green tops with white sleeves, like the Arsenal kit gone wrong.

Eddie Gray scored early on for us, after his first effort had been saved. That was about the sum total of the excitement. Gary

Sprake nearly gave another stupid goal away, while Peter Lorimer had one disallowed for offside in the second half. Sprake had been holding the ball in his hands and was set to drop-kick it forward, as he often did, so he bounced it on the deck but too close to their striker Colin Stein. Stein stuck his foot out and prodded the ball into the net. The referee even awarded a goal at first but then noticed the linesman waving his flag. Thank the gods. They had definitely smiled on Sprakey. Me, I'd have awarded the goal if I was a ref.

Different people get different levels of tension when they watch football. Some get animated and can't keep still, like they're actually playing in the match, while others just seem to hunch up and freeze, they're so nervous. Having watched them both a million times, I can vouch that Les Cocker definitely fitted the first description best, Don Revie the second. The Don looks like he's waiting for surgery, while Les looks like he's got big, vicious ants in his pants. I was never too bad watching, but I was bad listening to games on the radio. The really close matches were the worst: they were torture, whatever competition Leeds were in.

We'd beaten Luxemburg team Spora 7–0 away earlier on in the Fairs Cup, not exactly edge-of-your-seat stuff, but with tight matches I felt ill with nerves, I really did. Normally, I'd listen to the Leeds away games at home on the radiogram (as my grandma called it) while she'd try to watch television and pretend not to be that interested.

'Turn it down, James,' she'd say, when all the time it was her television making most noise.

I'd lie on the floor, never able to get comfy, restless like a flea-bitten dog. I'd rest my head close to the radiogram speaker with its wire mesh covering and try and visualize wherever it was Leeds were playing. No chance of that with European games, they were in different worlds, apparently. There was hardly ever any relaxing when a game was on the radio. In the Peacock, Aitch had a portable radio behind the bar and he'd turn it up loud so customers were forced to listen to it whether they wanted to or not. I usually listened at home though, like I say, because I wanted to stay away from beer when I could, even with Christmas not long gone.

111

In the world of the real Jimmy O'Rourke, Leeds matches outshone St Anthony's. Supporting Leeds United never stopped me from playing well for St Anthony's but when it came to being motivated I was always more nervous about the next Leeds match than I was the next Ant's one. I wasn't sure but it might have been the fact that no one seemed too fussed any more about me returning to playing. I'd just turned fifteen when I played in that trial match, now I was approaching eighteen – in the eyes of the Leeds scouts I bet I was too old. Not exactly fair, but maybe that was it. I mean, this was my second season back, St Ant's had won the league last term and were vying for it this time around, plus we reached two cup semi-finals. And after a shaky start, I was back to my old self – and of course I still trained once, sometimes twice a day. I'd not lost any skill but I had lost plenty of fitness when I'd slobbed around in pot.

I was at ours on the night of the second leg of the Hibernian tie. It promised to be edgy because we were only 1–0 up from the home leg. Hibs were no mugs and were keen as green mustard to beat us. To help me picture it in my mind better, I had the match programme with me. Not that there were ever many photographs of the players to help you visualize, but at least there were black and white photos of both squads. Other bits were more interesting. They'd have short articles about the opposing players and manager and club history and how well the team was doing and stuff. It was all three cheers for the opposition, all nice-as-pie credit and respect, before the players kicked ten bags of stuffing out of each other on the pitch.

Don Revie was on the radio before the game at Easter Road, being asked about our chances after the first leg 1–0 lead. 'We're not out yet,' he said. 'It is bound to be difficult now but all matches are hard for Leeds these days, so that is nothing new to the players. If we get one goal up there, Hibernian have to score three to beat us.'

I couldn't work out what he meant by 'We're not out yet' – making Hibernian sound like world beaters and that we were favourites to lose and be eliminated. But then the game, in Leith, near Edinburgh, kicked off.

The radio said it was another freezing cold night and the pitch hard as rock. The bad conditions affected football all over Great Britain and most matches were called off. This meant that lucky Leeds and Hibernian fans were treated to extended coverage as I think there was only one other game still being played – Plymouth Argyle and Norwich City in Division Two. Not much comparison really.

Hibernian levelled the tie in only the fourth minute with a well-taken goal by Stein. It wasn't looking too promising. But I had a positive in my mind: we'd only ever once conceded more than one goal away in Europe, and that was in the final last season. But the radio commentator said Hibernian looked easily the likelier to score again. We were under the cosh, as he put it, though defending valiantly too. Times like that, the match programme was a welcome distraction.

*Get all your meat requirements at Fred Dring Butchers in Leeds Kirkgate Market.*

Hibernian nearly scored with a deflected shot, from Stein again.

*A spectacular night of entertainment to be had at the Bradford Lyceum, Bingo Cabaret & Social Club.*

Hibs had four corners in a row within two minutes. Ten Leeds men defending. Cormack hit a shot from outside the area, just over Sprake's crossbar.

*Wallace Arnold: excursions to all Leeds United away matches.*

It didn't sound like many had travelled up from Leeds tonight, if the noise from the stadium was anything to go by.

It sounded like Mick Jones was on a lonely journey as well, playing in attack on his own. At least I could relax a bit whenever 'Jonah' got the ball, because he held it up so well, fending off his markers, waiting for the other Leeds players to catch him up and support him in attack. The trouble was, he wasn't receiving the ball anywhere near enough.

*Jacomelli: the perfect rendezvous after the match.*

*Jowett & Sowry Ltd Printers, for personal and commercial stationery.*

*Man Fang Chinese Restaurant.*

*The Wheel Licensed Grill Bar (Lands Lane).*

Mercifully, the referee blew his whistle for half-time, Hibernian one up, 1–1 on aggregate. We needed to buck our ideas up or we'd be going out.

Waiting for the second half, I made a pot of tea for me and my grandma. She'd started having a teaspoon of honey in hers, reckoning it was good for your chest and throat. I'd not noticed any improvement.

It was torture, not being at a Leeds game and having to listen to the radio, especially in cup matches, where any time we'd concede a goal I'd feel a bit sicker. I'd probably done Hibernian a disservice, underestimating them – I'd read about them beating Napoli and Porto to get to this stage of the Fairs Cup and you never got pushover teams from places like Italy and Portugal, it just didn't happen. Hibs must have played really well to knock both those out of the competition.

*Brady Bros. (Roofing) Ltd, Brown Lane, Holbeck, Leeds.*
*Step up with Johnstone's Paints Ltd.*
*Finch Batteries.*
*Leeds Shaver Centre.*
*If it's Barrels and Drums, then it's E Pease & Son Ltd, Ravell Cooperage.*
*Frank Fletcher Motor Cycles Ltd.*
*Reliant Sales and Service, D. G. Cheeseman, York Street, Leeds 9.*
*See the world and join the Royal Navy.*

And miss your football team, and get seasick or drowned or torpedoed while you're at it. No thanks, Admiral.

*Come work for the National Coal Board!*

I'd rather be in the Navy.

*Get a career with Britannia Metals.*

And breathe in even worse muck than down the pit.

Leeds were playing better in the second half, it was like The Don had given the players a bit of a bollocking, told them to pull their socks up. They were not so lacklustre now, even though Hibs were still causing us a few problems. At least we were pressing them, though. I was feeling more confident and relaxed.

But then the commentator suddenly gets all agitated and it's all gone wrong – Hibs had scored! But Colin Stein hadn't scored, he'd hit the side-netting. Dozy man.

*John Collier: the window to watch.*

114

Unless you're the commentator – he'd be looking in the wrong shop.

*Griffin Hotel – luxurious rooms at affordable prices.*

*British Rail – to and from the match.*

Well, not really.

*El Toro Coffee Bar.*

*Bentley's Yorkshire Breweries. There's no better beer than BYB.*

Yes there is. Tetley's for one.

*The Ancient Order of Foresters Friendly Society.*

An insurance company. Not as exciting as it sounded.

Not much seemed to happen in the game after the imaginary goal. There was plenty of effort from both sides but not much action in either penalty area or by way of shots. Our defence was winning just about everything, and Terry Cooper especially was playing well at left-back, linking up well with Eddie Gray in attack too. The Don had said that if ever Leeds played on snow, Eddie Gray never left footprints he was so fleet of foot. Maybe it had started snowing up there. The radio said Eddie was beginning to put in some good balls for Mick Jones and Jimmy Greenhoff to feed on, but we hadn't properly tested their goalkeeper yet.

Both teams were looking to score, and the longer the match went on the more likely the next goal would seal it. Or if it stayed the same until full time then there'd have to be thirty minutes' extra time. Every year Leeds seemed to have fixture pile-ups near the end of the season, so thirty minutes more in a midweek game was definitely something we could do without, especially as the pitch was hard as bone. The harder a pitch, the more chance of injuries, from broken bones or torn muscles or just plain cramp.

But with five minutes of normal time left, Hibs' goalie, Wilson, was penalized by the referee. No one seemed to know why though, and obviously the bloke on the radio was confused again. Seemed the referee had given Leeds an indirect free kick in the Hibernian penalty area due to the goalkeeper committing the crime of taking more than four steps whilst holding the ball. It was a new-ish rule, to stop goalkeepers' time-wasting tactics. It sounded harsh to me, bearing in mind that Hibs were the home team and going for the winner.

115

There was a queue of Leeds players wanting to take the kick – John Giles, Peter Lorimer, Jimmy Greenhoff, even Mick Jones. Hibs had formed a defensive wall ten yards in front. It had to be Lorimer taking it: he had such a brilliant shot on him that there was always chance the ball would end up in the net with an opponent attached to it.

The referee blew, Lorimer ran at the ball, about to whack it and if not provide the killer goal then at least to inflict major damage on one or two Hibs players in the wall. But he was pretending, he changed his mind and just jogged away from the ball. Then Greenhoff did the same, exactly the same. And straight after him, Mick Jones did exactly the same too. It was like a Marx Brothers routine, and the commentator wasn't the only one out of breath because of it.

In fact it was Giles who took the free kick. He walked up to the football and casually chipped it over the Hibs wall to Jack Charlton, who simply nipped in to meet it, jumping unmarked and heading it down and past the defenceless goalkeeper into the net. The equalizer and winner on aggregate! We were in the next round, the quarter-finals, because no way could Hibs come back now. They needed to score two goals to win, in less than four minutes. No chance.

8–5

'None of my players is for sale. I want to repeat that in the most emphatic way. My staff have not spent those thousands of hours searching for capable young footballers and grooming them in order to strengthen teams of other clubs. We want such players to win something for Leeds United and not for other clubs.'

This was Revie's angry response to newspaper gossip involving Leeds players leaving the club. He went so far as to say he was considering asking the Football League to investigate any further transfer rumours. Sunderland reputedly wanted Eddie Gray and Spurs and Arsenal were hunting Paul Madeley, yet no official enquiries had been submitted to Leeds.

With the potential match-winning qualities of Eddie Gray, a young player capable of scoring and creating sublime goals, it is transparently obvious why other clubs would want to buy him.

But match winners do not exist solely in the attack of a team; the genuinely great sides have champions throughout. Paul Madeley's gift was his versatility, in that he could play in any position and do a good job there, a very good job. He was a good striker of the ball with both feet and so had the ability to play in any of the back four positions, while many football supporters believed his best position was as a defensive midfielder. Paul Madeley was a class act in any of the defence's roles, but in central midfield he was regarded as a world-class act. Gray and Madeley were just two Leeds players mentioned in the football transfer gossip columns, but it is likely Revie needed to fend off many more enquiries, for his entire squad.

On another extremely cold Saturday afternoon in late January, on another heavy-going, debilitating, muscle-wearing mudheap of a pitch, Leeds edged past Derby in the FA Cup third round 2–0. Second-half goals from Jack Charlton and Peter Lorimer, in front of nearly 40,000 at the Baseball Ground, settled part two of the Peacocks–Rams 1968 trilogy. Part three, the Elland Road leg of the League Cup semi-final, was scheduled for the first Wednesday in February, kick off 7.30pm.

1–0 down from the first game, Brian Clough's men entered the pitch with instructions to attack from the first whistle. It was the all-white of Leeds against the all-red change strip of Derby. Taking the game to Leeds had to be the right approach: United were near masters at defending a lead, especially in cup competitions, so if Derby didn't force the pace then stalemate or a defeat was the likely outcome. Clough decided that if his team was going out of the competition then they might as well do it with a fight. It was the Clough way and would become the Derby way, and on twelve minutes Kevin Hector levelled the aggregate score, latching on to a long ball from John O'Hare to flick it into the net past Sprake with a brave header. 1–1 on aggregate. But their lead didn't last long. Less than two minutes, in fact – Peter Lorimer was fouled on the edge of the Derby penalty area. The Derby players, especially those in the resulting defensive wall, were understandably distracted by the threat of physical damage from a Lorimer missile and more concerned with self-preservation than defending their goal. Lorimer, though, does not shoot, instead he cleverly chips the ball over the wall to the advancing Paul Madeley who heads it across the goalmouth to Rod Belfitt. Playing in place of the League Cup-tied Mick Jones (he had played in an earlier round for former club Sheffield United), Belfitt controls the ball neatly and connects with a sharp shot to equalize, the ball going in off the Derby right-side post, with goalkeeper Reg Matthews stationary on his line. 1–1 on the night, 2–1 to Leeds overall.

The goal didn't discourage Derby, as they tried to keep attacking and pressing the Leeds defence. Their battle became even more difficult just before half-time, with Eddie Gray shooting Leeds further ahead. Fed by Johnny Giles, he gracefully dribbled the ball past three Derby defenders before striking a low, angled shot from the edge of the area. Matthews stretched and managed to make contact but he couldn't stop the ball from entering the net. To the Derby players and supporters, conceding again would have felt unfair, as they had been the more adventurous team, but teams chasing a result are liable to focus too much on attack, leaving themselves vulnerable at the back. That is exactly what Derby had done, and good teams know how to exploit those weaknesses. In the second half, Leeds controlled the game, due partly to Derby's desperation to score and thus keep in the tie. Saving a John Giles penalty, goalkeeper Matthews certainly helped them do that, but Belfitt notched his second goal of the evening with a cool finish to make it 3–1 to Leeds with less than twenty minutes to go. Very late on, Derby's Stewart made it 3–2, but it was too little too late for Derby – Leeds won 4–2 on aggregate and were set for their second Wembley final in three years. It was a deserved victory, but Brian Clough's Second Division Derby had contributed greatly to the tie and had made a good account of themselves. Leeds' opponents on March 2 would be Arsenal, who had thumped Huddersfield Town 6–3 on aggregate.

Three days after the Derby win, mid-table West Ham were the Elland Road visitors, in the League. It would be Leeds' forty-fourth game of the season, and it was only early February. The season was not even six months old yet. Revie had warned his players that, at this stage of the season, their fitness was nearly as important as match results. Injuries and fatigue could easily lose them matches. Therefore, with around ten minutes of the match to go, with Leeds leading West Ham 2–1, the Leeds players were keeping possession of the ball near the West Ham penalty area, preventing them from getting the ball rather than trying to score a third. They were conserving their energies and not pointlessly busting a gut. In other words, they were time-wasting, but Revie was angered to hear boos, whistles and slow hand-claps from home fans, aimed at their own players. It had been an entertainingly attacking match with Leeds the better team.

After the match, Revie snapped back at the dissenters: 'We had provided far more than our fair share of entertaining football in the previous seventy-five minutes – in fact, that was one of our best performances of the season! It was our third match in seven days, all of them being played on heavy pitches, so naturally the lads were feeling the effects a bit. When you're involved in so many important matches, no team can afford to do a lot of unnecessary tearing about. Any team would do the same as Leeds in this situation – if they had the skill.' And he was right: even the press agreed.

Their final match before the League Cup Final was the FA Cup fourth round tie at home to Nottingham Forest on February 17 1968. They would then have the rare luxury of a two-week break. Fellow finalists Arsenal, meanwhile, would not: they would be playing Manchester United in the League as the Leeds players relaxed and, in certain cases, tried to recover from injury.

### 8–6

'Why don't you go to the doctor's?' I'd ask her whenever her coughing and breathing sounded bad, which happened to be most of the time.

'Because there's no need,' my grandma would reply.

119

Her coughing on mornings was as reliable as an alarm clock and it made me want to work that much harder when I went out running, as if the cold air could at least help to cleanse my lungs, if not my grandma's. I just assumed she had a smoker's cough, she never seemed worried by it so what was the point in me worrying? Besides, she never listened to me. Smoke from our coal fire nearly always made my throat sore and my chest hot. I'd get a nasty dry, burning feeling in my lungs, which would make me wheezy and whistly as I breathed. Maybe it was that.

The February night we beat Derby in the League Cup semi-final second leg to get to Wembley it was dead cold with frost and freezing fog. The weather might have affected the crowd as well: less than 30,000 attended. We were possibly ninety minutes away from Wembley, but that crowd was rubbish. As a rule, I always liked fog; it made things deathly quiet and mysterious, especially on a night. Our street, when it was foggy, with its cobbles and street lamps, definitely did have a look of Jack the Ripper London about it.

After the Derby match about forty of us in total helped to mend the pitch, flattening it with the massive roller, replacing divots and then finishing off by covering the whole surface with straw to help protect it from more cold damage. We were due to play West Ham in the League on the Saturday and then Forest the week after in the FA Cup, so the pitch was in for more hammer.

For as long as I remembered Ces and John (more so) – and Ray Hardy now – had always got frustrated about the pitch being overused in winter. But the attitude of The Don and the coaches, at least then, seemed to be that the quality of the playing surface wasn't that important. Normally, the Don could wrap Ces and John around his little finger, but not where this was concerned. They'd keep on at him about it.

It was well known that The Don had this *way* with people. Just a few words or a smile from him could make your day, it really could. Over the years I saw him, on dead cold days (and nights), come out on to the pitch to talk the groundsmen and ground staff tending the turf, giving them glasses of whisky and brandy to help keep warm.

He came out to thank us after the Derby match. I'd been close to the players' tunnel when he'd walked out, so he couldn't really have missed me. Even though he'd only said 'Hello Jim, how's the leg?' I couldn't describe how much his words meant to me. Truly, I felt like a VIP. And maybe that was the point. If Don Revie knew and liked you, then you really were a very important person, at least to him. He didn't dish out any booze this time though.

When I got home, my grandma had already gone to bed. It was quite late so I didn't think anything of it. I had a couple of nips of sherry to warm me up then made myself a slice of unbuttered toast and a mug of tea and read the Derby match programme. A couple of sherries later, I fell asleep on the settee. The fire had gone out and it must have been the cold that woke me up. Going up the stairs to my bedroom, I could hear a strange scraping noise coming from my grandma's room. It was her snoring. I'd never heard it as bad as that.

I slept in the next day, not by much, but enough to miss my run. I thought my grandma must have forgotten to wake me up, but as I was going down the stairs I heard her voice, saying my name. I poked my head round her bedroom door. She was still in bed and the room smelt musty and wasn't warm.

'You alright, grandma?' She didn't look it. I could see that, even in the gloom. I pulled the curtains open.

'I can't seem to get out of bed,' she said. 'No energy or anything I've been coughing so much.'

'Have you had a nosebleed or summat?'

'No, I must have coughed some blood up, that's all.'

*That's all.*

She told me to run over to Clarkson the chemist's on Cemetery Road and get whatever their strongest cough medicine was. But I knew this was more than just a bad cough. So I rushed downstairs, took a couple of pence from her purse and then ran outside, down our street and along Elland Road, not to a chemist shop as none would have been open at that time anyway, but to the telephone kiosk opposite the stadium gates. I'd never used a telephone in my life before, and it felt like I took longer working out how to make a call than it did for the ambulance to turn up.

When I eventually got to work that morning I explained to Ces what had happened (before he had chance to bollock me for being slightly late). 'Well done,' he said. I'd done the right thing calling the ambulance. They wouldn't let me go with her to the hospital. I didn't see them examine her but when they carried her out of the house they'd put a mask over her mouth to feed her with oxygen from a little air tank. Already she looked a better colour.

It wasn't smoker's cough, it wasn't a bad cold and it wasn't influenza or bronchitis or emphysema. None of them. My grandma, somehow, had caught tuberculosis. The hospital kept her in for two nights until she came home the Saturday morning.

She wasn't exactly right as rain straight away but she was in much better nick than I expected. I never let on to her but those two nights when she was in the Infirmary were the loneliest and most miserable I ever had in my whole life, even though I knew the neighbours were looking out for me. It was even worse than when I had my leg and ankle broken. I couldn't help but think what an unfair life she'd had. She'd had to cope with the death of my granddad in World War Two, and as a widow she'd had to bring up her son on her own. And then, when that coward had grown up, she'd had to cope while his wife, my mum, had died when I was born. And then, when the spineless bastard ran off because he was scared of the responsibility of being a widower and young father, my grandma was lumped with having to bring me up as well. And now she was really ill. Where was the fairness in that?

Tuberculosis used to be a major killer right up to the early 1960s, I found out. They used to call it Consumption in the old days. Michael Caine had it in *Alfie*. Scientists and doctors had developed a cure, here at least – my grandma had these yellow tablets to take, one at a time, four times a day, before food. And she had strict instructions to look after herself better, eat regularly and get as much fresh air as possible, because she'd been overdoing it and was run down. I don't think there was any criticism of me in that, but just in case I started helping more around the house. She insisted on going back to work less than a week after. And she walked there.

She had to go for routine check-ups at the Leeds Chest Clinic once a month for a while but the doctors said the tablets should work without any problems and that she should be fully recovered within six months.

Saturday March 2 1968, Wembley Stadium, London. The Football League Cup Final. Attendance 97,887. Leeds United (white shirts, white shorts, white socks): 1 Sprake, 2 Reaney, 3 Cooper, 4 Bremner (captain), 5 Charlton, 6 Hunter, 7 Greenhoff, 8 Lorimer, 9 Madeley, 10 Giles, 11 Gray, 12 Belfitt. Arsenal (red shirts/white sleeves, white shorts, white and red socks): 1 Furnell, 2 Storey, 3 McNab, 4 McLintock (captain), 5 Simpson, 6 Ure, 7 Radford, 8 Jenkins, 9 Graham, 10 Sammels, 11 Armstrong, 12 Neill. Referee: L. J. Hamer.

The Football League Cup is regarded as a poor relation to the League Championship, the FA Cup and the European trophies, even with Wembley Stadium as the final's host. The Leeds–Arsenal match was expected to be a hard-fought, close-run and tense match – but it was not expected to be negative and dour a display. The continually rough and unattractive play produced by both teams upset many people, and the lack of excitement throughout provided only meagre fare for the spectators. It was generally low-calibre entertainment with precious few enjoyable moments, while both teams' shooting caused more work for the Wembley ball-boys than either goalkeeper.

The *Guardian*'s Eric Todd described it as a 'poor do' (as Yorkshiremen would put it, he said) and many spectators suggested it was the worst final ever played at Wembley, with the players more interested in battering each other than scoring goals.

Since promotion to the First Division in 1964, Leeds United had finished as losers in two major finals and runners-up for the League title twice. They were the classic chokers of football, said the cynics, who lost their nerve at the most crucial stages. And so, Revie pondered ways of motivating his players so they could avoid another failure and emerge, at last, as trophy winners. He even considered showing them the club's trophy cabinet, in all its glory – gloriously clean and gloriously empty of major silverware – to coldly show that all their hard work and endeavour so far had won them nothing of note apart from the Division Two title and a West Riding Trophy which, frankly, did not really matter. He decided against the ploy though, worrying that it might actually do more harm than good to their confidence, especially if Arsenal beat them.

In the week prior to the match, it seemed Leeds were already up against it, with the 'architect' Johnny Giles suffering from a heavy cold, Jimmy Greenhoff not fully fit and Mick Jones cup tied. Revie had tried to learn from his mistakes during the 1965 FA Cup final preparations, he knew that he should relax more and that the players should not see how anxious he himself was. But Revie was no actor, concealing his emotions and anxieties never came easily to him. Rarely enjoying a sound night's sleep at the best of times, the week up to the League Cup final caused even more sleep deprivation for the Leeds manager.

The big day arrived. That morning, a coach carrying Leeds supporters to Wembley was near wrecked after being attacked by missile-throwing Arsenal followers. And in the match itself, the Arsenal team was accused of 'unpardonable behaviour', and blamed for a number of skirmishes on the pitch. Leeds were far from innocent, though. Referee Hamer was criticized for not taking a firmer stance with the culprits, but in his defence, the final is a major event, with royals and television cameras in attendance, so he could be forgiven for wanting to control the game calmly and civilly, as well as expecting both teams to act correspondingly as well as show suitable sporting respect for each other.

In the match, Arsenal were to gain far more possession than Leeds but achieve very little of attacking note with it. Billy Bremner, the Leeds captain, leader and all-round superhero, began the game like a greyhound tearing out of the traps. With white socks rolled down round his ankles, and no pads, only pearly white shins, the copper-topped spark – 'ten stones of barbed wire' – dared not even consider defeat this afternoon. And with around fifteen minutes gone in the game, he forged ahead down the Leeds right flank.

He linked up with Norman Hunter on Arsenal's left, close to their penalty area. Norman Hunter ventured forth with the orange ball at his feet towards the dead-ball line, hoping to cross the ball to a team-mate in the danger zone. His route however, was blocked by Arsenal's Jenkins so Hunter knocked the ball against his opponent's shin to earn United a corner kick. Left-footed Eddie Gray will take it, probably using the old Leeds ploy of aiming his cross for Jack Charlton, standing on the line just inside the near goal post.

The tall frame of Jack Charlton does indeed occupy a place on the goal-line inside the post nearest to Gray. George Graham and goalkeeper Jim Furnell are behind him, wary of the lofty Leeds defender's imposing presence. And, like a film director frames a camera shot using his hands and fingers, Charlton signals to Gray where exactly to deliver the ball. Exactly. He wants the ball inches above where his head is. It is a well-used, well-known Leeds tactic, which no one away from Elland Road seems to appreciate, probably because most opposing teams have failed to cope with it. Some claim that the scheme is unsporting or even illegal. It is not – it might offend the purists but it is entirely lawful and part of the game, and frequently effective.

Gray sends the corner kick in. It is not his best, missing Charlton's head by inches. Goalkeeper Jim Furnell, however, attempts to jump higher than his opponent and reach the ball but succeeds only in thudding into the tree trunk that is Charlton's back. And as he does that, Leeds' number 9, Paul Madeley, outwits his marker Ian Ure to race in from the edge of the area and leap prodigiously for the ball. But mid-air, Madeley's left elbow collides with the side of Furnell's skull, and the goalkeeper ends up in a heap on the floor, crying foul. Fortunately for the Gunners, Arsenal forward Graham is there on hand as defensive cover and calmly heads the ball away from the goal-line.

Madeley's assault on Furnell was not deliberate but it was a foul. A foul, however, missed by the referee, and play therefore continues. The penalty box is a throng of players from both sides, all watching the descent of the ball – four Arsenal men stand guard on the goal-line, while Furnell lies virtually incapacitated on the ground. Ten yards away from the goal, the ball slowly drops within the vicinity of the penalty spot. Each man watches closely, none more so than the man nearest, Terry Cooper, Leeds' left-back. Lining himself up to volley the descending ball, as it reaches knee-height, he strikes it with a clean, sharp connection. Anticipating the shot, the four Arsenal defenders all rush out bravely to try and block Cooper's rocket. All to no avail: the pace of the shot takes it millimetres over and past them, flashing towards the goal. And into the net. Seventeen minutes in, Leeds United 1, Arsenal 0. Eerily, for three consecutive nights running up to the final, Cooper had dreamt that he would score at Wembley, and the winning goal at that.

Like over-excited schoolboys on the sound of the last bell on the last day of term, the Leeds players reel away to celebrate. Ecstatic, they jump for joy, they run to congratulate Cooper and they hug each other, dancing, saluting the 30,000 or so Leeds followers, while the referee ignores heated Arsenal protestations.

Once they had taken the lead, manager Revie instructed his players accordingly and amended the configuration of the team, switching Paul Madeley from his makeshift centre-forward position to that of auxiliary defender, operating in the midfield just in front of Norman Hunter and Jack Charlton, while Jimmy Greenhoff became the lone Leeds attacker. These tactics of containment explained criticism of Revie and the team's 'spoiling' strategy, but really, understrength Leeds were simply playing to what strengths they had. It was not particularly attractive to watch, but after their disappointments in the recent past Revie could hardly be blamed for ordering the team to shut up shop.

Midway through the second half, Bremner chased a long pass into the Arsenal penalty area but Furnell got there first, easily. Bremner slowed but continued running and stuck out a foot as if trying to knock the ball out of Furnell's hands. It is quite obviously a fair if pointless attempt to nick the ball, Bremner connecting with neither the ball nor the man. However, in aggressive remonstrations with the Leeds captain, the Arsenal players' reactions were undeniably over the top.

Late in the game, it was the Arsenal captain's turn to be involved in controversy, in the match's main commotion. Arsenal won a corner, the resulting kick long and high, to reach a red shirt on the far side of the Leeds penalty area. The ball was headed back into the goal area where, under no pressure, Gary Sprake was able to leap high and easily catch it. Safe in his hands, the ball was unquestionably his, but the Gunners' number 4, captain Frank McLintock, appeared to disagree as he too jumped, a split second later, to hit Sprake in the back stoutly with his shoulder. It was not a particularly serious or harmful foul but it did floor Sprake. And to exacerbate the situation, as Sprake lay there still clutching the ball, Ian Ure, bigger than Jack Charlton, rushed in with feet a-blazing. Apparently trying to dislodge the ball from Sprake's arms, he succeeds only in kicking the goalkeeper, more than once. And all hell lets loose.

Leeds defenders dive in to jostle and manhandle the Arsenal offenders.

Sprake gets to his feet, aiming to land revenge on Ure.

Norman Hunter confronts McLintock.

The referee hurries to the scene but has very little influence in the melee. A linesman rushes in to help him and is equally as impotent.

Jack Charlton grabs McLintock by the neck, steering him away from Hunter.

Ure tries to defend McLintock from Charlton's handiwork.

Positioned behind him, Sprake aims a punch or two at Ure.

Terry Cooper and Billy Bremner grab Sprake by the shoulders, attempting to stifle his boxing instincts.

And Paul Reaney wades in, ready to intervene and help his team-mates however he can.

The silver, lidless, three-handled League Cup is shorter and less impressive to the eye than the FA Cup. And with not as long a history, it does not pluck the heartstrings as romantically either. But try telling that to the people of Leeds and the United players and staff as the team chair their captain Bremner around the pitch, holding the shining beacon, their first major honour, in his hands. For today, at least, the Football League Cup is the ultimate prize in football.

Wembley, so they always reckoned, was the 'Mecca' of English football, and getting there was the dream of every football player and fan in the country. What a load of old cobblers. Wembley was a dump, a right hole!

Not that I let it spoil my day there though, nothing could have, but it was a big letdown, the state of the place. Our seats, they cost a pretty penny as well, were just long wooden benches in need of a good sand-papering and at least one new coat of varnish – there were splinters all over the shop. This ground had hosted the World Cup less than two years before. What a joke.

My ticket was actually Ces's wife Lucy's, but she wasn't fussed about going. I can't say I blamed her after seeing Wembley with my own eyes. I was chuffed to be there of course and Ces let me have the ticket for a very reasonable price. 'A pint sometime.' I'm not sure I ever paid him. If ever anyone wanted more tickets but couldn't get them from the club officially, there was always a chance of getting some from the Leeds players. It was probably against the rules, but I doubt there was one single Leeds supporter who minded: it was the players who'd got the club to Wembley after all. The word was 'See Big Jack.' The players received loads of tickets and had pooled all the spares – Jack was like the box office manager. He was a right entrepreneur, opening his own stall on Elland Road opposite the gates, selling scarves and hats and rosettes and badges and probably anything else he could sell that was in the Leeds colours. He'd even be there on the morning of home matches he'd be playing in. I know that he went on to open up a couple of proper shops in his name as well. He had one on Roundhay Road, near the Fforde Grene pub, funnily enough (which he was *never* seen in, *not* smoking while he *wasn't* there) and Garforth, to name but two. Eventually the club would strike some sort of deal with him so that they opened up an official souvenir shop in the middle of the Fullerton club house, the five-a-side fenced-in pitch and next to the main gates. Terry Cooper went on to do the same, in town, on Lower Briggate, a few years after. I hope that any football boots he sold came in a box and not just wrapped in an old newspaper.

Jack was notorious, too, for being 'frugal' with money and for cadging cigarettes off people, even if he didn't know them. Billy Bremner was usually in cahoots with him, as the Leeds squad's 'secret smokers' society', and they were said to be two of *the* laziest trainers at the club as well. Gary Sprake was no angel either, he even smoked a pipe as well as cigars, and I'd even seen The Don with a cigar once, though I don't think he approved of smoking. I think he was alright about the players drinking in moderation. Billy and Jack would smoke their cigs, and if someone was about to catch them at it, Jack would always somehow palm his cigarette on to someone else. Usually Billy. Legend had it that it even happened in the team bath once, after a match.

Ces warned me to make sure to remember which stairway we went up to our seats, because the stadium was like a huge bloody labyrinth inside. Seeing hundreds and hundreds of folk waving blue and white banners and wearing scarves in the gold, white and blue of Leeds made me feel safe – if I did get lost I'd be in good hands. At half-time I was bursting for a wee so I searched out the Gents. It wasn't hard to find. I followed my nose and the hundreds of other desperate Leeds fans.

I was never anywhere near as superstitious as Don Revie, but I must admit, before the League Cup final even I was starting to think Leeds were cursed and forever doomed to never win anything big. But when Terry Cooper popped up to whack in that bullet of a goal, there and then I was just about convinced there was no such thing as curses, at least not where Leeds United was concerned. The fact that we'd won was the most important thing for us all in the White corner. Not the performance, not the prettiness of the play, not the number of efforts on goal and not the watching all those ruffian working class sportsmen kicking lumps out of each other.

Even though we were in the same stand as the Royal Box, there was no way of seeing the League Cup itself being presented to the team, there were too many people in the way, but at least I'd had a good view of the goal and of all the action, even if there wasn't much of it. And I saw the lap of honour of course, which was brilliant.

When the referee blew the final whistle, there was Billy jumping off the ground and then doing a forward roll, Leeds players hugging, dancing, shaking hands, and Norman Hunter clenching his fists, swearing that this trophy would be just be the first of many. And we fans, we were all feeling a part of it, sharing the brilliance, I really believe that. There were men and women around me in tears once that whistle went, and Ces took the mick, in a good-natured way, and I'm pretty sure he was misty eyed as well when he saw the players celebrating. I know I was but I've never tried to deny I'm a big softie. Me, I felt like I could explode I was that happy, and I'm surprised I wasn't roaring as well. It didn't matter in the slightest that the game was supposedly one of the worst Wembley finals *ever* – Arsenal should take most 'credit' for that anyway – the most important thing was that we never looked like conceding a goal. The only sad part as far as I was concerned was that Harry Reynolds hadn't been there, because he'd been too ill to attend.

Those saps who criticized Leeds obviously had never watched a Peter Lorimer or Johnny Giles special before, or Mick Jones trouncing centre-halves, Eddie Gray dancing around everybody, or our double agent full-backs Terry Cooper and Paul Reaney racing down the wings on attack, or nullifying opposing attackers. And they won't have appreciated the class of Billy Bremner, finishing off a move that he'd started in the first place, or immaculate Paul Madeley floating around the pitch tidying everything up and putting away a few goals too, or our wingers and attackers, Albert Johanneson, Mike O'Grady, Jimmy Greenhoff, Rod Belfitt, Terry Hibbitt and co, in full flight. And then there's the brilliance and bravery of the goalkeeping and the tackling and heading of the central defenders, all skills in their own right, big time. There were so many great things to see in this Leeds team. These critics, they were blind and they talked out of their backsides.

Being laid up in pot some time before, I'd put on weight, my lungs had been given a long rest and my leg muscles had withered away a bit. But once recovered, I was confident I'd be okay and be able to run all day just like I could before. Of those Leeds players I watched the closest, Billy Bremner always seemed to be the fittest, and for his age, Bobby Collins had been bloody amazing too, even after his injury. And then there'd been Grenville Hair, who was small and muscular but wiry as well, and he was fast and he looked like he could play until dusk, too. Fit as a fiddle he was, even as a manager like he was now, at Bradford City. So you can imagine the shock when, five days after Leeds won the League Cup, Grenville Hair died of a heart attack after a training session with his players.

He was thirty-six years old, thirty-six bloody years old. Grenville Hair, Rest In Peace.

Modern technology was great. A few weeks after Wembley, the 1968 League Cup Winners were away at Glasgow Rangers in the Inter-Cities Fairs Cup quarter-final. We'd stuttered through to get this far, and Rangers would be the hardest tie, I reckoned. It was a sell-out at Ibrox so the Leeds board decided to arrange to transmit the game from Scotland to here by 'closed circuit' television, and put it on a special big screen built on the Lowfields Road terrace. I did ask one bloke from the company who were setting the screen up how closed circuit television worked but he might as well have tried explaining logarithms, in Chinese and from another room, to me. I bet he could hear his own words echoing in my head.

Credit to the Leeds board for screening the game, I'm sure Harry Reynolds would have been proud of the idea even if it might have been risky, money wise. I don't know how much it cost to hire all the equipment and to get the match relayed here, but there was a 20,000-or-so crowd at Elland Road to watch, so there'll have been a tidy little profit made on the night no doubt, plus a good little public relations exercise. I can still remember when that number would have been rated as a pretty good crowd for a real game of football.

The Rangers away game was predictable – we played to contain them and then take them on the break and grab an away goal. The weather was what you'd expect: just like everyone says it rains non-stop in Manchester, in Glasgow it was either blowing a gale, throwing it down or sleeting. And there were 80,000 mad Jocks for the Leeds team to put up with as well. On the face of it, we were really up against it and would do well to get just a draw, but I just had a good feeling due to most of the Leeds Scottish players being Celtic fans. I thought they'd use the hostile atmosphere to motivate them. I mean, could Billy, for one, really be scared of a big and loud Rangers crowd? Doubtful.

In Europe, Rangers had played more games than any other British team without winning any of the trophies. It was our fifty-second game of the season as well, already. Not that the players looked tired or anything, they battled for every single ball all night. The match was a tight affair. Sprakey didn't have a difficult save to make, but neither did their keeper, to be fair. By the end, The Don seemed very pleased with the 0–0 draw.

'This is the result we came for. Rangers played much as we expected them to, but it isn't over yet. Don't forget we have to take some risks at Elland Road in order to win the tie, and Rangers are an extremely accomplished and experienced side. However, I got one of the forms of result I wanted, a good result, and I think the boys were splendid.'

The newspapers agreed with him too. Wonders will never cease. They were nearly complimentary to Leeds as well, saying that the team had struck a severe blow to the pride of all Scotland. That was more nonsense. I'm *sure* Celtic fans were deeply upset at Rangers not winning.

Two weeks after, it was the home leg at our place. We'd beaten Sheffield United twice in that time, with our Paul Madeley getting the only goal in the FA Cup sixth round home tie, followed by a steady 3–0 League win the Saturday after, Madeley getting one again and Giles two penalties. The Cup tie had attracted 48,000; the League tie on April 6, against the same team, got 17,000 less. I always remembered that date because two days before was when Martin Luther King was murdered in Memphis.

Rangers had been allocated 3,000 tickets for Elland Road and, like we'd done, they'd arranged for the match to be transmitted on closed circuit television up to Ibrox. Before, Hibs had brought maybe 500 fans, but it seems obvious that Leeds had underesti-mated the Rangers support. There were millions of them, drunken, growling and weird sounding, and they wrecked half the pubs in town while they were here. The crowd was over 50,000.

It was bad-natured stuff. The referee even stopped the game in the first half because the Rangers fans were throwing stuff at David Harvey: beer bottles, coins, ball-bearings, the bloody lot. Their captain, John Greig, had to ask his own team's supporters to pack it in. Their behaviour was disrespectful to say the least – the Leeds players were wearing black armbands because chairman Morris had died a couple of days before. At that stage we were 2–0 up, so I don't know if the Rangers fans were trying to get the game abandoned, even before half-time, but it wasn't going to work.

Rangers started well enough but they didn't really look like scoring. They battled hard though and tried to take the game to Leeds. The fact was we were a bit fortunate to take the lead with a Johnny Giles penalty after Alex Ferguson had handballed. Peter Lorimer got a second after latching on to a cross that Jimmy Greenhoff had just missed. I don't know how many Rangers supporters were inside Elland Road but there were groups of them dotted all over the stadium. There were scraps and scuffles all around the ground.

We won. Which meant we were current League Cup holders, Inter-Cities Fairs Cup semi-finalists, joint top of League Division One and still in the running for the FA Cup with the semi-final against Everton coming up. In other words, Leeds were going for the full four trophies. *Four*. Four bloody trophies.

At this stage we were about twenty games unbeaten, in all competitions, but there were other strong teams with their eye on winning the League as well – Man United, Man City and Liverpool. Newcastle were sniffing around a bit too, but they wouldn't last the pace, Geordie teams never did. And Everton were a good side and only had the FA Cup to aim for.

### 8–9

Three days after beating Rangers, Leeds were at White Hart Lane in the League against Tottenham. It was the first of three games in six days. At Spurs, Leeds conceded goals for the first time in seven matches, losing 2–1, their first defeat in twenty-six matches. And to add to their gloom, with three weeks to go,

Manchester United took over at the top of the table with a 4–0 win at Fulham.

On the Leeds board of directors, Alderman Percy Woodward succeeded Albert Morris as chairman. He had been vice-chairman for over twenty years and was described as a traditional 'old-school' type of businessman. The day after the defeat at Spurs, Leeds visited Coventry and edged a 1–0 win thanks to a fine and rare Terry Hibbitt goal. It was the first of three hard-fought wins on the trot, with a revenge win over Spurs (1–0, a Lorimer penalty) and West Bromwich Albion 3–1 (Gray, Charlton, Madeley) during the following week. The victories left Leeds looking in a good position to win the League Championship for the first time ever, even though Manchester United remained top of the table, and Leeds, in truth, were not in the best of form.

The League Division One table (top), April 20 1968:

| 1 | Manchester Utd | Played 39, | Points 54 |
| 2 | Leeds United | Played 38, | Points 53 |
| 3 | Manchester City | Played 38, | Points 50 |
| 4 | Liverpool | Played 37, | Points 48 |
| 5 | Everton | Played 37, | Points 47 |

When comparing the teams in Division One, man for man, Leeds United probably were the best, but even the ambitious Revie had said that one team winning three trophies in a season was impossible. And here they were, vying for four. Having played around sixty games so far, there were extremely tired and not fully fit players lining up for Leeds. Many were the times when certain players ignored immense pain to play full matches, when just walking without hobbling was an accomplishment in itself. There were players who played despite being ill or who were suffering with broken toes or chipped ankle and foot bones, or swollen, over-stressed knees and fatigued, tender hamstrings. Pain could not be allowed to matter; keeping on working was the most important issue, keeping on winning, keeping on fighting and keeping on marching on together. Revie's preference was to select the same twelve men for every important match – don't change a winning team, don't upset the rhythm, don't tempt Fate by meddling with team selection when it doesn't need it, and say your prayers every night.

Leeds had a game in hand on Manchester United and could regain top spot on Tuesday April 23, St George's Day, with a win away to second-bottom Stoke City. Theoretically, it would be a straightforward two points for Leeds, but theory doesn't put the ball into the opponent's net, and things were rarely straightforward when Leeds were concerned. Stoke City were battling to preserve their place in Division One and thus gave Leeds a torrid time. By half-time, Stoke were leading 2–0, both scored by striker Peter Dobing. For the second half, Leeds came out fighting. Goals from Greenhoff and Charlton levelled the scores, but thanks to a combination of the woodwork, poor finishing and superb goalkeeping by Gordon Banks Leeds weren't able to snatch a third. To make matters worse, in the dying minutes, Dobing completed his hat trick to seal a fine 3–2 win for Stoke and inflict a severe dent to Leeds' hopes of winning the League.

Four days later at Old Trafford was the FA Cup semi-final against Everton. As was often the case against the Toffees, the match was not a pretty sight to watch, nor was it entertaining or good natured. The Everton team normally had what fans called the 'Holy Trinity' of Colin Harvey, Howard Kendall and a certain Alan Ball in midfield, but not today, as Ball was suspended. His typical never-say-die attitude was prevalent at Everton FC, with the team capable of beating anyone on their day, with or without Ball. In goal for Leeds was Gary Sprake, whose reputation had taken a beating a few months before at Anfield – incredibly, he had thrown the ball into his own net, against Liverpool, when trying to hurl it to one of his defenders. And in the FA Cup fifth round tie at home to Bristol City, Sprake was sent off for punching City striker Chris Garland. The referee, unfortunately, did not see Garland spit in Sprake's face first.

Another Sprake incident was to set Everton on their way to Wembley. Sprake had caught a cross intended for striker Joe Royle, the young and burly forward who liked throwing his considerable weight around to let goalkeepers know they were involved in a battle. Sprake, notoriously short tempered during games, unsurprisingly resented such antics from opponents, especially as he spent most of the game injured. In a few seconds of madness, the hurt goalkeeper allowed his temper to get the better of him. As he was in the motion of drop-kicking the ball, he seemed to be trying to exact some retribution on Royle. As well as the ball, it appeared Sprake tried to strike Royle as his kicking foot followed through. The crucial point was not whether Sprake struck Royle or not or if he intended to, the crucial point was the ineptitude of the kick. The ball, like a damp squib, travelled a pitiful twenty or so yards, straight to Everton's Jimmy Husband.

The surprised Husband kept his composure to fire in a quick shot towards the unguarded Leeds net, only to see Jack Charlton race in and prevent the ball from entering the net. But Charlton used his hands — so no goal for Husband but the reward of a penalty. Johnny Morrissey scored the spot-kick and Leeds' hopes of being the first team to win both the League Cup and FA Cup in the same season drained away. For all the great displays Gary Sprake had made for the team, his inconsistency and lack of concentration were now earning him the description of Leeds' weak link. Sprake's mistake brought the only goal of the game and a Cup exit for Leeds, leaving them, realistically, with just the Fairs Cup to aim for. At the final whistle, Everton supporters ran on to the pitch, prompting aggrieved Leeds fans to throw coins, toilet rolls and other objects at them.

Leeds' form marginally improved in the Fairs Cup semi-final first leg against Dundee at Dens Park on May 1. Paul Madeley was 'Mr Versatile' again, deputizing for lead striker Mick Jones, and he got the first goal in the match on twenty-six minutes, making an impressive personal total of ten for the season. Although Dundee soon equalized, for the second half Revie had ordered his players to ease off and conserve energy. Keep it tight and that away goal could be vital — besides, this was Leeds' sixty-second game of the season.

Three days later, with just three League games left to play, Leeds were in third place and set to play fourth-placed Liverpool at Elland Road. Thanks to Mick Jones smashing a Lorimer cross into the net after quarter of an hour to make it 1–0, Leeds were deservedly in front for most of the match. They also hit the bar, had a strong penalty claim for a Yeats handball declined and missed a couple more good scoring chances as well. And then it all went shockingly, miserably wrong, in the match's dying minutes.

Six minutes from the end, first a scrappy, fortunate goal from Lawler brought Liverpool level and then soon after another scrappy and fortunate goal, this time from substitute Graham, won the match for Liverpool and brought Leeds' first home defeat of the season. With Manchester City winning well at Tottenham, and Manchester United thrashing Newcastle, the late Liverpool goals had badly hurt Leeds' title aspirations.

League Division One (top), May 4 1968:

| 1 | Manchester City | Played 41, | Points 56 |
| 2 | Manchester Utd | Played 41, | Points 56 |
| 3 | Leeds Utd | Played 40, | Points 53 |
| 4 | Liverpool | Played 40, | Points 53 |

Just three days later was their game in hand – away at Arsenal, a team with revenge in mind after the League Cup bruiser. Sprake and Charlton were injured and worse news for Leeds was the enforced absence of Norman Hunter and Terry Cooper, both called up for England duty away to Spain the night after. David Harvey had shown he was more than a capable replacement for Sprake, but three of the famous Leeds back four 'wall' were out, while regular right-back Paul Reaney would play on the left against Arsenal, with Nigel Davey making his League debut on the right. Revie understandably was furious at having to play such an important match without Hunter and Cooper and he made his annoyance clear to the FA. But, as usual, club managers carried little sway with the game's rulers and Revie's complaints were dismissed.

In a dramatic, entertaining battle Arsenal took the lead three times, only for a weakened Leeds side to draw level each time, through Lorimer, Jones and Giles, who were virtually camped in Arsenal's half for the last fifteen minutes of the match. Unfortunately, try as they might they couldn't find a fourth goal and, just seconds from the final whistle, they fell to another late, late show with Arsenal getting the winner. The next evening, of scant consolation for Leeds, Norman Hunter scored the eighty-first-minute winner in England's 2–1 win over Spain to take them into the European Championship semi-finals.

On the final Saturday of the League, fourth in the table, unable to win it and already qualified for the next Inter-Cities Fairs Cup, Leeds' last League game, at Burnley, was somewhat meaningless. With the semi-final second leg against Dundee still to play, Revie's team selection for the Burnley match was unusual if not wholly surprising. Paul Madeley was accompanied in the centre of defence by Eddie Gray, and Nigel Davey would make his second League appearance. Full-back Bobby Sibbald would be making his first full League appearance while it would be Terry Yorath's Leeds debut and Jimmy Lumsden's second ever League game. Yorath was another of United's Welsh scout Jack Pickard's recommendations. Notwithstanding, Burnley won the match comfortably, 3–0.

Of eleven League defeats all season for Leeds, four had taken place in the disastrous last month of the campaign, while ten of them had occurred away from home. If Revie's Leeds had travelled with stronger intent to win games rather than just avoid defeat – in other words, if they had attacked more in away games – then there were claims that they would have won the Championship, and quite comfortably.

A confident Dundee side visited Elland Road in the Fairs Cup semi-final second leg, the score at half-time in the tie 1–1. Revie recalled the first team regulars except for Jack Charlton, who was still out with an ankle injury – Paul Madeley deputized for him in the centre of defence again. Less than 24,000 attended: the closure of the Gelderd End was partly responsible for this low figure, as a roof was being constructed for the Kop.

Despite the weekend rest for most of the Leeds players the match still proved to be a struggle for them, with little in the way of incisive or fluent attacking football until the second half. Was it complacency or weariness? After giving them a stern talking-to at the interval but seeing only slight improvement, Revie believed it to be the latter, though a couple of the players may have been guilty of under-estimating Dundee. The Scots were, after all, fortunate to be in the competition at all due to the Fairs Cup rule of 'one city, one team', plus they had received a bye in an early round. They did, though, battle well and never made it easy for Leeds, who were firmly in command thanks to their away goal in the first match. But Eddie Gray's shot in the eighty-first minute sealed the tie and put Leeds in the final. His left-foot piledriver hit the roof of the net after somehow piercing the crowded penalty area and beating two Dundee players on the goal-line. More good news for Revie and Leeds was that UEFA had decided, due to fixture congestions, to play the two legs of the 1967–68 Inter Cities Fairs Cup final at the beginning of the following season.

A lucrative advantage of Leeds' prolonged interest in all competitions, of course, was the increase in revenue. Whether the public agreed or not, professional football was a business, and every league club had to be run as such. Leeds' sustained financial success enabled the directors to continue with their plans to expand and improve the stadium and make it 'the Wembley of the North'. The summer of 1968 would see the north end of the ground, 'the Spion Kop', on the Gelderd Road side, rebuilt and covered by the new roof. The capacity of the Kop reduced as a result, from 19,000 to nearer 15,000. The new stand encroached on the playing area less than the old one, meaning that the football pitch needed to be re-sited thirty or so feet closer to the North Stand. The renovations were at a cost of well over £100,000.

# Chapter 9

*To hell with Man United, to hell with Liverpool,*
*For we fight, fight, fight, for United,*
*'Till we win the Football League!*

A great song, and it made a change from the usual 'Leeds Leeds Leeds' chants, which droned on a bit too much for my liking. And if fans got bored of singing something then it wasn't really likely to get the players' pulses racing either, was it?

The fans singing a new song proved that the team had come a massive way under The Don, but it showed that some supporters had got greedy and complacent, as if they had a right to expect Leeds to beat everybody and win everything. Complacency was an accusation aimed at the team last season, especially in the final run-in where we blew the big two, the League and the FA Cup.

On the face of it, the 1967–68 season had been bloody great, but the way it fizzled out over the final four weeks tainted all the success a bit. We lost to Everton in the FA Cup semi-final due to Gary Sprake, plus he'd scored that bloody awful own goal against Liverpool. If only his handling was as good as they said it was in the Mecca and Phonographique nightclubs – handling pint glasses and women – then he'd hardly let any goals in at all! The problem being a keeper is that one tiny mistake can result in conceding a goal, and poor performances are always remembered. Definitely the case with Sprakey. Who'd be a goalkeeper? Not me. You needed to be at least a bit barmy, especially with maniacs like Peter Lorimer shooting at you. David Harvey had been knocked unconscious more than once in training by a Lorimer thunderbolt.

To hear supporters whingeing about The Don or the team would tempt me to try and slap a bit of sense into the critics, but there was too much violence at football as it was. Now there were gangs from various parts of Leeds who'd go to matches with intention of fighting opposing teams' gangs. It was a 'disturbing new trend', according to the papers. Their publicizing it will have done a lot of good, of course. The new Leeds chairman Percy Woodward said that he wouldn't ever bring his grandchildren to Elland Road because of all the abusive and filthy language and atmosphere of aggression. The chairman of the club said that! But as much as violence among the supporters was wrong, I loved a good old battle on the pitch.

Up it went, proudly pinned on my bedroom wall, the Football Honours 1967–68.

**Division One winners**: Man. City. Runners up: Man. United.
**FA Cup winners**: West Brom. Runners up: Everton (shame!)
**League Cup winners**: Leeds United. Runners up: Arsenal.
**European Cup winners**: Man United. Runners up: Benfica.
**European Cup Winners' Cup winners**: AC Milan. Runners up: Hamburg.
**Inter-Cities Fairs Cup winners:** Leeds United (with luck) or Ferencvaros (without it).
**Football Player of the Year**: George Best, Man United.
**European Footballer of the Year**: George Best.
**Attendance average, home games**: 36,828.

All in all it had been a good year so far to follow Leeds, at soccer or rugby league. We won the Football League Cup and the rugby team won the Challenge Trophy for the first time, at Wembley as well. They were spawny though. I watched it on the Peacock television. The commentator Eddie Waring sounded like a jungle bird laying an oversized egg, because Wakefield's Don Fox missed the easiest conversion ever, right in front of the posts, with the very last kick of the match. Seriously, my grandma could have kicked it. But it had absolutely belted it down cats and dogs all day, the pitch was just about flooded and the game shouldn't have been played – they didn't nickname it the 'watersplash final' for nothing. It was a bit of a farce, but what the hell, Leeds won and Don Fox got the man of the match award. Mind you, I bet he'd felt like telling them where to stick it. Another reason to look forward to the new season was that Yorkshire Television would be showing highlights of League matches on Sunday afternoons.

The first leg of the 1967–68 Inter-Cities Fairs Cup final was to be played at Elland Road on the Saturday before the official League season started. Not only was it a cup final, it was a *major* cup final, and against one of the best teams in Europe, the green and whites of Ferencvaros, Hungary's most successful team ever. Bill Shankly, Jock Stein and Matt Busby had all said that Ferencvaros were the finest side in European football – they had won the Fairs Cup in 1965 and were reigning champions of the Hungarian league, meaning that after this final they'd be competing in the European Cup. Good as we were, everyone expected Ferencvaros to beat us.

The crowd of a little bit more than 25,000 was, in my opinion, pitiful. Okay, it was the official holiday time in Leeds and the match was shown live on television but still, it was embarrassing. Leeds had recently beaten Celtic up in Scotland in a friendly match. Match reports said that they'd played well, with a fresh, much more attack-minded approach than in previous seasons. With a trophy finally under their belts, Don Revie had given the players permission to 'express' themselves more, the papers said.

Any adventurous new tactics weren't very evident in the first leg of the Ferencvaros tie, I could state that categorically. It was a tight and cagey game all the way through, but we managed to grind a 1–0 win with a scrambled goal from Mick Jones. It was stop–start throughout, the referee used his whistle more than a Bank Holiday train guard. Leeds deserved to win although it wasn't a great performance – we couldn't seem able to get past or behind their defenders, all eleven of them. If a Leeds move looked promising then one of the Ferencvaros players would chop ours down or obstruct him.

So we were going into the away second leg with a 1–0 lead, which definitely would not be enough to win the Fairs Cup, according to most people. They were forgetting though that Leeds enjoyed being the underdog. In fact, the game was in doubt for a while as there was trouble brewing in Europe, due to the Russian Commies and the poor bloody countries they'd already taken over. There were rumours that it would be too dangerous for the Leeds team and any supporters to travel.

Having Mike O'Grady back was grand news, especially as Jimmy Greenhoff had decided to join Birmingham City, for £70,000, soon after the first leg of the final. He'd come on as a substitute in it. It was a decent fee but I'd have liked him to stay, he had a lot of quality about him. I couldn't quite fathom what his thinking was. He'd played in most of the games the last season, it wasn't like he was being ignored or anything – *and* the Brummies were in Division Two. It was also looking a bit bleak for Albert Johanneson's career as well, I didn't have a clue what was happening, just that he didn't seem to be involved much any more.

I know he liked a drink. Didn't we all? But whether that was affecting his football playing, I didn't know. After a good win, The Don would tell captain Billy to make sure the players had a good drink to unwind after, in moderation. To be fair to Albert, there were always stories about Leeds players drinking too much, not just him, and getting involved in scrapes with cars or ropey women and that.

A couple of years before, Albert had been substituted at half-time in a game, against Forest I think, so he stayed in the dressing room and supposedly polished off a whole bottle of whisky. And that's when it started, when he got a taste for the booze. How much of it is true I was never sure, but the players definitely had a bottle of the hard stuff available to them if they wanted a nip to warm them up. Leeds players were seen regularly 'on the town', places like the Windmill Club on North Street and the casino, and various pubs and clubs. Even though I heard a rumour that Billy Bremner had been found asleep on a Leeds golf course one Saturday morning before a match, there was never much to suggest that the Leeds players ever really went overboard or anything with the drinking. Besides, Don Revie had 'spies' all over Leeds and if a player was seen in an 'unseemly' state (pissed up), then the club would know about it soon enough.

Not that any footballer should need more reason to beat opponents other than it's infinitely better than losing to them, I put a list up on my wall of all our Division One opponents of 1968–69, plus The Reasons Why We Have To Beat Them.

| | |
|---|---|
| **Southampton** | Red and white stripes. Taff striker Ron Davies, top scorer, Terry Paine, John Sydenham, Mick Channon, Jimmy Gabriel. And Southerners. |
| **QPR** | Small London club = big headed and cocky Cockneys. Mick Leach, Rodney Marsh. |
| **Stoke** | Red and white stripes – Gordon Banks, Terry Conroy, Peter Dobing. We owe them big time. |
| **Ipswich** | Centre-forward Ray Crawford who's played for England. Country bumpkins. |
| **Forest** | Red shirts, Ian Storey-Moore, 'Slim' Jim Baxter and Joe 'the Jock' Baker who sounds Scottish but has played for England. And Robin Hood is from Yorkshire, really. |
| **Sunderland** | They probably do really hate us and they wear red and white stripes. Colin Suggett, George Mulhall. Some of their fans are a bad lot. |
| **Liverpool** | 1965, all red, Bill Shankly, Roger Hunt, Ian St John, Yeats and others. That accent, and the rotten abuse some of their fans gave Albert at Wembley. Cilla Black, Jimmy Tarbuck. |
| **Wolves** | Derek Dougan and Peter Knowles. The people talk funny. |
| **Leicester** | Peter Shilton and record transfer fee £150,000 striker Allan Clarke. |
| **Arsenal** | They hate us, and some of their supporters are proven to be right dogs. McLintock, Graham, Storey and Ure, who Gary Sprake knows all about. Red. |
| **Man City** | Joe Mercer in charge, League Champions. Colin Bell, Mike Summerbee, Francis Lee and Tony Book. Lancashire = red rose. |
| **Newcastle** | 'Magpies'. Wyn Davies and Bryan 'Pop' Robson. Geordies speak foreign. That ugly black and white kit. |
| **Spurs** | Bill Nicholson, rich club. Jimmy Greaves, Alan Gilzean, Martin Chivers, Pat Jennings, Cyril Knowles, Alan Mullery. Cockneys. |
| **Coventry** | Boss is ex-Man United player Noel Cantwell, took over from mouth almighty Jimmy Hill. |

| | Willie Carr, Lady Godiva and Coventry people's funny accent, possibly dafter than Wolves'. |
| **West Ham** | Snotty manager Ron Greenwood, Hurst, Peters, Bobby Moore. East End Cockneys. |
| **Man Utd** | European Cup holders, Busby, Best, Charlton, Law, Stiles. They wear red, have lots of supporters who can't take losing. Lancashire. They hate us. |
| **Burnley** | More Lancastrians. Big-mouthed chairman Bob Lord. Ralph Coates, Andy Lochhead, Dave Thomas. Some horrible supporters. |
| **West Brom** | Jeff Astle, Tony Brown, people from West Brom talk even weirder than Coventry and Wolverhampton. |
| **Everton** | They really hate us, have some very good players and possibly the worst fans around. |
| **Chelsea** | FA Cup semi-final, Villa Park, 1967. Cockneys. Most of their players and fans. |
| **Sheff Weds** | Stalwart Don Megson, Jim McCalliog who'd been at Leeds as a kid, Tommy Craig. Their supporters probably hate us because we're the strongest team in Yorkshire. |

### 9–2

'I took one look and thought he might never play again.' The articulate voice was followed by the signature tune. It was fair-haired, bespectacled Dr Matthew McCleary's turn in the spotlight.

Orthopaedic surgeon Dr McCleary, a small, quietly spoken man, informs Eamonn Andrews that twenty-one year-old Don Revie had broken three ankle bones and dislocated a joint while playing for Leicester against Tottenham. Dr McCleary treated him, and he quoted Revie's chances of a return to playing professional football as one thousand to one against.

How, asked Eamonn Andrews, was it that only eight weeks after having the pot off that Revie was back playing for the Leicester first team again?

146

'I think,' replied the surgeon, 'it was Don's grim determination to be a footballer.'

Grim determination indeed, and it would influence the attitudes of the Leeds coaches whenever they were required to treat injured players. Many times, player injuries and cases of fatigue were treated with disdain more than anything. If a player could walk quickly then he could trot, if he could trot he could run, and if he could run he could sprint, and if he could sprint then he was available for selection.

Footage of the 1949 FA Cup semi-final between Leicester and Portsmouth is screened. Black and white images show Revie scoring the first goal, then team-mate Ken Chisholm the second and Revie slamming in his side's third, 'to sink Pompey lower than a submarine!' There are cheers from the evening's audience. Revie smiles sheepishly, probably recalling more misfortune that struck him not long afterwards, forcing him to miss the final.

Wife Elsie tells how her husband had challenged for a header in a match against Blackburn Rovers and had his nose and teeth smashed inadvertently by his opponent. The loss of blood would prove to be life threatening.

In July at Elland Road, Revie gathered his Leeds squad together in the Players' Lounge to outline his plans and aims for the forthcoming campaign. This was the beginning of his eighth full season as manager and it was business as usual. What was far from usual though was the challenge he issued to his men. No fuss or drama, only words spoken in a simple and matter-of-fact way: 'You're going to win the Championship this time lads, and what's more you're going to do so without losing a single league match.'

Club captain Billy Bremner asked Revie if he was in fact joking, while other players wondered, privately, whether the Boss had taken leave of his senses. So Revie said it again, adding that he was indeed being entirely serious.

If ever Don Revie became dissatisfied with how the team was performing he would employ his 'cheque book ploy'. He would threaten the players that if they weren't up to the task or weren't prepared to play 'his' way, then he would not hesitate in buying players who were.

With the League Cup in the trophy cabinet, possibly to be joined in the near future by the Inter-Cities Fairs Cup, Revie was satisfied with the players available to him, despite the team's League burnout late last season. He believed the squad to be the best around, although the English public had only seen Leeds United Mark One, the pragmatic rather than entertaining team designed to win matches efficiently, systematically and in a no-nonsense manner rather than provide thrills and lots of goals. For away games, the intention had always been to win (of course), but with little if any emphasis on doing it impressively. But for the 1968–69 season that would all change.

The highest compliment that the critics seemed able to bestow on Leeds was that they were a powerful 'machine' built by an efficient manager. If that was praise then Revie didn't want it. Instead of being admired as a great manager who had built Leeds up from virtually nothing, it felt as though he was regarded more as a cold and calculating autocrat, guilty of creating a monster of a football team. Revie was anxious for his men to receive rightful recognition for their achievements. Much as he respected managers like Busby, Shankly, Nicholson and even Ramsey, their successful teams had always been built around players with strength and 'bite' and no little devilry, yet it only ever seemed to be Revie and his Leeds who were criticized for aggressive style. The FA's 'dirtiest team' tag of more than four years before had stuck, and still rankled with the club. Revie wanted to be liked, he wanted to be popular, and he wanted his team to be loved, because he believed they deserved it.

Four days after the narrow home-leg 1–0 win over Ferencvaros, on August 7, the new League campaign kicked off, and Leeds had a total of seven matches to contest before the return leg in Hungary. A hectic schedule again for the Peacocks, but this 1968–

69 campaign was to witness a revitalized Leeds. The mood within the camp was one of high confidence, and for every game the players would enter the field of play, staunch and dogged in the belief that they would not, perhaps even could not, lose.

An away win at Southampton started the assault on the Championship. Despite going a goal down very early on, Leeds responded superbly and goals from Lorimer, Jones and Hibbitt (on as substitute for Lorimer) resoundingly won the match 3–1. And so exciting was the victory that the *Guardian*'s David Lacey wrote: 'Many of the crowd must have wondered how Leeds had earned their reputation for mean mindedness and spoiling tactics.'

Four days later, at home, goals from Jones, Giles, Reaney and Hibbitt brought a 4–1 win over newly promoted Queens Park Rangers, though Leeds had more difficulty than the scoreline suggested, and it was to be Johnny Giles' last game for a while due to knee trouble. His injury did not seem too severe at first, more a 'niggle' which would eventually fade, but in fact it was a potentially career-threatening one. Fortunately, Giles was treated by specialist Mr Rose, a director of Manchester City, and the prognosis was good. Rose had helped Jack Charlton's recovery from broken knee ligaments before, a serious injury for a footballer and for which nine out of ten operations reputedly failed to work successfully.

The following Saturday, August 17, without Madeley and Lorimer as well as Giles, Leeds strove for a hard-earned win against Stoke City, Mick Jones and Albert Johanneson scoring.

On the next Tuesday, the long journey to newly promoted Ipswich Town resulted in two more Leeds points as goals from Belfitt (in the first twenty seconds), O'Grady and Hibbitt provided a 3–2 victory. Ipswich had fought back from two down to level early in the second half but Hibbitt's third of the season sealed it, a thirty-yarder deceiving the goalkeeper. Four wins out of four, eight points out of eight. The next Saturday, at Nottingham Forest, Hibbitt was a central figure again, but for very different reasons.

One of the Leeds players' favourite pre-match pastimes was to play bingo – a fun way of keeping them relaxed and entertained.

And there was usually a lot of money riding on it. Before the Forest game, Hibbitt had won the bingo and thus pocketed a tidy little sum as a result. As he was one of the younger first teamers, he was paid accordingly too, so the winnings were a welcome bonus. At the City Ground at half-time, Don Revie was instructing the Leeds players in their dressing room, in the main stand of the ground. The score stood at 1–1 and Leeds had not played particularly well. While the players were listening to their manager, Gary Sprake smelled burning and then noticed smoke coming into their room under the door.

He tried to calmly inform the rest of the group but was told 'Shut up, the Boss is talking!' They eventually noticed the hazard and without any panic made their way out to safety away from the City Ground, to a nearby hotel across the River Trent. Not before Terry Hibbitt had dashed back into the changing room, however, to retrieve his winnings from his trouser pockets. He returned safe and sound, and relieved to still be that bit wealthier, but he had to endure much ridicule from team-mates for not thinking to bring the trousers with him.

As usual, Dave Cocker, with younger brother Ian, had been at the match to support Leeds. As the flames began to consume the stand in which they were sitting, their dad Les wasn't sure where they were and spent a frantic few minutes searching for them. With flames shooting through the floorboards, they'd realized they were in danger and so had fled into the standing paddock in front of the seats and then on to the football pitch, with hundreds of other spectators. An electrical fault was considered to be the cause of the fire, though lit cigarettes were also suspected. As there had been no casualties the fire was not regarded as a serious incident. People there though, including the Cocker boys, knew only too well that they had had a lucky escape. Forest had to play their home games at Notts County's ground for a number of weeks as the stadium underwent repairs.

Four days later, at Elland Road, Leeds disappointingly dropped their first point of the season in a 1–1 draw with Sunderland, Belfitt getting the goal. Aware that injuries to key players was a distinct threat to the team's chances of glory, Revie put in a bid for Burnley's exciting and versatile winger Willie Morgan, a Scotland international. But Burnley chairman Bob Lord turned the offer down and Morgan later signed for Manchester United for a fee of £117,000.

Revie and the fans' disappointment with the Sunderland result was short lived as they beat Liverpool 1–0 at Elland Road, Jones getting the all-important goal after a mistake by Yeats gave him a free run in. Jones rounded the advancing Reds' keeper Lawrence to jab the ball into the unguarded net with his left foot. Leeds were top of the table, but they weren't the only team to have started the new season very impressively – Arsenal too were on song.

Midweek, Leeds made hard work of beating Charlton Athletic in the League Cup second round, 1–0, before notching up another decent League win at the weekend, over Wolverhampton Wanderers, 2–1, Cooper and Charlton getting the goals.

## 9–3

They were all heroes – September 11 1968. Not my words, the newspapers', local *and* national.

I watched the second leg against Ferencvaros away in Budapest, Hungary 'live' on the Peacock's television. The pub was pretty packed, but not too uncomfortable. *All* the Leeds team played heroically, especially Gary Sprake in goal, in the best attempt at self-redemption since Pickles the dog found the World Cup just after crapping in his master's slippers. He played fantastically well (Sprake, not the dog) and definitely kept us in the match. The way he played and the way the team, especially the defence, battled was what Leeds United was all about for me – the team, the supporters, the city itself, even with the mucky aspects. Persevering, resisting, fighting for each other, all for one and one for all. And the harder life gets, the harder you fight to put things right. The team had been expected to just give in and roll over and accept what was coming to them – a good beating, in other words – but that was very possibly when Leeds were at their most dangerous. You underestimated or dismissed this team at your peril.

151

So good was Sprake in this match that it was possible he would be forgiven for those stinkers he conceded against both Scouse teams. Possible but not probable – make one bad mistake and football fans will never let you forget it, ever. He looked to be wearing a new kit against Ferencvaros, I thought – though it was only a black and white picture – black shirt, black shorts and white socks. He'd worn black shorts in the League Cup Final as well so maybe black was a good omen. It never seemed to do Lev Yashin any harm. Personally, I always preferred Gordon Banks's yellow England shirt, but Sprake could wear anything he liked if it meant he played as well as this match – purple, pink, even red. We were 1–0 up from the first leg and Sprake and the lads made sure that it stayed that way with a 0–0 stalemate over there. There was no doubt in my mind, at all, that the whole of Great Britain would have been proud of tonight's Leeds United. If they weren't then there was something wrong with them.

So up they went on my bedroom wall, the match reports and other articles about Leeds and Ferencvaros. I was running out of wall space, my bedroom was only pokey. The Don Revie quotes just went to show what I'd thought about him since way back: that there was a public Don Revie and there was a private one as well. I'm not meaning he was two-faced or anything, just that he was a different person on match days, like he was obsessed or something, and not his usual relaxed and friendly self. I wish I'd known him better than I did, but I couldn't complain: at least he knew my name, said hello to me every now and then and he knew enough about me to know I was on his side, whatever happened, just like probably everybody else involved with the club.

I worshipped the fella even though I didn't always understand him.

*Aye aye aye aye,*
*Gary is better than Yashin,*
*Albert is better than Eusebio,*
*And Arsenal are in for a thrashing.*

September 21 was Leeds versus Arsenal. Kenneth Wolstenholme was here with the *Match of the Day* television crew – it was to be the featured game. He'd called us 'the number-one team in the country at the moment' but that didn't mean much, Arsenal were top of the table and still smarting (so the papers said) about the lost 'battle' of Wembley the previous March.

Just a few minutes before kick off The Don sent two of the juniors out to parade the League Cup and the Inter Cities Fairs Cup around the pitch to the crowd. I was jealous as hell. But after some tosspot, probably but not definitely an Arsenal fan, threw a coin at Peter Hearnshaw, one of the juniors, and cut his head open, I was glad it wasn't me out there. 'We want the crowd to see what we have been working for these past few years,' The Don said, but I can't have been the only one thinking that he'd done it more to show the Arsenal team what they hadn't won.

It had poured it down in the morning and the pitch was soaked. There was nothing much you could do to protect pitches against heavy rain bar covering it all up, which just wasn't possible, or keep forking it to stop it turning into a lake. There were ways of sponging surface water off, but the most effective measure was to sweep it off with big brushes over the touchlines and on to the cinder track. You needed to be quick as hell when doing that though, and it was proper tiring work, but it was good physical exercise and I enjoyed it. It beat carting tons of straw about all night, that was for sure.

The Leeds team was read out over the tannoy, each player was cheered. Some cheers were more vociferous than others, Billy Bremner's was usually the loudest. 1 Gary Sprake, 2 Paul Reaney, 3 Terry Cooper, 4 Billy Bremner, 5 Jack Charlton, 6 Norman Hunter, 7 Mike O'Grady, 8 Peter Lorimer, 9 Mick Jones, 10 Paul Madeley, 11 Terry Hibbitt, and today's substitute for Leeds United, number 12 Eddie Gray.

Three o'clock kick off and the crowd was lively and singing from the off, mainly the Scratching Shed end. All sides of the ground were pretty well crammed nice and snug though, so there were songs from all quarters, even from our side, the West Stand. Staff got a typed team sheet the same time as the announcer did, so I knew already that Norman would be playing in midfield whilst Paul Madeley was in the centre of defence alongside big Jack.

*We're the greatest team in Europe, and Revie is our king!*

Then a couple of choruses of *The Whites are going to win* and *We shall not be moved* and then it's on to chanting the names of the individual players. Sometimes it's like the singing is all orchestrated.

    *M – I*

    *M – I – C*

    *M – I – C – K – MICK JONES!*

Jonesy would always look embarrassed I thought, but he'd give a little wave to thank his fans. What a great bloke.

    *Bremner Bremner Bremner Bremner!*

Not that Billy ever needed motivating; he wasn't Leeds United captain for nothing. And every time he heard his name, his songs, you could see him grinning proudly, wherever you were watching from. This season there was a new song to add to his little collection, too.

    *His eyes they shone like diamonds,*
    *as he lifted the cup from the stand.*
    *And there stood Billy Bremner,*
    *stood there with the cup in his hands.*

Just in case any of the Leeds players felt left out, if they had time before the game started, the Leeds fans would try and make sure they all got a mention. Even the sub. Jack would always be at the back when the team came out on to the pitch. He'd done it for as long as I could remember, with a few exceptions when he'd been captain. Did it make you superstitious if you had a set routine that actually worked most of the time?

    *Jackie Charlton*, clap clap clap, *Jackie Charlton!*

Then a big roar just before the first kick is about to be taken, to roar the Leeds players on to victory whilst putting the wind up the opponents, good and proper. We're off. Even without the midfield mastermind John Giles, we had more of the play than Arsenal. Billy looked the liveliest of everyone but he had more than decent help with Norman Hunter and Terry Hibbitt doing well in the centre and Mike O'Grady and Peter Lorimer both out wide on the flanks. Mick Jones was more or less up front on his own, though that didn't have a negative look to it at all as he was seeing plenty of the ball. He was so involved, even alone, I definitely thought he'd get on the score sheet today; he looked to have the better of all the Arsenal defence. If he wasn't trying to take advantage of passes from midfield or running in on goal with the ball himself, he was supplying the oncoming midfielders whenever he could, laying the ball off for them. Looking at him, shielding, dribbling, controlling the ball, fending off defenders, scrapping fairly for every single ball that came near him, I couldn't quite believe that he'd needed extra training to improve his ball control when he first arrived at Leeds.

When the Gunners did manage to mount an attack, Sprake was having another good day – every catch stuck to his hands like glue. Maybe it was something to do with all the chewing gum thrown into his net by his little fan club behind the Kop end net.

*Leeds! Leeds! Leeds! Leeds! Leeds! Leeds!*

The Whites press forward as often as they can, and the crowd urges them on.

*Leeds! Leeds! Leeds! Leeds! Leeds! Leeds!*

Me being more a defensive, tackling and 'holding' sort of player, what I've always liked about the Leeds style is that they don't just clear the ball away from the penalty area unless they need to, they pass it out of defence or even dribble away with it if they've the space. All in all what that means is that Leeds can attack and score from just about every position. Besides the goalie of course, and even then that's not completely impossible. The players hardly make a wayward pass or aimless punt, not even the goalkeeper, who tries to throw or roll the ball to one of the full-backs. Paul Reaney and Terry Cooper would bomb it down the wing whenever they could, or link up with the player there in front of them.

In the first half, Jack had one of his brilliant giraffe-striding runs from the edge of our penalty area up into the middle of Arsenal's half. It wasn't all brilliant football of course, but it was a good game, and there was a bit of needle too, with Arsenal giving a load of free kicks for fouls away.

*Dirty Arsenal, Dirty Arsenal!*

*Animals! Animals! Animals!*

Terry Hibbitt was tripped and it looked to me that Jack got a bit of a whack in the mouth as well when Leeds had a corner. The culprit was Bobby Gould, who looked like he only had one eyebrow. He ran around like he thought he was the cock of the playground, but he'd come to the wrong place for that.

*Leeds! Leeds! Leeds! Leeds! Leeds! Leeds!*

Every time we got a corner: *United*, clap clap clap, *United!*

Even though the Scratching Shed mob behind him give him plenty of grief, Arsenal keeper Bob Wilson's not had much trouble so far, and he's dealt with the corner kicks easily enough. It's the same again with this corner, except the ball is half-cleared by Arsenal, ending up on our left touchline near the Lowfields terraces. Cooper's in possession of the ball and you can tell he's trying to take a swing with his trusty left foot and get a cross in, but the Arsenal bloke keeps blocking the chance. So, tricky Cooper feigns a kick with his left, nudges the ball to his right and then lofts a cross into the penalty area with his right foot. Long and high, the cross veers inwards, but it's gone over Mick Jones and seems just that bit too high and far away from Mike O'Grady, who's darting in from the right flank. Amazingly – I don't know how he manages it – O'Grady dives forward and *upwards* to head the ball. He meets it dead right, connecting with his forehead as hard as if he had kicked it, and the ball arrows over Bob Wilson's arms, scrapes the bottom of the crossbar and hits the net. A truly fantastic goal and it's 1–0 to Leeds.

Half-time. The players leave the pitch, the Leeds lads in all white with lots of black mud all over them, the Gunners in their usual red and white 'tanktop' shirt, all filthy as well. Hot teas for most of the players, though I wouldn't be surprised if there was a nip of the strong stuff for anyone who says he needs it. Half the crowd disappears from the terraces too, most of them go to the toilets or get more beers in. There are snacks available too, and gravy drinks, but the prices are as unappetizing as the tastes.

The grass has churned up big time, as expected, so it's as many ground staff (and casuals) on as possible to replace divots or flatten any rough muddy bumps and holes. People could be forgiven for thinking that I get a thrill every time I get to go on the hallowed Leeds pitch, but the truth of the matter is that feeling's long gone now. It's not much of a thrill any more and what's worse is – the way I see it at least – the more times I go on that pitch to tend it, the less times I'm likely to go on it and play as a fully fledged Leeds United player. That all probably sounds mixed up or even superstitious of me, but I know what I'm on about. So, yes there is a sort of feeling in me when I'm out there helping that I am quite important compared to many of the thousands there to watch the game, but it's not exactly an exhilarating 'buzz' – and

I'd wager that most of the people in the crowd get a miles better rate of pay than I do, casual workers or full-timers.

The second half is much the same as the first. The players come out, the same eleven on each side, and all wearing the same mucky kits. The play is much the same too – Leeds taking the game to Arsenal for most of the half. It's good to see us beat teams convincingly, but when the other team is top of the League, you expect a better and harder game. I wasn't meaning to put them down but for their sake I hoped that this was just an off day as there wasn't a lot of quality play from Arsenal. Maybe they had too many injuries – there was no John Radford, Peter Storey or George Graham or that big bugger Ian Ure.

With one of his regular headers on the goal-line from a corner, Jack made it 2–0. He's great is Jack. When he scores he doesn't dance around or celebrate with the other players, even though everyone runs to him to congratulate him. He normally doesn't even thank the man who's taken the corner and landed the ball right on his head to score the easy goal with! With today's goal, Jack stood on the goalie's line as always, and all Bob Wilson could do was try and push Jack out of the way. It's like The Don always says, there's nothing in the rules to stop it – and if anything, Bob Wilson fouled Jack.

When that second goal went in, that was it, the game was over and Arsenal were knocked off their perch above us.

*U-nited, U-nited, top of the League, top of the League.*

The full-time whistle goes, the Leeds supporters cheer and applaud the new League leaders. Both teams' players congratulate and shake hands with each other, as well as the referee and the two linesmen, as they all walk off the pitch and down the tunnel, good-naturedly chatting with each other and maybe arranging to have a pint in the Players' Lounge after. Usually the crowds leave as quick as they can, though you sometimes get a few oddballs hanging around on the terraces for no apparent reason. Me, I just want to get in front of the television so I can watch the football results being announced, but it hardly ever happens, too much work to do. If the pitch is in a real state, which it virtually always is, we have to do what we can to make it better as quick as possible. Even though it's like trying to plait fog.

So, we were first now, while current champions Man City were nowhere, same with Man United. Even with less than a third of the season gone, there was only one other team who could stop us – Bill Shankly's Liverpool.

Division One table, September 21 1968:

| 1 | Leeds | Played 9, | Points 16 |
| 2 | Arsenal | Played 10, | Points 16 |
| 3 | Liverpool | Played 10, | Points 14 |
| 4 | Chelsea | Played 10, | Points 14 |
| 5 | West Ham | Played 10, | Points 14 |

My own playing career (poor choice of word that, 'career') wasn't exactly headline material any more. It wasn't even footline material, if there was such a thing, it was sod all, that's what it seemed like. I still trained virtually every day before going to work, afterwards as well, and I was fitter than the proverbial butcher's dog, I really was. My place in the St Anthony's first team was assured and we won stuff and I usually played well, but no one outside of St Anthony's seemed to take any notice of me. Ces would come and watch sometimes, maybe John too, and I'd ask them if The Don and co knew I actually existed as a football player any more.

Ces would say 'They know' and stuff, but I had this rotten little suspicion that I wasn't being taken seriously any more, or that Ces was trying to save my feelings. Or maybe he didn't want me to know that my chances had slipped away, either when my leg and ankle were broken or when I'd let myself go too much, with too much drinking and the like.

9–4

A week after their famous European Fairs Cup success, Leeds began their defence of the trophy with a 0–0 away draw with Standard Liege. The same evening, West Bromwich Albion made their European bow in the Cup Winners' Cup, also against a Belgian team, FC Bruges. It was a night of shocks, as Bruges beat them 3–1 and then scores of their supporters invaded the pitch at the end of the match, with Albion striker Jeff Astle needing hospital treatment after being attacked.

On their return from Hungary to the English League title race, Leeds had earned a point away at Leicester City, thanks to a Paul Madeley goal. Liverpool were sitting handily in third place in the table, as if in wait for their two main rivals (Leeds and Arsenal) to falter and allow them to steal the big prize. Late September, in midweek, Johnny Giles returned to the Leeds team in the 2–1 League Cup third round win at Bristol City.

Many people considered the Leeds team's strongest point the 'engine' of the midfield, which was the perfect partnership of Billy Bremner and Johnny Giles. Bremner would look for attacking positions where he would force things to happen, while Giles would get into positions to guide and *persuade* things to happen. With Giles recovering from treatment and Leeds already top of the table – on goal average, above Arsenal – it could justifiably be said that things were looking very promising for the Peacocks. However, careful Revie rested Giles for the tricky League game at champions Manchester City on September 28. At this stage, City were in mid-table and by all accounts not playing very well. Nevertheless, they were the reigning champions and could not be discounted as a threat, but Revie did not want to rush Giles' recuperation, especially as the Maine Road match would be more physically exerting than the Bristol City one. Selecting a less-than-hundred-percent Giles was risking longer-term injury.

Despite a sixteen-match unbeaten run, Leeds were outplayed by Manchester City and deservedly lost 3–1. And so the critics pounced, as if it was their sixteenth consecutive game without a win. They placed the majority of blame at the door of Sprake, Charlton and Hunter, who had all been jittery in the match, and Leeds were clearly lucky City only scored three times. Colin Bell, with two goals, had been outstanding but also the most wasteful in front of the Leeds goal. After the match, Revie did not seem too worried, putting the poor performance and result down to too many of his players being off form.

Manchester United had enquired about the availability of a certain player who went by the name of Pele. Nothing would materialize, but it was a sign that the Old Trafford club was ambitious. Or was it desperate, due to the club directors' increasing anxiety at the team's inconsistency?

Meanwhile, with the Leeds board aware that Manchester United sooner rather than later would lose the services of Sir Matt Busby as manager, they were more than a little concerned that Don Revie would be their target. The Old Trafford club was one of the richest around and, were they to approach him, Revie might not be able to resist. Therefore, the Leeds directors decided to act swiftly and prepared to offer Revie a new, improved contract. Although Revie scotched the rumours in the *Yorkshire Evening Post,* the board didn't want him to feel underrewarded, as then there could be trouble. But Revie's present contract, for seven years at around £7,000 a year, with four years left to run, was far from measly. And now the board was offering him an improved deal to keep him at the club until 1975. In comparison to the other top managers in Britain, the terms were very generous. Manchester would have to look further afield for a new manager.

After the Manchester City defeat, within eight October days Leeds returned to winning ways with three League wins in a row – two 1–0 victories, at Newcastle and Sunderland (scorers Charlton and Jones), and a scrappy, bad-tempered 2–0 win over West Ham at Elland Road (Giles and an unstoppable Lorimer free kick). They followed that with a midweek and weak fourth round 2–1 defeat at Crystal Palace, the holders casually waving goodbye to the League Cup with barely a hint of emotion.

Leeds' League Cup defeat may not have mattered too much, but the following Saturday was serious, as a young Burnley team outpaced and outplayed them at Turf Moor. Frank Casper, Dave Thomas, John Murray, Steve Kindon and Ralph Coates enjoyed a fine time to help incur only the second Leeds League defeat of the season. Two quick Burnley goals to Leeds' one in the first half helped them to a thoroughly deserved 5–1 victory. Five goals to one, an almost incredible result, against the most renowned defence in English League football.

Five minutes into the second half of their Wednesday night Fairs Cup return tie against Standard Liege, the seemingly now shaky Leeds defence had conceded another two goals, albeit against the run of play. They were now 2–0 down on aggregate with less than forty minutes of the tie remaining. It looked like Leeds were releasing their hold on the Fairs Cup as meekly as they had done the League Cup. But thanks to a very quick response with a header from Charlton and then a seventy-second-minute free kick missile from Lorimer, Leeds had drawn level and at least regained some respect – it looked like they would go out via the away goals rule. But then again, with just two minutes left, the midfield dynamo and captain Bremner was perfectly positioned to tap the ball home after a Leeds corner had eluded the Liege defenders. 3–2 to Leeds and one of the most dramatic Elland Road European ties ever. Bremner celebrated emphatically, grabbing, punching the net with glee and drop-kicking the ball into the roof of the goal. Leeds' reward was another tough tie in the next round, with Napoli of Italy. Standard Liege had shown themselves to be formidable opponents and would march on to win the Belgian League Championship.

Leeds' recent less-than-impressive defensive displays had prompted media comment that their famous back five wall was weakening and had had its day. Of course, Revie knew differently, believing that the Leeds defence needed a boost, that was all. So he ensured that his defenders – the first team as well as the reserves and juniors – were put through 'refresher' courses by the Leeds coaches. Three clean sheets in a row in the League followed. The trouble seemed now to be in attack, as the games against West Bromwich, Manchester United (away) and Tottenham were all goalless. Three 0–0 draws were hardly a disastrous statistic but they did cause a fall down the table.

Division One League table (top), November 9 1968:

| 1 | Liverpool | Played 18, | Points 26 |
|---|-----------|------------|-----------|
| 2 | Everton | Played 18, | Points 26 |
| 3 | Leeds Utd | Played 17, | Points 25 |
| 4 | Arsenal | Played 17, | Points 23 |
| 5 | Chelsea | Played 18, | Points 22 |
| 6 | Burnley | Played 18, | Points 22 |

Next up came the visit of Napoli in the second round of the Fairs Cup. The first leg, at Elland Road, was played on the thirteenth night of November but the only bad luck for Leeds was that goalkeeper Dino Zoff was on top form – Leeds were unfortunate to have only scored twice, with headers from Jack Charlton before the half-hour mark, while Mick Jones had two goals disallowed as well as his face punched by an Italian defender for his troubles.

Napoli had earned notoriety over recent years for violent misconduct, on and off the pitch. Last season in Naples, for instance, a Burnley party, plus English journalists, needed escorting from the stadium by mounted police, an armoured lorry and nine military jeeps.

After the first leg of the Leeds–Napoli tie, unhappy Don Revie commented, 'Some of my players said they had fingers poked in their eyes and faces in scrambles, and then there was the punch in the face Jones took and some other unsavoury moments.' He later added, 'We have asked for special observers to be at the game in view of the fact that Naples have been fined twice for crowd disturbances in the last two seasons and the trouble when Burnley played in Naples,' prompting media criticism, again, that he was overreacting and guilty of preaching double standards. However, managers of other teams who had played in Europe, especially Italy, expressed support for Revie. The away leg promised to be interesting, very interesting, though Leeds had two League games before the trip to Naples - Coventry away and Everton at home.

With a 'technically faultless' performance and a fine twenty-five-yard strike from Paul Madeley, Leeds beat Coventry 1–0 and followed it up with a hard-fought but deserved 2–1 win over Everton. A penalty from Giles and a well-taken goal from Eddie Gray earned Leeds the two points, in front of nearly 42,000.

The Napoli match went just as Revie had feared, with the Italian players kicking and snarling their way to victory. Leeds' Mike O'Grady received a booking from the referee, for being headbutted by Napoli's Omar Sivori (who then dived as if felled by an invisible assailant). Revie revealed later that he had been very close to taking the team off the pitch as the violence rained in, threatening to cause serious injury to the victims. With stalwarts such as Giles and Bremner and Charlton and Hunter and co in the side, all of who liked a good old battle, it is unlikely the Leeds players would have really appreciated such a gesture. The Leeds manager and chairman, unusually, were in complete agreement – that despite the club earning good money from the Fairs Cup competition, the risk of serious injury to their players might be too high and that competing in Europe might not be worth doing again. With respect to the actual Napoli–Leeds football match, 1–0 up from the first half, Napoli finally squared the tie 2–2 with a penalty, six minutes from time. The scoreline stayed the same and thus the result had to be settled on the toss of a disc. Billy Bremner called and guessed correctly, and so Leeds won the tie thanks to not their football skills but the lottery of a coin toss.

After a good 1–1 draw at Chelsea (O'Grady) on November 30, Leeds beat Sheffield Wednesday 2–0, both goals cracked home by Peter Lorimer. However, an injury to Terry Cooper had necessitated changes to the team – Paul Madeley (who else?) was switched from midfield to left-back, and Lorimer was recalled to the starting line-up after being dropped some weeks before. Unhappy at the situation, Lorimer had asked to leave Leeds, so Revie added his name to the transfer list. It stayed there for most of the season. There were reports that he would be used as part-exchange for players such as striker Joe Baker of Nottingham Forest, Hibernian's Peter Cormack and Sunderland's Colin Suggett, but no deal ever materialized. It is unlikely that Revie ever had any intention of letting Lorimer go.

On December 14 1968 Leeds took their unbeaten League run to eight games with a 1–1 draw at West Ham (Gray). Revie and the players knew very well that they weren't scoring enough goals; they missed more chances than they were converting, but on the positive side, it was also becoming clear that they were the hardest team to beat in Division One. On the Wednesday night, Leeds exploited the freedom and space allowed them by a rather weak German side, Hanover 96, by winning 5–1. Lorimer grabbed himself a brace while O'Grady, Charlton and Hunter scored the others. Hanover's coach, Zlatko Cajkovski, praised Leeds as the best English team he had ever seen.

Four days before Christmas, Leeds most definitely were not in festive mood: they were out for revenge, over Burnley. The players needed little motivation from their inspirational boss to exact it – memories of the 5–1 drubbing in October were more than enough incentive. With the exception of Gary Sprake in goal (because he had little work to do), every Leeds player contributed to a superb team performance that saw them tear Burnley apart right from the kick off. A splendid chip from Burnley's Ralph Coates from outside the area, early in the second half, made it 4–1 to Leeds but only sparked them into increasing the pressure on Burnley even more. In all, goals from Lorimer (two), Bremner, Jones, Giles and Gray signified a superb 6–1 Christmas cracker of a Leeds win.

A Boxing Day Elland Road crowd of 42,000 enjoyed a proficient Leeds display against Newcastle and a 2–0 win, a Lorimer penalty and Madeley shot sealing the points. Mike O'Grady had substituted the injured Johnny Giles early on, and whilst the Leeds central midfield was unquestionably weakened, Newcastle never looked like rescuing the tie. Liverpool were still top, by two points, but Leeds had two games in hand. The first two games in 1969 for Leeds, though, were cup ties against Sheffield Wednesday.

They had drawn 1–1 at Hillsborough on January 4 in the FA Cup third round, so a replay was needed, played at Leeds on the following Wednesday. Leeds were the country's form team at the time and the bookmakers' favourites to win the Cup. Although they were without the injured Cooper, Giles and O'Grady, Leeds still fielded the stronger team. Sheffield Wednesday certainly weren't there to just make up the numbers, though. Making only his second start of the campaign, Albert Johanneson hit the first goal of the tie early on, but it was an end-to-end, typical FA Cup tie, with both teams going close a couple of times as well as hitting the crossbar. Shortly before half-time, Wednesday equalized with a deft, curled lob from Brian Woodall to make it 1–1 at the interval.

When the visitors took the lead early in the second half, again through Woodall, Leeds were forced to push more players up in attack to try for the equalizer. But the visitors defended stoutly and prevented Leeds from breaking through. Finally, after resisting another Leeds barrage, Wednesday exploited the overstretched home defence to grab a third, well-taken and decisive, goal, through striker John Ritchie. The Cup favourites had fallen at the first hurdle.

Perhaps, to some, Leeds losing in the Cup was more down to bad luck than anything, but their next match – against Manchester United – had a large slice of good luck in it. Thanks to a scrambled goal from Jones and an O'Grady cracker from the corner of the Manchester penalty area, which soared into the top corner of the net, Leeds were 2–1 up. However, late in the second half, the referee awarded Manchester United a free kick just outside Leeds' penalty area. When George Best instead of Bobby Charlton took the kick, he caught the Leeds keeper and defence by surprise. When his chipped shot landed in the Leeds net, their surprise turned to shock, seeing as Best had equalized and nicked a point for the visitors. Except the referee disallowed it, stating that the free kick was 'indirect'. From an indirect free kick, the ball must be touched at least once more for a goal to be given, if it goes in. Leeds' luck was definitely in as Johnny Giles admitted Best's strike had brushed his head before hitting the net. The goal should have stood.

It was also fortunate for everyone there that there were no serious injuries on the Elland Road terraces. Crowd trouble began well before the three o'clock kick off, with Manchester United fans attempting to invade and 'take' the Leeds Kop, walking from their allocated end of the ground, the south stand, across the pitch. An estimated 2,000 supporters were locked out of the ground too, and numerous exchanges were made between rival fans – exchanges of insults, fisticuffs, bottles, coins and other missiles – with nearly 50 people injured. The St John's Ambulance volunteers were kept busy all afternoon, just like the police of course, but the following week, chairman Percy Woodward surprisingly denied that any trouble had occurred.

On January 14 Sir Matt Busby announced that he would be retiring as manager of Manchester United at the end of the season (FA Cup final day in fact) but would be staying on as general manager. Commenting that the pressures of football management were becoming too much for a man of his age (nearly sixty), he said it was the perfect time for a younger, 'track-suited' manager to take over. On hearing the news, forty-three-year-old Leeds manager Don Revie wagered £10 with Johnny Giles that he himself would retire from football management by the time he was fifty-two.

The next Saturday, Leeds earned a point in a 0–0 draw away at Spurs. Unfortunately, Liverpool outdid them in the capital by beating Chelsea 2–1, going three points clear at the top of the League, though Leeds had games in hand. They managed to play one of those on Friday January 24, again in London, against QPR. Both teams had exited the FA Cup and so had a fixture-free weekend while the Cup fourth round took place. Revie, keen to avoid the usual end-of-season match pile-up, took advantage of the situation and sought official permission to rearrange certain Leeds' fixtures. With the clubs agreeing to bring forward from Good Friday their League tie, QPR hosted Leeds on the Friday night. Alarmingly for Leeds, the plan looked to have misfired as foot-of-the-table QPR gave them a hard time, even hitting the post in the first minute and having a Bobby Keetch penalty saved by Sprake early in the second half. By then Leeds were leading, having taken the lead in the first five minutes, Mick Jones putting away a parried Paul Madeley shot.

Next up for Leeds was Coventry at Elland Road on February 1 1969, and a deserved win followed, though the 3–0 scoreline flattered them (Bremner 2, O'Grady), while Liverpool beat Sheffield Wednesday at Anfield. Leeds were still in Europe too, of course, unlike Liverpool, who had been knocked out in the first round of the same competition by Athletico Bilbao.

Division One League table (top), February 1 1969:

| 1 | Liverpool | Played 29, | Points 45 |
|---|-----------|-----------|-----------|
| 2 | Leeds Utd | Played 28, | Points 44 |
| 3 | Everton | Played 28, | Points 40 |

Leeds flew to Germany soon after the Coventry match for the return tie with Hanover on Tuesday February 4. Revie would later describe the Hanover team as brutal, even though it was Leeds' Terry Cooper sent off late in the game. Leeds won 2–1 on the night and 7–2 on aggregate and would meet mighty Hungarian side Ujpest Dozsa in the next round.

On February 12 Leeds took the opportunity to use their League game in hand and, they hoped, gain points on Liverpool to take over at the top of the table. The match, versus Ipswich Town, had been brought forward from Easter Monday, but it could easily have been called off due to more bad weather on the day. The match was played while heavy sleet and snow fell throughout, making the pitch heavier and the playing conditions much more difficult. But Belfitt and Jones secured the two points for Leeds in the one-sided 2–0 victory.

The next Saturday, Leeds were at home to Chelsea, and Liverpool to Nottingham Forest. With Forest toiling at the foot of the division, and Chelsea faring relatively well in the top half, Liverpool looked to have much the easier task. However, in one of the major shocks of the season, Forest snatched a fine 2–0 victory at Anfield while a second-half Peter Lorimer strike beat Chelsea, putting Leeds three points ahead of Liverpool.

The week after, February 22, winter struck harshly in the north and Leeds fell behind Liverpool again, at least in terms of matches played. Sheffield Wednesday versus Leeds was a casualty of the weather but Liverpool's visit to West Ham went ahead. Bill Shankly probably wished it hadn't, a second-half goal from Roger Hunt earning them a point in a 1–1 draw.

Tuesday February 25, Leeds caught up again with games played with their visit to Nottingham Forest at the City Ground, the main stand rebuilt since their last flaming visit. Tonight the only semblance of fire came from Leeds, on the pitch, as they dealt comfortably with all Forest's attacks and then burned through their defences with ease. Goals from Lorimer and Jones won it 2–0 but it should have been by more. Leeds were now four points clear of Liverpool, both teams having played thirty-one games.

The fifth round of the FA Cup saw Liverpool away at Leicester, leaving Leeds an opportunity to extend their lead, with a home game versus Southampton. Curiously, Leeds played nothing like the masterful football seen at Forest the Wednesday before: it was Southampton who looked like champions-elect, taking the lead twice. A Johnny Giles penalty, an own goal from Southampton's Kirkup and Mick Jones pouncing on a parried Giles shot gave Leeds the points and the unlucky Saints nothing.

In the Fairs Cup, Ujpest Dozsa, despite their famed fast and adventurous football, defended en masse at Elland Road and only looked to score from breakaway counter attacks. Leeds had the majority of possession but toiled to make any impact on the opposition's goal. Johnny Giles even had a penalty saved in the second half. Late on, the visitors took the lead – star striker Antal Dunai smacked in a shot from outside the penalty area, which speared into the top-right corner of the net – and the score stayed 1–0 to the end. Even though Leeds were the holders of the Fairs Cup and the League leaders, few people expected them to overcome the one-goal deficit in two weeks' time,

Unusually it wasn't the inclement weather to blame for the next Liverpool postponement but a flu bug sidelining eight of

Arsenal's players ahead of their game at Anfield. Leeds therefore had further chance to extend their lead in the table, while the Liverpool players could only kick their heels and hope that Revie's men slipped up at relegation candidates Stoke City. As the adage goes, animals are often at their most dangerous when wounded, and unfortunately for Liverpool and most certainly Stoke, Leeds owed Stoke for the crucial defeat there last season. They annihilated them and were 3–0 up at half-time, 5–1 winners (Jones, Bremner 2, O'Grady 2) at full time and eight points clear of Liverpool as a result.

Division One League table (top), March 8 1969:

| 1 | Leeds Utd | Played 33, | Points 54 |
| 2 | Liverpool | Played 31, | Points 46 |
| 3 | Everton   | Played 30, | Points 43 |
| 4 | Arsenal   | Played 30, | Points 42 |

England manager Sir Alf Ramsey had been paying attention, and called on Paul Reaney, Terry Cooper, Jack Charlton, Norman Hunter and, after seven years out of international football, Mike O'Grady for the midweek friendly against France at Wembley. As it turned out, Hunter and Reaney did not play in the 5–0 England win, but the other three Leeds men did. O'Grady even opened the scoring and he and Cooper received excellent reviews for their performances.

At the top of the First Division table, Liverpool reduced the points gap to six with a steady 2–0 win at Sunderland on March 15, as Elland Road fell to the weather with the Leeds–Nottingham Forest game snowed off. On the very same day, at Wembley, Arsenal were playing Division Three side Swindon Town in the League Cup final. They lost, after extra time, 2–1, in one of the shock results of football history. Humiliated though the Arsenal players were, some of them drew strength from the whole sorry affair, while later citing that particular match as the turning point in their careers.

Wednesday March 19 was Leeds' Fairs Cup quarter final return leg with Ujpest Dozsa. Leeds' preparations could hardly have been worse as influenza and cold bugs affected the squad.

Too ill to play, Reaney, Charlton and O'Grady were withdrawn. Most of the remaining Leeds players were not well, but not ill enough to drop out. Billy Bremner would play at right-back and Mick Bates fill in the gap in midfield. Terry Yorath and Terry Hibbitt were named as substitutes and Jimmy Lumsden travelled with the squad. The changes unsettled the weakened Leeds team even more and, in the last twenty-five minutes of the match, the Hungarian champions-to-be scored twice to win it. The Purples deserved to win the tie and were now hot favourites to win the trophy.

After the Fairs Cup defeat, a League visit to Wolverhampton Wanderers on Saturday March 29 followed, as did one more point in the bag with a 0–0 draw. Hardly disastrous, mid-table Wolves' home record was good, but Liverpool gained a point with a win at QPR and now sat five points behind Leeds with a game in hand. Third-placed Arsenal were not out of the running just yet either.

A major frustration for Liverpool, though, was the number of postponed games affecting their challenge, the most unpalatable of them being the home match against Leeds, scheduled for March 22. Following their game in Hungary Leeds had ten players ill or injured and so asked the Football League to call the Liverpool game off. After some consideration, the League duly did so, bringing about more insinuations of favouritism as a result. The criticism showed that the Football League could not really win whichever choice it made, whilst Liverpool simply could not win, lose or draw due to so many postponements. Over the next four weeks, to the joy of Leeds supporters, whenever the Whites dropped a point, the Reds seemed equally as wasteful.

Liverpool's March 31 1–1 draw at home with Arsenal practically ending the Gunners' title challenge even with eight games to go, and Leeds' 0–0 draw at Sheffield Wednesday on April 1 maintained the gap between the top two sides.

League Division One table (top), April 1 1969:

| 1 | Leeds Utd | Played 35, | Points 56 |
|---|-----------|-----------|-----------|
| 2 | Liverpool | Played 34, | Points 51 |
| 3 | Arsenal | Played 34, | Points 48 |

The top two both seemed to have stopped playing entertaining football now, and on Saturday April 5, while Liverpool scraped a 1–0 win at Wolves, Leeds won at home to champions Manchester City by the same scoreline. The *Guardian* described Liverpool about as inspiring as watching a concrete mixer at work, and about Leeds' display it was written that 'Gray and Lorimer were profligacy gone mad and poor Jones had as much support as the average working man's application for a pay rise. Giles and Bremner wove beautiful patterns all over the field but the end product … oh dear!'

Liverpool could only draw 0–0 at Stoke City on April 7, plus they had to suffer the loss of Roger Hunt, taken off injured with a dislocated shoulder. And two days later it was as you were as Leeds' drew 1–1 at West Bromwich, restoring their five-point comfort zone. However, comparing both teams' remaining fixtures, Leeds seemed to have much the harder run in. They had to face the other three teams at the top, Arsenal, Everton and Liverpool, and all away from home, plus difficult home games against Leicester City and Nottingham Forest, both fighting hard against relegation and both, incidentally, victors over Liverpool earlier in the season.

## 9–5

April 12 1969. It would have been worth noting in my diary, if I had one. I took back what I'd said in the past about referee Ken Burns. Well, most of it. He definitely went up in my estimation after the Arsenal–Leeds League match. Arsenal were third in the League, and Liverpool second (and they'd won 2–0 at Leicester the same day).

'That bloody idiot Gary Sprake!' Ces grumbled, the Monday after, 'You'd think he wanted us to lose.' Ces had gone to Highbury with John; the club had laid on a special coach for full-time staff. If I'd got on my knees and begged I probably would have been able to go as well, but it would have cost me too much.

In the first five minutes of the match, Sprake and Arsenal's Bobby Gould – him with the eyebrow – went up for a high cross. It was breezy and due to the wind both of them missed the ball.

171

And so Gould decided to kick them belonging to Gary Sprake instead. Apparently he added a few verbals too, about Sprake's being Welsh. So Sprake lamped Gould with a proper champion left-hook. It was Gould's turn to hit the floor now, while referee Ken Burns came rushing in to intervene and probably to send them both marching.

Except Ken Burns is Welsh, and he'd heard what Gould had said. Instead of sending them off, he gave them both a good talking to and only booked them.

Anyway, Keystone Cop defending by Arsenal's defence, especially Ian Ure and Bob Wilson in nets, let Leeds in twice on goal (Mick Jones and then John Giles) and we won 2–1. Great result. If Sprake'd been sent off, God knows what the score would have been.

Next we were at home to Leicester. Though he never came right out and slagged off Leeds supporters, The Don could never quite keep his feelings to himself about the less-than-impressive Elland Road attendances. This season there'd been only about six home matches where more than 40,000 people had turned up, which was plain daft bearing in mind that we were top of the League virtually all the time. Maybe too many Leeds folk were misers. Or lazy. Or just plain skint.

38,391 watched us beat Leicester 2–0 on Saturday April 19, and this was a game that if we won while Liverpool lost, it meant we were near definitely the winners of the League. It wasn't a great game by any chalk, but did anyone really care, as long as the result was the right one? Leicester played alright for a team looking into Division Two next season, but Mick Jones and Eddie Gray got the goals, while Liverpool were winning at Ipswich 4–0. You couldn't really argue with that sort of performance from the Scousers, though we were still five points clear of them. We had three games left and they had four. The only way Liverpool could beat us to the League title would be for us to not win any of our games and them to win all of theirs. And one of those games just happened to be Liverpool v Leeds. I couldn't wait for that one.

Ces made sure I was booked on the staff coach for the game, on April 28. If needs be, I'd said I'd travel in the luggage compartment. I didn't care, just as long as I got there. These games that

Leeds and Liverpool had left were rearranged fixtures due to loads of postponements, and next Saturday was the Man City–Leicester FA Cup final, and League games weren't allowed on that day. Fair enough: as a football fan I always loved FA Cup final day, even when Leeds weren't involved.

We were at Everton the coming Tuesday, April 22, and then at Liverpool two days after the Cup final, and then at home two days after that to Nottingham Forest. I listened to the Everton game on the radio at ours with my grandma. There wasn't proper commentary, only 'updates'. 'And here's a special report from Goodison Park ...' *Shit, someone's scored*, I'd think, *I hope to God it's us*. Usually, nothing would have happened at all, bar a throw-in or something. The match stayed goalless all the while and it seemed like nothing happened at all. Leeds hung on to a 0–0 draw. The reporter said we had a couple of half-chances to score but a draw was the right and fair result. Drawing at Everton was a good point earned any time of the season, and with Liverpool only drawing at Coventry as well, it was a bloody brilliant result.

There must have been thousands of Leeds supporters at Everton as well, because it was a massive crowd, something like 53,000. Everton's supporters had a bad reputation as hooligans, but loads waited after the final whistle to applaud the Leeds players. I suppose they'd applaud anyone who stopped Liverpool from winning the League, though.

We had two games left and had sixty-four points while Liverpool had fifty-nine points and three games left. But because the teams' next game was against each another, Leeds only needed a draw for the League Championship.

Liverpool versus Leeds, to decide the 1968–69 season. This was our time. We were the best team in England. This was what English football was all about, why football was the greatest sport of all and why it didn't matter who you were, where you were born or how rich or poor your family was.

Liverpool–Leeds games were always something special, something *else*. This time, I was there to witness it too. The Liverpool fans inside Anfield that night were fine supporters. They backed their team whatever, they hardly stopped singing or applauding, there was red and white everywhere, and a fair bit of white, yellow and blue too. The trouble, the big trouble, was that there were thousands of Scousers locked out and not happy at missing the match, which did turn out to be the title decider after all, but not how they would have liked it.

The papers said that Liverpool and Leeds had slugged it out like two mighty heavyweight boxers, that Leeds were magnificent in defence as usual, that Alun Evans up front for Liverpool missed two good chances, that Leeds were happy to defend en masse and intent on attacking on the break only. They said that Liverpool really should have won it and that Leeds set out their stall to stop them scoring and that Tommy Smith was the best player on the pitch, closely followed by Paul Madeley.

But what you wouldn't see in the newspaper reports was all the locked-out Liverpool supporters' aggression, all the trouble they caused. All the cursing, all the insults, all the threats. Coach and car windows put through, bottles, stones, bricks, ball-bearings, pelting anyone caught up in it all. Coppers not sure who they were protecting or attacking, pushing people around, truncheons always ready for using.

There was probably no word even of the fact that the Leeds players' and officials' coach got bricked and had a window smashed. Actually, it wasn't a brick that broke the window: it was a piece of concrete. John Reynolds brought that piece of concrete back as a souvenir, as it had gone through the window and landed on his lap. It's still kept at Elland Road. He'd been seated next to Paul Madeley on the coach and apparently everyone was very concerned about Paul's welfare, but no one gave a second thought to John's!

### 9–6

On the Sunday evening, the night before the English League season's biggest game, David Harvey and Johnny Giles watched *Rosemary's Baby* before returning to the hotel for bingo and bowls with the rest of their team-mates. Given the sinister theme of the film and Don Revie's generally odd superstitions, it was surprising that he allowed any of his squad to go anywhere near

174

it. Back at the hotel, Revie announced, 'If you get anything at Liverpool tomorrow night, lads, I think you'll be home and dry.' The players had heard it all before, because Revie had said virtually the very same thing prior to every League match of the previous two months.

The final scoreline was 0–0. Leeds had achieved the result they had hoped for. And around 27,000 Liverpool Koppites stayed behind after the last whistle to salute the visiting team, the new League Champions.

The champagne flowed in the Leeds dressing room. Liverpool manager Bill Shankly had arranged for the club to provide the bubbly and had handed each Leeds player a bottle in congratulation. The players could finally celebrate, but not too much: they had Nottingham Forest to play in two nights' time and a win would give them a historic sixty-seven points, beating the previous record of sixty-six.

Bill Shankly asked Don Revie if he could address the Leeds players. Above the clamour and chatter of press men and the Leeds contingent, Revie demanded everyone quieten down. 'Mr Shankly wants a word.'

In his famous Glaswegian growl, Shankly said, 'All I've got to say to you boys is: you're a great side and you deserved to win it. You didn't pinch it, you didn't fluke it. You're a wonderful team.'

It was one of the proudest moments of Revie's life. Such a tribute from a brilliant man like Shankly was high praise indeed. Speaking to reporters soon after, however, Shankly was more like his normal droll self, saying that Leeds really were a great side but that 'the best team drew'. Throughout the second phase of the season he had regularly predicted Leeds to 'blow it all'.

Two nights later, at Elland Road, before the third-highest gate of the season (46,508), an anxious and erratic Leeds somehow managed to squeeze out a 1–0 win over Nottingham Forest, thanks to John Giles, arguably Leeds' best player of the campaign. He had managed to stop a cross-shot from Cooper, then bring it down and under control and turn and shoot in one sweet, swift sequence. Leeds had not only won the Championship for the first time in history, and brought it back to Yorkshire for the first time since Sheffield Wednesday in 1930, they had broken a number of records along the way. They had won the most points in a season with sixty-seven, the most home points (thirty-nine), won most games in total (twenty-seven) and the most at home (eighteen), with the fewest overall defeats (two), whilst also remaining unbeaten at home. And the total of just twenty-six goals conceded was a new record, as was the number conceded at home: nine.

# Chapter 10

A true and rare thing of beauty, the Honours List of Football, 1968–69:

**Division One winners**: LUFC. Runners-up: Liverpool.

**FA Cup winners**: Manchester City. Runners-up: Leicester.

**League Cup winners**: Swindon Town (Division 3!). Runners-up: Arsenal (the shame of it).

**European Cup winners**: AC Milan. Runners-up: Ajax.

**European Cup Winners' Cup winners**: Slovan Bratislava. Runners-up: Barcelona.

**Inter-Cities Fairs Cup winners**: Newcastle Utd. Runners-up: Ujpest Dozsa.

**Leeds crowd average, home games**: 36,955.

**Player of the Year 1969**: Shared by Dave Mackay (Derby) and Tony Book (Man City).

**European Footballer of the Year**: Gianni Rivera, AC Milan.

**Manager of the Year 1969**: Don Revie, LUFC.

**Charity Shield winners 1969**: LUFC. Runners-up: Man City.

**New British transfer record fee**: £165,000 for Allan Clarke, stumped up by LUFC to Leicester.

When we bought Allan Clarke, he'd just been on tour with England in South Africa, and he'd caught gastroenteritis. Leeds signed him at his house, while he was in his dressing gown. He said he felt like death warmed up and hardly had the energy to lift the pen to sign the forms. Even better for us was that Clarke had chosen us over Man United as he thought we were on the up while they were sinking.

This year, the supersonic airliner Concorde flew for the first time and the Yanks had put men on the moon for the first time. More importantly, Don Revie said that the new season would see a team win the triple for the first time in history. He had told the

Leeds players that we were aiming for the League Championship, the FA Cup and the European Cup.

We needed to win the League again because hardly anyone managed to do that. We needed to win the FA Cup because we hadn't won it yet and doubles were as rare as rocking horse manure. A triple was unheard of. A football team needed to set itself targets, just like people should. They help you get out of bed on a morning, for one thing. We needed to win everything, to show that it could be done.

Looking at what The Don had done for Leeds, it was like he'd performed a miracle. When he started the job, eight and a bit years ago, he'd inherited good coaching staff and made them even better by setting targets and making plans for and with them. And he inherited a couple of good players and sorted them out, made them fulfil their potential, and he brought loads of new young lads in too thanks to the brilliant scouts already at the club. No way would he have done it all without Harry Reynolds and his money, but still, Don Revie, The Don, was a genius.

So, we'd follow up last season's magnificent League display by being magnificent again, this time in every competition and this time with no slip ups. And now we had Allan Clarke, who the papers were saying was the most 'complete' centre-forward in football – he was thin, but he was tall but fast, he could head the ball well but had great footwork, and he had a poacher's instinct but could score from just about anywhere, with either foot. They reckoned he would be the perfect partner for Mick Jones in the Leeds attack. And they reckoned it was Don Revie's way of treating himself to a sort of luxury item, like Clarke was a twenty-four-carat medallion or something. Anyway, this was the season where we'd go hell for leather to cop the absolute lot. The Elland Road trophy cabinet would need to be extended.

The season started well, really well: we beat FA Cup holders Man City to nab the Charity Shield for the first time in our history. We had a pretty good run straight from the off, with two wins and four draws up to the end of August, when we lost 3–2 at Everton. Thirty-four League games unbeaten.

Selling Mike O'Grady to Wolves in September was a surprise. We got a good fee of £80,000 for him but I wasn't sure why we sold him. He'd had a few injuries, a bad back quite often, but I liked him, a lot, plus he was Leeds born and bred. John commented that Mike was the only player in the first team squad not yet married, sort of implying that he was a bit of a bad influence on the more settled lads.

First to go was the League Cup. We'd beaten Fulham 1–0 away in the second round but then lost away in a third round replay at Stamford Bridge to Chelsea. 2–0. The League title was going nice and smoothly again though, putting the Everton result to one side. Our first attempt at the European Cup was going okay too – we just scraped through the first round against Norwegian side SK Lyn Oslo, 10–0 at home and 6–0 away. To be sporting to the Norwegians, even though they'd made it to last year's Fairs Cup quarter-finals, they were only a part-time club. In truth we could have scored double what we did but I was quite sure I'd never see ten goals scored in a Leeds game again, by one team alone or in total.

In the second round of the European Cup we drew old enemies Ferencvaros. I always felt the Leeds players saved their best form for Europe. Put it this way, we were in really good form in the League – we'd beaten Forest 6–1 and Ipswich 4–0 in our last two home games – but in the first leg v Ferencvaros, we really hit form and went at them non-stop. They can't have known what had hit them. It was one of those nights when every Leeds player peaked, where we looked dangerous from every part of the pitch. Ferencvaros might not have been as strong as they had been in the past but that was no excuse, Leeds gave them a whipping, which should have been more than the 3–0 result. The attendance for the second leg, in Budapest, said it all: 5,400. The Hungarian supporters had given up on the match and it sounded like the players had too. We beat them 3–0 again, and one of the younger lads made his Leeds debut too, coming on as substitute for Eddie Gray – winger Chris Galvin, who I thought had a good chance of making it. We were drawn against Standard Liege in round three. For whatever reason, though, the match wasn't due to be played until March 1970.

Eamonn Andrews mentions Revie's days as a player at Hull City and Manchester City, including the 'Revie Plan', which even now, in 1974 and so many years after the event, embarrasses the Leeds manager a little. And more footage is shown, of Revie's England debut and first international goal, against Northern Ireland, and a glimpse of his FA Cup final appearance for Manchester City against Birmingham City in 1956. He played well and the Revie-inspired team went on to win 3–1, but darker events in the match would cause it to be always remembered as 'the Trautmann final'. Revie remains seated as kind words are spoken and flattering images are played. As Andrews continues speaking, Revie looks up at him as if he is a schoolteacher about to dole out a punishment.

Saturday evening, October 25 1969. *Match of the Day*. There's been a keenly contested, exciting First Division match played, between last season's champions of Division One and Division Two. With two expertly taken goals from record signing Allan Clarke – a flicked header from an Eddie Gray corner, and a one-on-one victory following a long-range, defence-splitting Mick Bates pass – Leeds have beaten new boys Derby County 2–0. But Brian Clough has developed Derby into an impressively strong force, similar to Revie's Leeds of 1964.

Standing inside the West Stand of the Elland Road stadium, the two managers are interviewed by presenter David Coleman. On screen it seems that Don Revie stands seven maybe eight inches taller than Brian Clough. Both wear smiles as authentic as that of a ventriloquist's dummy.

The familiar, nasal voice of Clough replies, 'We've been through the Leeds machine,' when asked by David Coleman how he thinks his team has performed today. Clough is cool, cool and annoyed – annoyed, it seems, because he has lost to such a systematic team. His remark is not designed to be affectionate or humorous and he makes little eye contact with Coleman as he says it. And none at all with Revie. As he talks he looks away, in the off-camera distance, as if wishing he were somewhere else.

He goes on, 'I'm not quite sure why we didn't win. Perhaps it's because he works harder than me or he's a better manager than me.'

Revie smiles but it is not a content or even nearly satisfied smile.

David Coleman seems oblivious to the cool atmosphere; viewers across the country are probably thinking Clough's words are intended as complimentary and respectful. They would be wrong. Finally, Clough remarks that he doesn't think Leeds were better than Derby, there was 'nothing' between the teams, they were evenly matched.

Coleman then asks for Revie's thoughts on the match. While the Leeds boss speaks, Clough bows his head, looking down at the floor. 'I just wondered what Brian was on about, a "machine".' His words belie his facial expressions and body language. Revie is annoyed at Clough's clear lack of respect to the Leeds team and to himself.

Coleman asks Revie: 'Now you've often said that you want to be respected for your football here at Leeds ... Today it was all there wasn't it?'

Although the compliment is welcome, Revie does not want to hear it from a television commentator, it should come from the opposing manager, as well as the football authorities and every single team manager who has ever fallen to the strength and skill of his Leeds team.

He responds to Coleman's question as if he has rehearsed it. 'Now they're starting to come on song. When you've nine or ten internationals in your side who can play a bit, eventually they will respect us.'

'They will respect us.' Likely to be a wish rather than a prediction.

In November 1969 chairman Manny Cussins sold off his luxurious suburban house to Leeds United to in turn pass on to Don Revie. The detached house in Alwoodley, Leeds, had five bedrooms, a four-car garage, two bathrooms and a sun lounge, with annex accommodation too. As Revie was the highest-paid manager in England, it was clear the club was treating him very well. By Christmas, with nineteen League wins clocked up, Everton were setting a formidable record at the top of Division One, with less than half of the season still to play due to it having commenced early in order to help England's 1970 World Cup preparations. Leeds were by no means having a poor campaign but had played more games than Everton and won fewer, fourteen, with ten draws. A last-minute mistake by Gary Sprake cost Leeds a point at Crystal Palace, the unfortunate goalkeeper dropping a 'freak' shot from full-back John Sewell into the net. Two days after Christmas, Leeds and Everton met at Elland Road. 46,770 watched a pulsating game in which a second-half Alan Whittle goal was Everton's only reply to two Mick Jones strikes before the interval. 2–1 to Leeds, but the Championship race had not suddenly swung in their favour, though it did lift their spirits significantly.

Division One League table (top), December 27 1969:

| 1 | Everton | Played 26, | Points 41 |
| 2 | Leeds Utd | Played 27, | Points 40 |
| 3 | Chelsea | Played 26, | Points 34 |
| 4 | Liverpool | Played 25, | Points 32 |

The beginning of January 1970 brought another boost to Leeds when Revie was named in the New Year's Honours List, for Services to Football. Posing for photographs on New Year's Day outside Buckingham Palace, standing proudly with Elsie, Duncan and Kim, the family is dressed to the nines, with Don in a smart blue suit. He is now Don Revie OBE.

He tells journalists, 'My award should be recognized as a club rather than personal achievement, because without the talent, character and dedication of everyone connected with the club, my success as a manager would not have been possible. When I went to Buckingham Palace I collected the award on behalf of Leeds United.'

Division One and Two clubs entered the FA Cup fray on January 3 in the third round. Leeds had been paired with Fourth Division Swansea Town and had squeezed through to round four with a 2–1 win. The slender win was even more remarkable as Swansea had led for much of the game, but later had a man sent off. The Leeds goals came after the dismissal. Everton fared even worse in their Cup tie, losing 2–1 at Second Division Sheffield United. Leeds' next League match was away at Chelsea, with over 57,000 people attending, hundreds locked out and scores of thousands more watching Saturday evening's *Match of the Day*. It was a dogged battle: Leeds, in white shirts and shorts and red socks, turned a 2–1 half-time deficit into an amazing 5–2 win. Four goals within twenty minutes of the restart from Cooper, Giles (a penalty), Lorimer and Jones added to Clarke's first-half tap-in, went some way to wooing the football nation and announced that the champions most certainly were not ready to relinquish the title easily. The match would be named the programme's Match of the Season too.

Two weeks after, Leeds romped through the Cup fourth round with a 6–0 drubbing of non-league Sutton United, Allan Clarke bagging four goals and Peter Lorimer two. Interestingly, Mick Jones failed to score and Sutton defender John Faulkner, charged with marking him, played so well that Jack Charlton advised Revie to sign him. Revie reacted accordingly, signing 'Max' Faulkner for £10,000. In conjunction with their FA Cup exit, Everton's form in the League was arousing suspicions that they wouldn't be able to maintain their challenge for the title. As well as the defeat to Leeds, they had lost 3–0 at deadly rivals Liverpool in December. And in the coming weeks, Everton defeats and draws were to outnumber their victories while Leeds progressed quite nicely in the League and the FA Cup. The European Cup was to reconvene on March 4, against Standard Liege.

Since a Boxing Day defeat at Newcastle, Leeds had embarked on a fine run in all competitions. In the League there was the win over Everton and the crushing of Chelsea, they had gained a point away in tough games at Manchester United, Tottenham, Stoke City and Liverpool, and they had coasted to home wins over Coventry and Crystal Palace as well as giving a 5–1 thrashing to West Bromwich Albion. In the European Cup third round against Standard Liege, the highly rated Belgian champions, Leeds won 1–0 away as well as at home, with excellent performances in both matches. In all red, Leeds' winner in the first leg in Belgium came from Peter Lorimer, driving home a low-angled shot that Christian Piot, the Liege goalkeeper, believed he should have saved.

In that return tie, on another very heavy pitch, Norman Hunter damaged a knee. His own knee. Painful but not excruciating, the initial signs were that it was relatively minor an injury, but it would flare up again soon and badly affect his season. He would miss some crucial games as a result.

Next up in the European Cup for Leeds was a potentially classic semi-final pairing against the 1967 winners and current Scottish champions Celtic. Revie and Celtic manager Jock Stein were good friends and rivals, in both football and golf.

Celtic had decided to hold their semi-final home leg at Hampden Park so as to be able to accommodate more of their fanatical supporters. But tickets for the first leg, at Elland Road, would create major problems for both clubs. The capacity of the Leeds stadium was now 48,000, and while Celtic could sell over 20,000 tickets for this game, Leeds would only provide them with an allocation of 6,000. General Secretary Keith Archer explained that the home fans had to take priority over Celtic's. This simply was a notable occasion when the stadium wasn't big enough to accommodate everyone wanting to see the game.

Leeds' Assistant Manager Maurice Lindley travelled up to Glasgow to watch and gather notes on Celtic. After a 3–0 win against Ayr United, he declared, 'I saw enough to realize that this match with Celtic will be the toughest we have ever had to play in almost ten years of European competition.'

The Leeds United FA Cup quest continued impressively, with a fifth round home win over battling Mansfield Town (2–0, a crowd of 48,093) and then a sound 2–0 quarter-final victory at Swindon Town, last season's League Cup winners. Leeds were well and truly in contention to make footballing history. But the moment the FA Cup draw was made and the numbered balls of the four remaining teams came out, pairing Chelsea and not Leeds with the overwhelming underdogs Watford, Leeds' problems really were about to bite. Leeds were drawn to play their fiercest of rivals, Manchester United.

March 14 1970, three days after the Liege decider, Leeds met Manchester United at Hillsborough. 55,000 crammed into Sheffield Wednesday's stadium to watch an absorbing tussle between two giants of football. It was, as expected, a tough, unflinching conflict but nothing like their previous violent, unsavoury encounter there in 1965. Unfortunately, at least from the Leeds camp's perspective, the result was a 0–0 stalemate, nearly as bad as actually losing.

The replay took place at Villa Park nine days later, Monday March 23, two days after the Saturday League games in which Leeds beat Wolves 2–1 away and Manchester United lost by the same scoreline at high-flying (and new FA Cup finalists) Chelsea. Chelsea had beaten Watford 5–1 in the Cup, all the goals coming in the second half. Norman Hunter had to miss the Villa Park replay due to his knee injury so the king of adaptability himself, Paul Madeley, replaced him.

62,500 travelled to Birmingham to watch the match to decide Chelsea's FA Cup final opponents at Wembley. Allan Clarke had a headed goal disallowed by referee Jack Taylor, while Brian Kidd swung and missed a seemingly easy chance for Manchester United. The scoreline stayed the same after ninety minutes as well as thirty minutes' extra time, necessitating a second replay – to be played three days later at Bolton Wanderers' ground.

And at Burnden Park, with another fine crowd (56,000) watching, at long last the deadlock was broken. Both sides – Leeds in all white, Manchester in red shirts and socks, white shorts – had set out on the offensive. After around ten minutes' play, a half-cleared cross bounced out of the Manchester penalty area. Bremner pounced to get to the ball before Pat Crerand, to rifle a half-volley with his left foot, which the red shirt tried in vain to block. The ball whizzed in low, towards goal, skimming the surface before settling into the corner of the net past Alex Stepney's flailing right arm.

Even with a fine array of attacking talent including Best, Charlton, Kidd and Willie Morgan at their disposal – and Law as substitute – Leeds' defences could not be broken. Even without Hunter, they possessed a formidable back-line which by tradition rarely let a lead slip. The fact that Paul Madeley was in Hunter's place can only have discouraged Manchester United. The score remained 1–0 to Leeds – they had made it to Wembley again, thanks to a FA Cup semi-final win over Manchester United again, the winning goal coming from the indefatigable Billy Bremner, again.

## 10–3

A 'machine'? Bit of an insult in my book. It wasn't meant as a compliment, I knew that. It implied that we played the same way all the time; that the players were robots going through the same motions. What a load of crap.

When things went right, Leeds were the most balanced and skilful side going. They could attack from every angle and score from just about anywhere. Every outfield player was like a double agent: each of them could defend and attack/attack and defend/tackle and create/create and attack, make short passes and long passes, and all the players had the combination of speed and stamina. Aye, when things went right, Leeds were the best team around by a mile.

Five semi-finals, two FA Cup finals and seven League games. That's what we had to play from March 14 to April 29 1970. Too many big matches, too many injured players, or at least not enough fully fit ones. Doctor Adams had said to Don Revie in late March that five or six of the first team squad were close to nervous and physical collapse. It looked more likely that rather than win the big three, Leeds would lose them.

March 14 1970. Man U, FA Cup semi-final. 0–0.

March 21. Wolves (away) in the League. 2–1. A good win.

March 23. Man U, FA Cup semi-final replay. 0–0. Nail-biting, nerve-jangling stuff.

March 26. Man U, FA Cup semi-final replay part two. 1–0. Thank you captain Bremner.

March 28. Southampton (home) in the League. 1–3. That tore it, we were losing our grip on the League title.

March 30. Derby (away), League. 1–4. Just about sealed the title for Everton, and Leeds got fined £5,000 for playing mostly reserve players in the team as well.

April 1. Celtic (home), European Cup semi. 0–1. Rubbish performance, rubbish goal, we just didn't seem able to get going properly even though Eddie hit the bar with a right-footer. Billy cracked his head, got knocked out in the second half and was taken off, with concussion. He looked in a right state, even paler than normal, chalkier than chalk, and he was wandering around the tunnel and rooms and offices, still concussed, not knowing what he was doing. The Don said 'We never give up hope' after the match, but I think he knew we'd had it. Celtic had one of the best players I've ever seen – Jimmy Johnstone on the right wing, the sort of player every defender hates playing against. Fast, skilful, adventurous, fiery, never-give-in attitude.

April 2. West Ham (away), League. 2–2. Poor Paul Reaney broke his leg. That's him out of all our big games as well as the England squad for the World Cup in Mexico. Sickening, absolutely sickening, he's been on brilliant form.

April 4. Burnley (home), League game. 2–1, nothing riding on this match, and the Grand National was on the telly, so only 24,691 bothered to turn up. But it was a memorable game. Faulkner made his debut and Burnley's goal went in off him. So thank the Lord for Eddie Gray's two beautiful goals. Reaney wouldn't be able to play for ages, obviously, and Sprake, Cooper, Charlton, Hunter and Jones were all out injured. Eddie's goals were fantastic – one a lob from miles out which beat their goalie, and the other he must have dribbled round half the Burnley team before toe-ending it with his right foot into the net. And as he did that, Albert Johanneson was lying in the penalty area, injured, but watching Eddie dancing. In a way, that said something poetic and significant about them both.

April 11. Chelsea, FA Cup final. 2–2 after extra time. Eddie danced all over Chelsea but Sprakey was asleep. Some reporters called it a 'pudding' of a pitch, thanks to the Horse of the Year Show the night before. It wasn't that good. We should have had the game sewn up – but we didn't. Eddie Gray hit the bar with a right-foot shot when it was 2–2, while Sprake made some good saves in the second half. Half the papers seemed to agree that Leeds had played some of the best football ever played at Wembley. Typical of us that we still only drew.

April 15. Celtic (away), European Cup semi, second leg. 1–2. Billy took the lead with a scorcher but Celtic were too much for us and Johnstone was brilliant again.

April 18. Man City (home), League game. 1–3.

April 21. Ipswich Town (away), League. 2–3.

And April 29 was to be Chelsea, in the FA Cup final replay at Old Trafford. They nicked the match off us. Webb's winning goal was weak as dishwater but we'd had enough chances to have wrapped the match up before the extra time.

The papers said Chelsea committed thirty-five fouls in the replay, while we, the dirtiest team in the whole land, committed a disgraceful eleven. The fouls weren't the reason we lost the match though, even though Eddie McCreadie had kung-fu kicked Billy Bremner in the head and we should have been awarded a penalty. It was that blatant and violent a foul, even the Chelsea fans and players appealed for it! If someone had done that in the street, they'd have been jailed, but the nauseating fact of the matter was that even though we had most of the play and created more chances, we didn't make it count and in the rotten end we got sucker punched for it. Every bugger knew we were better than Chelsea. Fatigue beat us, I reckon – physical and mental.

### The Football Honours 1969–70

**Division One winners**: Everton. Runners up: Leeds United.
**FA Cup winners**: Chelsea. Runners up: Leeds United.
**League Cup winners**: Manchester City. Runners up: WBA.
**European Cup winners**: Feyenoord. Runners up: Celtic.
**European Cup Winners' Cup winners**: Manchester City. Runners up: Gornik Zabrze.
**Inter-Cities Fairs Cup winners**: Arsenal. Runners up: Anderlecht.
**Football Player of the Year**: Billy Bremner, Leeds United.
**European Footballer of the Year**: Gerd Muller, Bayern Munich.
**Manager of the Year**: Don Revie, Leeds United.

For the new season we had our orders to create a new Elland Road playing surface, to replace the old pile of dying earth that was sometimes called the pitch. A new, fresh beginning.

Out of the house, right foot first, think the thought again. *To Achieve Personal Greatness.* Stretches and bends on the pavement, a trot up our street and on to the patch of waste ground. Star jumps and crouches to brace my calves and then I'm on Elland Road in seconds, the song and rhythm helping the beat of my footsteps.

*We've got the best team in the land, we've got the best team in the land ...*

Forcing each word out, growling, barking, grunting, to achieve personal greatness ...

*We've got Gary Sprake at number one,*
*we've got the best team in the land.*
*We've got Paul Madeley wherever he wants,*
*we've got the best team in the land.*
*We've got Paul Reaney at number two,*
*we've got the best team in the land.*
*We've got Terry Cooper at number three,*
*we've got the best team in the land.*

Past the Scratching Shed, the shops and houses, the training pitches, the giant Greyhound Stadium stand, the workshops and factories and under the railway bridge.

*We've got Billy Bremner at number four,*
*we've got the best team in the land.*
*We've got Jackie Charlton at number five,*
*we've got the best team in the land.*
*We've got Norman Hunter at number six,*
*we've got the best team in the land.*

All the way along Elland Road until it rises into Churwell Hill, under another railway bridge while I'm looking out for my old, old friend the Morley Milestone.

*We've got Peter Lorimer at number seven,*
*we've got the best team in the land.*

Right round the New Inn, careful not to fall over any stray drunks or bottles at the back, and back down the hill I'm heading, under the railway bridge and the billboard sign.

*We've got Allan Clarke at number eight,*
*we've got the best team in the land.*
*We've got Mick Jones at number nine,*
*we've got the best team in the land.*
*We've got Johnny Giles at number ten,*
*we've got the best team in the land.*
*We've got Eddie Gray at number eleven,*
*we've got the best team in the land.*

Past the nice Cottingley houses and cemetery and land and where the council's planning to build two great big sod-off high-rise blocks of flats and a ton of houses nearby.

*We've got Mick Bates and the rest,*
*we've got the best team in the land.*

And then it happens, without any rhyme or reason, the smallest of incidents. As I'm running, near the crematorium, I hear this tiny little cracking sound like a dry twig being snapped, and with it massive evil pain in my left calf muscle like a bullet's daggered into my leg.

## 10–4

Leeds United were not the first club to be punished for fielding a weakened team in a League match, Burnley had been fined £1,000 nine years before, and Everton £2,000 in 1966.

With respect to the £5,000 fine imposed on Leeds for fielding their 'second string' against Derby, Football League President Len Shipman said, 'We took into consideration all their problems and felt sorry for them, and it took us more than an hour to reach our decision because we were conscious that they were struggling especially hard as the season had been shortened. But it must always be borne in mind that the League can, after all, forbid clubs to take part in European competitions if they cannot fulfil commitments at home.'

Revie had been unrepentant. He had, after all, possibly lost the League title as a consequence of his changes to the team, so financial punishment represented just another kick to the club while it was down. Everything seemed to be going against Leeds, everything and everybody, and his stance was that he had only done what he thought was best. 'I would do the same again. I can't describe how much those Manchester United games took out of the Leeds players.'

And concerning the Derby match, he said, 'The first team players who played for me against Southampton have been ruled out by the club doctor. Five of these players, Jack Charlton, Eddie Gray, Peter Lorimer, Allan Clarke and Paul Madeley, were too tired, both mentally and physically, to play in this game.'

Another seven players, including Billy Bremner and Mick Jones, were undergoing treatment for injuries at the time too. Leeds claimed they had asked Derby to postpone the match until a later date, but their directors had refused. Such a refusal seems to contradict Brian Clough's apparent disgust at the Leeds management for selecting so many reserves for the Derby–Leeds game. Regardless, Secretary of the Football League Alan Hardaker had no sympathy at all for Leeds or for Revie, saying that he had offered them various chances to rearrange games but they had rejected every single one. Hardaker's dislike for fellow Yorkshireman Revie was one of football's least-well-kept secrets.

After the two defeats to Celtic in the European Cup semi-finals, 0–1 and 1–2, Revie said, 'We lost our chance at Leeds. When we scored away I thought we could do something, but Celtic are a very, very good side. I sincerely hope they win the European Cup again.' Jock Stein acknowledged that Revie was one of the very few football men in England to show respect for his team. Celtic's hopes in the European Cup were to be destroyed, though, by Dutch champions Feyenoord in the final.

# Chapter 11

## 11–1

There it was, the first time I'd ever noticed it, sprayed on a Lowfields Road wall, in white, foot-high letters: DEATH TO ALL MANCHESTER FANS. I didn't know if it meant City or United, but by nightfall I thought it the most unfunny graffiti I'd ever seen in my whole life. Just a few hours later and it's all gone wrong, and I'm not talking about torn calf muscles or broken legs and ankles, I'm talking about a life that's suddenly torn and broken.

'I'm sorry to advise,' the doctor said, 'but your grandmother's condition is extremely serious.'

The nurses would make her as comfortable as was possible, but all we could do was wait and see if she regained consciousness. They said she had a blood clot on the brain, at the back of her skull where she'd banged it. She'd fallen down some stone steps at the side of the River Aire and cracked her head open. A woman had found her lying there, unconscious, at about eight in the morning and because of the blood and my grandma being so cold and pale the woman had thought she was dead.

I'd been at work, getting the stadium back to ship-shape for the new 1970–71 season. Ces had waved me down to the north-west corner tunnel, whistling, signalling me. I realized later why he hadn't shouted me: he'd been too choked up about it all himself.

In Leeds Infirmary, I wanted to blame someone, anyone, but I couldn't. Sometimes there's nothing or no one *to* blame.

She was lying in a side room, separate from the rest of the bed-ridden patients in the ward. Eyes closed, her head propped up on a pillow, she was as stiff as a waxwork. No movement, no twitching or anything like that, no eyelids flickering or eyeballs moving, not even a sign she was breathing. The nurse walked me into the room. I didn't want to, but I knew I had to. I had to try and be a man about it, deal with it like a responsible adult. I was twenty years old, after all, but I felt like a lost little child, that's the truth.

I couldn't look at her face. The nurse suggested I sit close to the bed, told me to touch or even hold my grandma's hand. Just because she was unconscious didn't mean she wasn't aware I was there. It could help if I spoke to her, the nurse said. She left the room, and there's me on my own, holding my grandma's cold hand. I tried to talk to her. 'It's me, Gran, Jimmy, I'm here ... I'm not going anywhere till you get better.'

My throat was dry. I couldn't swallow and it hurt when I tried to. I felt sick but ravenous too. I was sweating hot but I was cold inside and my stomach felt like I'd been punched. There was so much I wanted to say, so much I wanted her to know. I wanted to say sorry, sorry for everything, anything I'd ever done to upset or hurt her. I wanted to tell her that I did know, really, how hard she'd always worked to bring me up well and how difficult it all must have been for her. I wanted to thank her for everything – her care, her help, her sacrifices. I wanted her to stay so I'd get the chance to prove she was the most important thing in the world to me, over everything else: Don Revie, Leeds, St Anthony's, Ces. I wanted to tell her that I loved her more than anything else. But I didn't say it, I couldn't, because me and my grandma never did.

But then I couldn't stop myself. I wasn't just crying, I was wailing, whimpering, and saying all sorts of stuff to her, hoping she'd answer. I even swore at her, hoping that'd make her react. It didn't. I didn't want to lose her and I didn't want to go back to the house on my own and I didn't want to have to tell everyone what had happened.

'Please don't go, Gran, it's not your time, you've got ages, you've got years ...' Tears and snot were sliding down my face, tickling my jaw, dripping down my neck, drenching my collar. 'Wake up, listen to me.'

I kissed her cheek, it was soft but cruel and cold and the skin looked dry and yellow and grey. She wasn't my grandma any more. She looked so vulnerable and frail, so alone. People would be waiting for her, to keep her company and to look after her. People in heaven, or wherever we go when we die. Angels, ghosts, spirits, my mum. I felt light-headed and got a strange, reassuring feeling that someone was looking out for me too, like I was about to fall a long long way but someone would be there to catch me.

I sat at her bedside for an age, but probably less than an hour, in reality.

Then the strange noises started.

They were frightening, almost animal noises. Guttural, deep, deep breaths, almost snoring, almost growling. But worse. Long, unpleasant-sounding breaths that made me more nervous each time one began and then stopped. The breathing was slower, irregular, almost like a small engine fading, giving up.

The nurse hurried in. She must have noticed my panic even though I could hardly move, I was so shocked, scared. I half expected the nurse to tell me to leave so she'd be able to examine my grandma in private, but she didn't because she knew exactly what was happening. And so did I, deep down.

'She's been waiting for you,' the nurse said. 'You're here now, and she's finally decided to go, it's her time, James love, it's her time. Her body is shutting down.' She sat at the other side of the bed, took hold of my grandma's right hand and spoke to her, quietly, telling her it was alright to leave now, that everything was calm and there was nothing to worry about any more, James was here and he wants only what's best for her. She was just as upset as I was.

I sat on the near side of the bed and held my grandma's left hand again like I did at first. I'd no idea what she was going through but kept worrying that she was in a lot of pain, so the quicker this was all over with the better. I was willing the pain to leave her alone and to leave her in peace. In fact, I was actually willing my grandma to hurry up and die.

Her breathing slowed down, the sounds got softer until they weren't that unpleasant and more like gentle ocean waves or trees in the wind. Then her jaw dropped so, so slightly, opening her mouth a fraction, as if she was about to say something. It was only a tiny movement and wasn't life. The nurse sighed, a smile on her face and tears in her eyes. 'I'm sorry,' she says. 'She's gone.'

I don't know what time I got back home but it was dark. I couldn't think clearly and as well as being so horribly tired I was scared, no, *terrified*, of waking up in the early hours with a shock, remembering everything that had happened.

I never let on to anyone because it was probably a bit too odd and Norman Bates-like for them to understand, but I slept in my grandma's bed that night. The room was musky and smelt of lavender and dust, and there were far too many blankets, but I actually slept well, as if everything was peaceful and was going to be alright and that the day, in fact, had not been the worst day of my life.

## 11–2

Thankfully, the writers of *This Is Your Life* excluded Leeds United's disastrous 1969–70 season from the Don Revie script.

In April 1970, Paul McCartney left The Beatles. The World Cup in Mexico brought more disappointment to the country, as Sir Alf Ramsey's England team were dumped out of the competition by West Germany. Reigning champions England had been two up in the quarter-final but ended up losing 3–2 after extra time.

At Leeds, approaches from Birmingham City, Juventus and Torino for his services, plus the persistent rumour that he would take the Manchester United job 'tomorrow', meant that Revie was a much-sought-after man. The time, though, wasn't right for moving: there was still much to do at Leeds.

Hull City had issued an invitation to Jack Charlton to apply for the job as their player–manager. Charlton's reputation as a potentially top coach was growing, but, although flattered to be asked, he wanted to make the most of his playing days. Revie believed Charlton could carry on playing until he was forty. Charlton himself wanted to be remembered at his best and so would finish his playing career only when he felt, physically and mentally, the time was right. After their offer had been declined, Hull turned to Arsenal's Terry Neill.

In August 1970, in time for the forthcoming season, Leeds became the first-ever club to install a 'police station' within their stadium grounds, while the Football League's Alan Hardaker urged the civil authorities to take a harder stance against the trouble causers at matches because, he said, sooner or later someone would be killed.

In October, Jack Charlton mentioned in a television interview that he kept a little black book to list the names of certain players he intended harming or getting his revenge on for past skirmishes and quarrels. He had been speaking figuratively, referring to 'old scores' he intended to settle. Nonetheless, black book or not, the Football Association deemed his comments to be bringing the game into disrepute and a swift statement was issued to say that Jack would face a Joint Commission of the FA and the League for the remarks.

Two matches from the 1970–71 campaign will never fade from many minds. Both games featured on *Match of the Day* as the programme's main attractions, and both made for compulsive if, for some, excruciating viewing. February 13 1971, in the FA Cup fifth round: Colchester United versus Leeds.

In just short of a decade's tenure as the Leeds boss, Don Revie's team had played nineteen games on the thirteenth day of various months over the years. Not that he suffered from triskaidekaphobia. Leeds had lost just once.

So far, the Cup draws had been kind to Leeds. They had been drawn against lower-league opposition each time – Rotherham United of Division Three in the third round (winning the Elland Road replay 3–2 after a 0–0 draw), Division Two's Swindon Town in the fourth (4–0 home win) and now Colchester in the fifth. Colchester, a tiny club with an average gate of less than 3,000, and currently in the top half of League Division Four.

First Division high-flyers Leeds United flew down to Colchester for the match at Layer Road. Although it was a cold and windy Saturday, the conditions were better than most other venues in

197

the country, with postponements affecting the day's fixture list. Mick Bates replaced injured Billy Bremner while Paul Madeley stood in for long-term injury Eddie Gray on the left wing. Shortly before the three o'clock kick off, while the Leeds players warmed up on the pitch, as usual, Norman Hunter and Jack Charlton discussed their prospects. With the surface ridged and bumpy and the wind swirling, and with former England forward Ray Crawford leading the Colchester line-up against them, and with a partisan crowd crammed to capacity inside the tiny ground, Hunter and Charlton agreed that they would need to get stuck in, as it was going to be one hell of a battle.

The opening five minutes of the game were indeed a battle, and Leeds struggled to get out of their own half – Colchester set off with clear intent to 'rattle' them and disrupt any chance of rhythm. Just as the attendance for the match had swelled to 16,000, the Colchester players seemed to have grown in stature too. They looked like the famed honours-chasing First Division team, not Leeds United. Their early pressure was near relentless and when a Leeds player actually got the ball at his feet he had precious little time to do anything with it as Colchester players hassled at every opportunity. They were well organized, tightly knit, disciplined and physically fit, with a seething desire to win.

After around a quarter of an hour comes the match's first scoring chance. Neat and swift interplay between Ray Crawford, Brian Lewis and Mick Mahon, near the half-way line, gives Mahon a run-in on the Leeds goal. Racing through the Leeds half, easily eluding surprised defenders, he smacks in a good low shot, which Sprake does well to push by his left-hand post for a corner. Nothing comes of this attack, but that won't be the case for long.

Near the right-hand Leeds corner, Dave Simmons, Colchester's big target-man, gets to the ball before Jack Charlton. Simmons is better known for his heading ability and for throwing his weight around, but he shows good footwork to keep the ball and skip by Charlton with it. The defender thrusts out a leg to try and jab the ball away from Simmons but succeeds only in tripping him. The referee blows his whistle, a free kick is awarded and Simmons and Charlton jog into the penalty area, sharing a good-natured chat. More players take positions around the area and get ready for the free kick. Brian Lewis takes it, and the well-struck cross swings in close to and across the Leeds goal. Charlton and Simmons both jump to try and head the ball but it misses them both by inches and should be a straightforward catch or punch for Sprake, or failing that, a header clear for Norman Hunter. The two Leeds men need only to communicate and the problem is easily resolved. Instead, they hardly move and watch like spectators as the ball flies in towards them. Their indecision proves decisive, allowing Ray Crawford to steal in and pounce to head the ball firmly into the near top corner of the net. It's 1–0 to Colchester, and no more than they deserve. Leeds have yet to pose any serious threat on the home side's goal. Johnny Giles and Peter Lorimer have hardly touched the ball, while Allan Clarke and Mick Jones have made little impact so far.

Although more a hopeful punt than a calculated pass, ten minutes later a long and lofted cross from just inside the Leeds half floats towards the visitors' goal. As it approaches, Paul Reaney and Ray Crawford jump together to challenge for the airborne ball. It's fifty-fifty, and both players actually make contact with it, Crawford heading the ball, against Reaney's ribs. It drops softly to the ground while the two players land in a heap, with the ball nearby, minding its own business. Sprake scrambles out to collect it, but unfortunately for him Crawford's legs are much closer and he spots a chance. Still lying on the ground, he swings his left leg to kick the ball, albeit with very little power. But it's power enough. His kick deceives the advancing Sprake and the ball rolls slowly by him. It rolls, rolls, rolls, twelve, fifteen yards, towards goal. Colchester fans behind will it on, while Leeds supporters pray that it is heading wide of the net. It then gently collides with the left-hand post – the inside of the left-hand post – and comes to a halt, just across the goal-line. Striker Dave Simmons rushes in and whacks the ball into the net, just to make sure, but it is Crawford's goal and it is 2–0 to Colchester. The Leeds men in the tiny pitch-side dugout cringe with despair, and wonder if it is possible to feel any smaller or more uncomfortable in such a cramped space. Allan Clarke fails to hit the target with two half-chances. Half-time.

The second half begins, and the Leeds players have clearly received somewhat of a rollicking. They look more determined, more confident and more agile. The overall play, from both sides, is even faster and more frenetic. In the fifty-fourth minute, there's a significant mistake in the Leeds defence.

Another long cross comes in from the Colchester right, one yard inside the Leeds half. The football is high in the air for some time, and Gary Sprake should be able to judge it easily. But again his indecision is final and the ball bounces high towards the Leeds area, close to the penalty spot. Sprake hesitates, and when he runs out at last to catch the high ball it's too late. The unfortunate Reaney is made to look foolish too, as Dave Simmons beats both Leeds players to the ball to head it before either of them can intervene. The ball loops over Sprake and bounces smartly into the empty Leeds net. Fourth Division Colchester United 3, First Division Leeds United 0.

Mick Jones is having one of those games where very little goes right. He latches on to a low Peter Lorimer cross but his shot is weak and off target. Although they are three goals up, Colchester show some inexperience by continuing to attack Leeds and thus leave spaces at the back for Leeds to exploit. They really should defend en masse, but this is the only negative aspect of their performance so far. They might get away with it.

With room to advance and run with the ball, Paul Madeley has a thirty-yard shot deflected for a Leeds corner. Terry Cooper takes it, the Colchester penalty area packed with ten Colchester men marking nine Leeds. And just out-jumping all around him, Norman Hunter connects with the ball to score a rare headed goal, giving Leeds a glimmer of a chance to save the game. In the seventy-third minute, with Leeds on the attack and showing real urgency at last, a fine left-footed strike from Johnny Giles makes it 3–2. Jack Charlton is moved up into the front line to add weight and height to the Leeds attack as an emergency striker. It's now all Leeds, but the team isn't playing its typical style of football: it is long-ball play, kick and hope, and far from attractive stuff. But if it was going to be effective then who cared?

And in the seventy-ninth minute Charlton has a great chance to equalize. A strong Lorimer cross comes in and Charlton stoops to meet it. His bullet header ought to hit the target, trouble the keeper or at least go close, but it squirts yards wide of Colchester's left post. And a minute later, six yards from his own goal, Brian Garvey meets a low cross a fraction of a second before Mick Jones, sending the ball goal-bound, but straight at goalkeeper Graham Smith. His reactions are sharp and he makes a smart save. Seconds after, Mick Jones strikes a poor left-footed shot wide and Norman Hunter wastes a decent chance, skewing a free kick high and wide from just outside the area.

The referee blows his whistle for full time. Colchester players and supporters are ecstatic at Leeds' ignominious exit from the FA Cup. It's a major shock result. Colchester are through, and rightly so.

On April 17 1971 League leaders Leeds would meet West Bromwich Albion at Elland Road. Arsenal and Leeds had been virtually unstoppable at the top of the table for most of the season, and seemed to be running away with Division One. At one stage, Leeds held a seven-point lead, though the Gunners had a couple of games in hand. A home win today was imperative for Leeds if they were to maintain a serious challenge. West Bromwich, meanwhile, had the worst defensive record in the division. A comfortable Leeds victory was expected, though Albion had a powerful, proven strike force, and two players would regularly feature in the lists of top goal scorers. Tony Brown and Jeff Astle had upset the odds and opposing defences many times before, while the team had taken a point in impressive performances at Everton, Liverpool and Tottenham. For Leeds, Mick Bates replaced unwell Peter Lorimer, the sole absentee from an otherwise full-strength line-up. Nigel Davey, a local lad from Garforth, was number twelve and on the bench.

From the very start of the match, Leeds went on the offensive, hoping to get an early goal and thus weaken Albion's resolve and damage their morale. Perhaps the Leeds players were too keen though, or perhaps they had underestimated their opponents, because the Whites looked edgy throughout, especially in defence. The usual incisiveness of their passing and fluidity of their forward play was lacking also, whilst the Leeds midfield were struggling to mark their authority on the game. Full-backs Reaney and Cooper, too, were making little impact on the wings, and central defenders Hunter and Charlton looked uncomfortable each time West Brom counter-attacked. They were jittery, either due to nervousness or fatigue. Fortunately, Sprake looked to be in good form, and he had a busier-than-expected afternoon as Albion mounted various assaults on his goal with relative ease.

In the nineteenth minute the game's first goal arrives, following a mistake by Jack Charlton in the centre circle, inexplicably losing possession of the ball with a stray pass just inside the Leeds half. Albion break away swiftly, a quick couple of interchanges ensue and Tony Brown is free and in the clear outside the Leeds area. Running a few yards with the ball at his feet, he looks up towards Sprake's goal and slams the ball home with a low, well-struck right-footed shot. 1–0 to West Brom and it's half-time.

In the second half Nigel Davey replaced Mick Bates, and Terry Cooper moved up to left wing. Leeds looked livelier and were attempting to pierce their opponents' back line by whatever route possible. But Albion stood firm while continuing to be dangerous on the break. Sprake was playing well even though Tony Brown wasted a great opportunity to score again by shooting tamely straight at him from five yards.

On the Leeds right flank, seven or eight yards from the Albion goal-line and just inside the penalty area, Eddie Gray shimmied and swayed to deceive the defenders and place a right-foot, head-height cross into the box. Mick Jones, loitering with intent on the six-yard line, gets to the ball first and, with a powerful and accurate flicked header, the ball soars past goalkeeper Jim Coombes into the far corner of the Albion net. A superbly taken chance but, alas for Leeds, it doesn't count. Offside, and the correct decision.

A few minutes later, running shoulder by shoulder, Allan Clarke and centre-half John Wile chase a through-ball. Clarke gets there first but Wile is right with him and, just inside the area, he collides with the Leeds striker. Clarke is sent sprawling while the football rolls harmlessly through to Coombes as he dashes out of his goal. The crowd believe it's a foul and make the referee aware of it. Clarke believes it is a foul and tries also to make the referee aware of it, but no other Leeds players seem to be appealing for a penalty. The referee waves play on and the game continues.

A beautifully struck missile of a volley from outside the Leeds area seared in on Leeds' goal from inside-left Bobby Hope. It arrived through the crowded penalty area, and Sprake did well to see it as well as block it. The ball rebounded off him and landed at the feet of Colin Suggett to casually tap it into the net. Suggett, though, was at least a yard offside. The correct decision and still 1–0.

Sprake takes the resultant free kick, passing the ball to his left to Norman Hunter. Hunter paces down the left flank, reaching the half-way line with the ball at his feet. He pauses, in search for a team-mate to pass to whilst keeping tight possession of the ball. He spots Clarke in attack and attempts a diagonal pass to him, but only succeeds in finding Hope's backside. Luckily for Hunter, the ball gently ricochets back to him. He traps it and again looks for an available Leeds man while the other Leeds defenders vacate their own penalty area and make their way to the half-way line. To avoid being caught offside, the Albion players in attack follow suit. Johnny Giles signals to Hunter that he wants the ball. Hunter acknowledges and hits the pass towards Giles, but Albion's Tony Brown anticipates it to intercept the lay-off. Brown, not quite able to control the football, sees it hit his left boot and rebound into the Leeds half.

Paul Reaney is positioned way over on the opposite flank just inside the Leeds half. Colin Suggett, casually making his way back from the forward position he had occupied less than a minute before, is the only Albion player in that Leeds half, at least five yards behind Reaney and therefore at least five yards offside. As soon as the football enters the Leeds half, the linesman waves his flag. Players on both teams stop.

Except for Tony Brown, who continues to run, as he is watching the ball and nothing else. He tears after the loose ball while all the other players wait for referee Tinkler to blow his whistle and corroborate the linesman's decision. But the whistle blow does not come. Mr Tinkler has deemed Colin Suggett not offside as he was not interfering with play.

In the centre circle, Suggett seems surprised by the referee's decision. Seeing Brown's run, he swivels around and begins a sprint towards the Leeds goal to catch up. At the far side of the pitch, big centre-forward Jeff Astle shows a decent turn of speed too and chases after his team-mates. He races half the length of the pitch, with Paul Reaney hot on his heels, but not hot enough. Still in possession of the ball, Brown progresses into the penalty area. He looks up and sees Astle ready to accept a pass in his stride. Brown's timing, though, is imperfect, and he casually taps the ball slightly forward to Astle, who is two yards in front of him, and therefore two yards offside as well. But he's judged by Referee Tinkler to be onside. Astle receives the pass and rolls the ball into the net past the helplessly stranded Gary Sprake. 2–0 to Albion and at least two incorrect decisions.

Twelve angry men of various ages run on to the pitch to remonstrate with the referee. When the game eventually restarts, Allan Clarke nets for Leeds in the eighty-second minute to make it 1–2, but it is too little too late. West Bromwich hold out to win and steal the points, while Referee Tinkler is escorted off the pitch by police officers to protect him from any possible danger. Viewers could be excused for thinking he had been arrested.

It had been one of the most controversial, notorious football matches ever played in England, and the match result just about decided the fate of the 1970–71 season's League Championship. As if the result hadn't been bad enough for the Leeds supporters, the consequences of crowd disorder would have more serious and far-reaching effects.

Chairman Alderman Percy Woodward, never slow to lambast the loutish aggression on British football terraces in the past, was furious, but at the actions on the pitch. 'It is appalling that nine or ten months' work by all of us should be destroyed by one man ... I am not blaming the spectators. There was every justification for it. I am sorry it happened but there it is.'

The Lord Mayor of Leeds, Alderman Arthur Brown, himself a former professional referee for many years, commented: 'I can find no defence for the referee.'

When asked about the crowd trouble, Revie responded, 'Can you blame them for what happened today?' adding later, 'I have never been so sick at heart. The ref's decision on Suggett, the worst I have seen man and boy, was wrong and it wrecked nine months of hard work at our club. I regret the crowd scenes like anybody else but, by heaven, I can understand why they cut loose. Astle was also offside, in my opinion, when he took the pass from Brown to score.'

Bremner had his say too: 'Suggett was plain straight offside and the goal hung on that. We all stopped running. But the match got away from us.'

Referee Tinkler defended his actions. 'I am completely sure that Suggett committed no offence. He was in an offside position and the linesman had flagged him, but he was not interfering with play.'

Comments published in the *Daily Sketch* and attributed to the linesman, who was felled by an object thrown from the crowd for his troubles, contradicted Mr Tinkler's viewpoint. 'Suggett wasn't just a yard off-side, he was a good five yards and in my opinion must have been influencing play. He didn't touch the ball but he set off in support of Brown so there was a clear intention of interfering with the course of the game.'

League Division One table (top), April 17 1971:

| 1 | Arsenal | Played 37, | Points 58 |
|---|---------|-----------|-----------|
| 2 | Leeds Utd | Played 39, | Points 58 |
| 3 | Chelsea | Played 39, | Points 48 |

Even though Leeds went on to win their remaining three fixtures, including a 1–0 home win over Arsenal, the damage had been done and Arsenal went on to win the title with a last-minute victory at arch rivals Tottenham Hotspur in the last match of the season. The consequences of the West Brom defeat, the referee's decisions and the fans' actions went deeper than just a ruined title challenge, negative press and increased notoriety for Leeds.

Because of the pitch invasion the club was punished severely by the FA (too severely some said) and would be forced to play their first four home fixtures of the next season at neutral venues.

Although their 1970–71 season would be predominantly remembered for two shock defeats, Leeds' campaign was far from a disaster. As well as registering a record number of points for League runners-up (sixty-four, twelve more than third-placed Tottenham) in March the club announced a record profit of £171,951 for the previous season. Seven Leeds players were said to earn between £10,000 and £12,500. Leeds managed to win the Inter-Cities Fairs Cup too. They were Champions of Europe once again, albeit not in the European Cup.

Three days before the West Bromwich Albion nightmare, Leeds had been away to Liverpool in the first leg of the Fairs Cup semi-final. A surprise inclusion in the Leeds eleven was Billy Bremner, who had been out of action for more than two months. Renowned for scoring crucial goals, Leeds' very own copper-topped Captain Marvel played as a third attacker, not his usual midfield role. For Leeds, the first British winners of the Inter Cities Fairs Cup, the Anfield tie was, astonishingly, their fiftieth in the competition. And they had scored ninety-nine goals along the way.

Bremner as captain, having won the coin toss, decided to make Liverpool play towards their Kop, crammed with over 20,000 Reds supporters. Just as Leeds prefer to play towards their Gelderd End Kop in the second half of matches, Liverpool do the same at Anfield. Some minor psychological gamesmanship from Leeds on the night, then, which did seem to work. No matter what pressure Liverpool put the visitors under, they couldn't break the deadlock. At half-time it was 0–0 and the Leeds players were growing in confidence of spoiling Liverpool's unbeaten home record for the season.

The second half underway, just after the hour mark, in a predictably tight and hard-fought match, with few fouls committed, Leeds were awarded a free kick on Liverpool's left. Johnny Giles floats the ball into their penalty area but his cross is too high for Liverpool's defenders. However, their slack or absent marking leaves Bremner virtually overlooked and lurking on his own just inside the area. Probably the smallest man on the pitch, Bremner shows yet again superb heading ability belying his size. Gauging the flight of the ball, he dashes a few yards inside the area and launches himself, twisting his body mid-air to try and plant as much of his bodyweight into the ball as he can. He connects well, very well, smashing the ball with the top of his head towards Liverpool's goal. Bremner's header is truly a fine one and its power and trajectory beat goalkeeper Ray Clemence. The Liverpool faithful are stung into wounded silence. Liverpool 0, Leeds 1. The goal is enough to win the match and indeed put Leeds into the final, as the second leg against Liverpool at Elland Road produced no goals.

In late May and early June, with a 2–2 draw (Madeley, Bates) away at Juventus and a 1–1 draw (Clarke) in the second leg of the final at Elland Road, Leeds won the Fairs Cup for the second time in their history, this time by way of the away goals rule. The first game in Italy had had to be postponed at very late notice due to torrential rainfall. Whilst warming up on the pitch for the then still 'on' game, Eddie Gray suffered the excruciating injury of a dislocated shoulder.

Quite understandably, Juventus felt aggrieved at losing via the rule, because they had not lost one game in the competition. Leeds had, in the second round away at Dynamo Dresden, 2–1, the Mick Jones away goal taking them through. They made easier work of their other opponents, beating Norwegian side Sarpsborg 6–0 on aggregate in the first round, Czech side Sparta Prague 9–2 in the third, Vitoria Setubal of Portugal 3–2, and Liverpool 1–0 in the penultimate round of the competition. The truth of the 1970–71 season for Revie and Leeds was that the Inter-Cities Fairs Cup had not been high on their list of trophy priorities to begin with, but by the end of the season they were thankful in the extreme for it.

**11–3**

When the crappiest sort of luck hits you, I think it's safe to say that you either sink or you swim. With me, it was sink, I was sure of it, it all felt like I was up to my neck in it and drowning, everything had changed so much, so quickly, so rottenly.

But I was lucky. I would have been well and truly sunk without friends' help. Proper, true friends. Ces and John, and Aitch, and just about everybody else in our street. The funeral, the insurance, the money, the rent, the paperwork, the obituary thing in the paper, the Peacock for the wake, and so on and on and on. It all seemed to be neverending and I didn't even want to get out of bed most mornings, there just didn't seem much point. It was like I'd lost all my energy. But Ces and John would take it in turns at battering on the door each morning, even some Saturdays when we weren't due to work. I was only just twenty-one, I didn't know what you were supposed to do or how you're supposed to recover from being left totally on your own. I couldn't even play football to help kick out the stress because I had to rest my torn calf muscle until autumn.

I'd never known my grandma had so many friends. Everyone was so nice and sympathetic. I didn't know what to say or how to react but I think I did alright.

Sometimes things happen in the world, even if they happen away from your own world, that shock you and shake you out of personal dark times and make you realize that you're not the only one with problems. On January 2 1971, 66 people died and over 200 were injured at the Rangers versus Celtic match at Ibrox. Metal barriers collapsed, causing a pile-up of people, and most died of asphyxiation.

We all make mistakes. But Tinkler's wrong decisions in the West Brom game weren't just mistakes: they looked bloody deliberate to me, as if he was wanting to spite Leeds. And we should have had a penalty and all. When some of the fans got on the pitch I

208

really did expect him to get lamped. Tinkler was lucky he didn't, that's a definite.

Trouble at football matches was getting more and more common. You wouldn't hear about it on the television or radio so much, and the papers missed more than they actually reported, but there were always stories. Pub talk, terrace talk, talk at work, talk amongst the St Ant's lads. There were regular incidents within Elland Road but most of it was outside the ground, or in town or in and around Beeston and Holbeck.

In September Leeds played Chelsea at home. No love lost between us and them so there was plenty of scrapping, as you'd expect, mainly in town near or in the train station. October we had Man U at home. A 50,000 crowd, and plenty of arrests. The *Evening Post* reported Man United had 'many youths wearing crash helmets, heavy boots and wearing red', with lots of them ejected from the stadium. Bloody right and all. There were fights all over the place and the New Peacock pub supposedly got trashed. The Imperial Hotel on Princes Street in Holbeck had windows smashed, and lots more breakages as well. According to people who lived around there, trouble connected to the football was nothing new. Every time Leeds had a home game they reckoned there was always loads of violence and vandalism. Why not move house then? Eventually, Leeds banned helmets and steel-capped boots. God knows how they thought they'd manage it. And they banned banners and instructed the police to look out for 'aggressive clothing', too.

# Chapter 12

*This Is Your Life*'s writers discreetly omitted any mentions of Colchester and West Bromwich Albion, as well as Leeds having to play their first four home games of the 1971–72 campaign on neutral territory. They were not the only club in trouble at the time, however. At Old Trafford, after a knife-throwing incident in February at their match with Newcastle, Manchester United were also banned from playing at home, for two weeks. Their August 'home' game against Arsenal was switched to Anfield.

The Leeds players were well aware of their aim for the new season: the double of the League and FA Cup. But by the third month of the season, after twelve games, Leeds were eighth in the table, six points behind the leaders Manchester United. Plus they were out of the UEFA Cup at the first hurdle in September, and would exit the League Cup in October.

The new UEFA Cup competition replaced the Inter-Cities Fairs Cup, in which Leeds and Spanish side Barcelona had been the two most successful teams to take part over the years. UEFA arranged for a play-off between the two sides to decide the trophy's permanent owner. Barcelona had won the trophy three times, Leeds twice. The match, held at Barcelona's huge Nou Camp stadium on September 22, created less prestige than UEFA hoped, with just 35,000 people attending. Barcelona won 2–1, with Leeds' goal scored by Joe Jordan, signed from Morton for £15,000 in October 1970. A few hundred ardent Leeds fans made the trip to watch the Barcelona match but it is unlikely their disappointment at the result lasted much longer than the return journey home.

Jordan's early days at Leeds had been uncomfortable to say the least. In addition to relentless ribbing from his new team-mates for 'unusual' dress-sense (an oilskin coat and an Arran wool sweater his mum had knitted being the main offending articles) he had been kicked in the mouth in a Leeds reserves match at Coventry and his front two teeth ended up in the muck. They were followed soon later by the tooth at each side whilst he was forced to wait days for dentures.

Jordan had been a Morton team-mate of the one and only Bobby Collins. Don Revie had asked his former midfield general if there were any players north of the border he could recommend. 'Aye,' Collins had replied, and mentioned a boy called Joe Jordan who had a 'real chance'.

In the summer of 1971, *Goal* magazine had declared that the new Leeds season would be the last throes of a great side, while Peter Morris warned that if Revie were to depart it could cause the club's swift decline and its return to the low point of the early 1960s. The worry was a very real one for Revie. Players were getting older and slower, and perhaps losing the desire too, and some were hindered by persistent injuries. The beginning of the end of his 'Super Leeds' squad was approaching and there was very little he could do about it. With every passing day and with every new setback affecting his men, his anxieties grew. In the early days of his managerial career, he rarely got more than four hours' sleep each night. Ten or so years later, his sleep suffered all over again, but for very different reasons: achieving success rather than failure.

The four neutral-venue games turned out to be more an inconvenience than a heavy punishment as the team went unbeaten in them. Leeds gained a 0–0 draw with Wolverhampton at Huddersfield's Leeds Road ground, a 1–1 draw with Spurs at Hull's Boothferry Park, and wins against Newcastle United (5–1 at Hillsborough) and Crystal Palace (2–0 at Leeds Road again). United's early season problems in the League were more away from home. Although they beat Manchester City at Maine Road 1–0 on the opening Saturday, by late October they had lost at Sheffield United 3–0, Arsenal 2–0, Huddersfield Town 2–1 and 3–1 at Coventry. In the League Cup they went down 1–0 to West Ham, after extra time in a replay, and in the UEFA Cup lost 4–2 on aggregate to Belgian side Lierse SK. Despite Revie's pre-season confidence, already it was looking distinctly gloomy.

Leeds' main problem was inconsistent performances, but suspensions and injuries also forced frequent team changes and thus prevented a settled line-up. Changes upset a team's rhythm, regardless of how good the replacement players are. It is fair to say that injuries to key Leeds players did upset the balance. Allan Clarke, Mick Jones and Eddie Gray all missed matches early in the season, while Jack Charlton, Terry Cooper and Johnny Giles were occasionally rested.

The media didn't let up either. More and more opinions were expressed about the players being too old, being injury prone and no longer being strong or hungry enough. The death knell of Super Leeds was surely ringing.

After the October 9 defeat at Coventry, Revie's Leeds lions were portrayed as having been reduced to toothless cubs. But the wounded beasts followed the loss with four League wins in a row, at home to Manchester City 3–0, Everton 3–2 and Leicester 2–1, plus a fans' favourite 1–0 victory at Manchester United. But a November 13 2–1 defeat at Southampton spoiled the run.

Division One League table (top), November 13 1971:

| 1 | Manchester Utd | Played 17, | Points 26 |
| 2 | Derby County | Played 17, | Points 23 |
| 3 | Manchester City | Played 17, | Points 23 |
| 4 | Sheffield Utd | Played 17, | Points 23 |
| 5 | Leeds Utd | Played 17, | Points 21 |

Also in November, Leeds had all but bought left-sided midfielder Asa Hartford from West Bromwich Albion for more than £200,000. The Scot even trained with his new Elland Road team-mates, only for the club's insurers to cancel the deal due to Hartford having a past heart condition. And this despite cardiology reports giving the player the all-clear. Very sad news for the player and for the Leeds camp, too.

The team though went unbeaten in the League for nine games as well as easing through the third round of the FA Cup in mid-January 1972. Their eye-catching League run included a November 2–0 walkover at Nottingham Forest, an impressive 3–0 home

213

win over Brian Clough's Championship hopefuls Derby on December 27 and an excellent 2–0 win at old rivals Liverpool on New Year's Day, in front of nearly 54,000 spectators, to complete the double over Bill Shankly's team. The draw for the FA Cup fourth round would give him the chance to avenge. But a Gary Sprake blunder, gifting Martin Chivers the winner and Spurs the points in the 1–0 defeat at White Hart Lane, meant that by the end of January the Peacocks were just below top spot.

Division One League table, January 29 1972:

| 1 | Man City | Played 27, | Points 38 |
|---|---|---|---|
| 2 | Leeds Utd | Played 27, | Points 36 |
| 3 | Derby | Played 27, | Points 36 |
| 4 | Man Utd | Played 27, | Points 35 |
| 5 | Arsenal | Played 27, | Points 33 |
| 6 | Wolves | Played 27, | Points 32 |

With Sheffield United, Tottenham, Chelsea and Liverpool all loitering with intent, the title race was promising to be the closest and most exciting for years.

February 5 1972. FA Cup fourth round. Liverpool 0 Leeds 0. With around 56,600 making it Liverpool's highest attendance for over ten years, the hosts had most of the possession and attacking pressure. There were few clear-cut chances throughout though, while a combination of good goalkeeping by Sprake, solid defending by Reaney, Cooper, Hunter and Madeley (in for the ill Charlton) and inadequate finishing by Liverpool kept the scores level.

After a relatively slow start, tickets for the Elland Road replay sold out. As well as nearly 46,000 inside the ground there were thousands locked out, an even more astounding figure given that it was a midweek afternoon kick off due to power cuts. A hundred or so supporters managed to perch on the Peacock pub rooftop to get a view (of the Kop end of the pitch at least) while a few others tried watching from nearby trees and roofs. Leeds went into the replay still as the bookmakers' favourites to win the Cup. The general view was that Liverpool had missed their chance to beat Leeds on the Saturday. Don Revie would have none of it. 'Liverpool are still one of the hardest teams in the world to beat.'

Leeds won 2–0, thanks to expertly taken Allan Clarke goals in each half. Revie was proving to be a proper thorn in Shankly's side.

Less than two weeks later (with a stalemate at Everton inbetween) millions of television viewers in addition to a crowd of over 45,000 at Elland Road saw second-in-the-table Leeds annihilate fourth-placed Manchester United 5–1. Just a few weeks prior, Manchester had been top of the table, but were now stuck in a dismal run of form, despite a line-up including George Best, Bobby Charlton, Willie Morgan and Brian Kidd.

Leeds were now riding high in the League and doing well in the FA Cup. Next up for them was the FA Cup fifth round, away to Second Division Cardiff City. Leeds were expected to win but Revie, still haunted by last season's humiliation at Colchester, warned that Cardiff would not be pushovers by any means. There would be a big and partisan crowd of Welshmen roaring them on, and the players would 'chase everything and fight like tigers'. He was right.

On February 26, on a rainy Wales afternoon, close on 50,000 people attended Ninian Park to watch Cardiff take on Leeds, most of them hoping for another shock result. Leeds put on a faultless performance. No nerves, no complacency, no frills. With a goal in each half, the second a typically sweet strike, man of the match Johnny Giles steered Leeds into the next round. Cardiff played well and gave the Cup favourites a hard game but Leeds undeniably deserved the win.

'To say that Leeds are playing with Southampton is the understatement of the season. Poor old Southampton just don't know what day it is' *Match of the Day*'s Barry Davies commentated on Saturday March 4 1972. Even the *Daily Telegraph*, hardly fervent admirers of Revie or the club, praised Leeds' efforts.

Leeds thumped Southampton 7–0 at Elland Road. Less-than-sympathetic viewers claimed Southampton had been lucky to get nil. The scorers were Clarke two, Lorimer three, and Jones and Charlton one each. As Don Revie and Saints manager Ted Bates were good friends, during the rout Revie tried to send word to his players to take the heat off Southampton. Heeding the Boss's instruction, the Leeds players began to play 'keep ball' instead of trying to score more goals. And with the fans all around the ground cheering, crying 'Ole' with every Leeds pass, various ball-flicks and tricks ensued. Southampton barely got a chance to touch the ball. Ted Bates' players weren't embarrassed, they were humiliated. For the Leeds management and directors, the afternoon's one disappointment was the attendance: less than 35,000. One week later, nearly 9,000 more turned up for the League game against Coventry. Mid-table City made the match hard for Leeds and just one goal would settle it - fortunately for Leeds it was scored by Jack Charlton, and in his six hundredth League game for the club.

Next up: Spurs in the FA Cup quarter final. Goalkeeper Pat Jennings, a Northern Ireland international, played outstandingly well for Spurs and probably prevented a drubbing. But Tottenham took the lead shortly before half-time, albeit against the run of play and with a fortunate goal. It was the first time Leeds had been behind in that season's FA Cup. It wasn't for long.

Desperate defending by Jennings and co could not stop Allan Clarke stretching and toe-poking the ball home for the equalizer after a game of football pinball in the muddy penalty area. The ball fell kindly for Clarke. Early in the second half, an innocuous Martin Peters foul on Terry Cooper brought a Leeds free kick on the left, yards outside the Spurs penalty area. The Spurs defence's lack of concentration and organization allowed Jack Charlton to rise unchallenged in the area and thrust a net-rippling header past Pat Jennings. It was the winner, 2–1 to Leeds, in what had been a captivating end-to-end match.

The draw for the semi paired Leeds with Birmingham City, managed by former Peacocks defender Freddie Goodwin. Arsenal would play Stoke in the other. The Leeds–Birmingham tie was scheduled for Sheffield Wednesday's Hillsborough Stadium while Stoke and Arsenal were to meet at Aston Villa's ground.

### 12–2

### The Football Honours 1970–71

**Division One winners**: Arsenal. Runners up: Leeds.
**FA Cup winners**: Arsenal. Runners up: Liverpool.
**League Cup winners**: Spurs. Runners up: Aston Villa.
**European Cup winners**: Ajax. Runners up: Panithinaikos.
**European Cup Winners' Cup winners**: Chelsea. Runners up: Real Madrid.
**Inter-Cities Fairs Cup winners**: LEEDS. Runners up: Juventus.
**Football Player of the Year**: Frank McLintock, Arsenal.
**European Footballer of the Year**: Johan Cruyff, Ajax.
**Crowd average, home games**: 38,922.

Not the best reading, true, but a few years back I'd have given my right arm for it. At least we won *something*.

By April 1972, we'd sold Terry Hibbitt and Rod Belfitt. I think they wanted more first team action elsewhere. Hibbitt went to Newcastle for just £30,000, which was a snip, while Belfitt went to Ipswich for £80,000.

There were three League games to play before the April 15 FA Cup semi-final against Birmingham, plus two more within the week after it. No rest for the wicked. First up was Derby away. I saw the highlights on *Match of the Day*. There weren't many. Derby made fools of us, beating us 2–0, their second goal an embarrassing fluke.

Top of League Division One table, April 2 1972:

| 1 | Derby County | Played 36, | Points 51 |
| 2 | Man City | Played 36, | Points 50 |
| 3 | Leeds United | Played 36, | Points 49 |
| 4 | Liverpool | Played 36, | Points 46 |

The Wednesday after we were back on track with a home 3–1 win over Huddersfield Town (Jones, Lorimer, Gray). There were over 46,000 there for that one, I was impressed, though it probably had a lot to do with Derby losing on the Monday to Newcastle, 1–0, putting us back in with a chance of the title. On the Saturday we gave Stoke a bit of a seeing to with a 3–0 win at their place (Jones two, Lorimer), a great way to warm up for the FA Cup, except it was ruined by Terry Cooper breaking his leg whilst Nigel Davey broke his the same day, in a reserves match against West Brom. Sick luck is that, sick.

Hillsborough, April 15 1972, FA Cup semi-final. Possibly for the first time ever Leeds wore all yellow, complete with their Trevillion-inspired blue sock tags, while Birmingham wore red shirts (with a wide white stripe down the front), white shorts and red socks. Before kick off, City copied our pre-match routine of warm-ups on the pitch, presumably in an attempt to wind up the Leeds camp. Ces said it was the only thing City got right all day. But they started the match quite well and got the first shot in, even if it was tame. It woke Leeds up – we started to take control from then on.

After about twenty minutes, John Giles ran with the ball out of our half and passed it forward to Mick Jones. Jonesy laid it off for Billy Bremner on the left-hand side who quickly and neatly switched the ball to our right flank to the overlapping Paul Reaney, a few yards from the corner flag. 'Speedy' Reaney controlled the ball, and with two defenders blocking his own chance of hitting a cross in, passed it diagonally backwards and inside to Peter Lorimer on the edge of the penalty area. Lorimer lashed in a pinpoint cross for Allan Clarke at the back post. 'Sniffer' Clarke nodded the ball across and in front of City's goal to the oncoming Mick Jones to firmly plant an easy header past the keeper, who had no chance. It was clinical, like a technical blueprint drawing put into motion.

1–0 to Leeds, and I knew then, one hundred percent, that we were on our way to Wembley again. We scored another in the first half, a well-taken goal from Lorimer himself, feeding on a brilliant long ball from Eddie Gray, and we got a third goal in the second, from Mick Jones again after Gilesy had beaten three defenders to the ball and somehow got a perfect little cross in. The entire Leeds team played well, really well, but I think Jones gave Birmingham the most trouble, they just couldn't handle him.

I watched from the seats with the employees' coach load, but seeing how bloody mad and brilliant it was in the Leeds end behind the goal when we first scored I wished I'd been in with the standing fans, even at the risk of getting shoved and knocked about to kingdom come. I got well and truly tanked up in the Peacock that night but four days later we all crashed back down to earth when mid-table Newcastle beat us 1–0 in the League at their place. No excuses, we were a team supposedly chasing the double so it was a game we should have won. Newcastle had nothing to play for even though they had beaten Derby not long before, and they were vying for the title as well. We played West Brom three days later and grabbed a 1–0 win there, thanks to a John Giles penalty, but I couldn't help thinking we'd already blown our chances by losing to the Geordies.

## 12–3

Although *Observer* journalist Tony Parson likened a Leeds United without Terry Cooper to gin without tonic, the Whites were able to replace him with another fine international in Paul Madeley. Despite declining the opportunity to join Alf Ramsey's 1970 Mexico World Cup squad (in place of Paul Reaney) Madeley had finally gained his first England cap in 1971, at right-back, while Terry Cooper had played on the left. Notwithstanding, there were other fitness worries for the Leeds squad ahead of the 1972 FA Cup final. John Giles was the main concern, troubled by a groin injury, while Allan Clarke, Paul Madeley and Paul Reaney had all picked up knocks in the 2–0 win over Chelsea the previous week, while Eddie Gray would not be fully fit for the game. In the days before the final, Revie banned even the playing of golf, as a precautionary measure. All the Leeds players were forced to rest and put nothing at risk.

In the 1972 European Championships qualification stages, England were paired with West Germany, the victors going through to the June finals in Belgium. The two legs were to be played on April 29 (Wembley) and May 13 (Berlin). Consequently, the domestic League schedule was altered so as to accommodate international call-ups. Most First Division clubs were affected by this, but especially Leeds, as they were the FA Cup finalists and serious contenders for the Division One title. The fixture shuffling meant that Leeds would have to play the FA Cup final against Arsenal on Saturday May 6 and then finish the Division One campaign just two days later, on Monday May 8. Leeds' two most important games of the entire campaign, and the destiny of English football's two most prominent competitions, were to be decided within less than three days of each other.

With respect to who would keep goal for Leeds in the final, Don Revie was faced with one of the greatest dilemmas of his career. Both keepers were fully fit, so who to choose, David Harvey or Gary Sprake? On the Thursday, two days before the final, Revie took David Harvey to one side to tell him that he would be playing in the match. The rest of the Leeds players were told on the Friday.

When asked how Sprake had reacted to the bad news, Revie said, 'Gary accepted it. It is all part of the family spirit at this club.' But Sprake was stunned at the rejection, he had never been left out before by his manager, especially for such a prestigious match. He did not take the exclusion at all well.

The Centenary FA Cup Final between Arsenal and Leeds took place on Saturday May 6 1972. It was the competition's hundredth year but only the ninety-first actual final due to cancelled competitions during the wars.

In the Leeds changing room prior to the three o'clock kick off, Revie spoke to his players passionately and forcefully. He told them, in no uncertain terms, not to let themselves down, to be honest and to play to the best of their abilities. They were the best team around and, providing they followed their instructions, they would be taking the trophy back to Leeds.

12–4

Last time I'd been at Wembley, four years earlier, it was Leeds versus Arsenal too. Today, the pitch was in beautiful condition and the weather had been alright, with a bit of damp in the air making it a bit slippy but nothing serious. I'm sure there was scrapping and trouble between us and Gunners fans somewhere, but I never saw any, walking up Wembley Way in the massive throng of thousands and thousands of fans, of both sides. It was a great atmosphere – lively, loud, good humoured – people mixed without any bother, singing and clapping and chanting and waving their banners and flags about. There was some piss-taking and taunting but it had all been friendly enough. It's truly uplifting, walking up that road towards the Wembley twin towers with countless fellow fans, marching on together, ready to give as much as you can to help your team win the best trophy going.

I watched the whole game completely sober. Not a drop of alcohol had touched my lips. I wanted to stay clear headed so as to soak in the whole occasion and the sights and sounds and the band and centenary celebrations and, most importantly, all the match in detail. The tactics and strategies and moves and runs, the individual battles as well as the obvious eleven-versus-eleven game. I remember the goal because I had a really good view of it, and I'll never forget how brilliantly the Cup shines as it's held aloft. But

221

afterwards most of the actual match stayed as a blur, no matter how much I tried to remember it. I might as well have got tanked up before the game, seeing as I forgot so much so easily. A few weeks later I even bought the LP of the match commentary. I've still got it somewhere.

You can hardly hear yourself think when the teams walk out from the tunnel on to the pitch. Cheers, chants, whistles, songs, horns blowing. The Leeds twelve looked bloody great in their white socks and blue tags, white shorts and white tracksuit jackets with the blue collars and trim and LUFC in old-style script writing on the chest, plus the player's name on the back in blue. What I'd have given to be out there with them, with one of those jackets with my name on it.

The Don leads Leeds out, Bertie Mee his Arsenal, both smartly dressed in nice suits. Don's is dark blue, surprise surprise, it'll be a new 'lucky' one no doubt, specially made.

1 David Harvey, 2 Paul Reaney, 3 Paul Madeley, 4 Billy Bremner, 5 Jack Charlton, 6 Norman Hunter, 7 Peter Lorimer, 8 Allan Clarke, 9 Mick Jones, 10 Johnny Giles, 11 Eddie Gray, 12 Mick Bates.

1 Geoff Barnett, 2 Pat Rice, 3 Bob McNab, 4 Peter Storey, 5 Frank McLintock, 6 Peter Simpson, 7 George Armstrong, 8 Alan Ball, 9 Charlie George, 10 John Radford, 11 George Graham, 12 Ray Kennedy.

The Scottish lads on both teams seemed to get on well with each other, smiling, sharing laughs, whereas none of the other players seemed to be talking much at all. Clarke and Giles had passed fitness tests that morning, while Arsenal's regular goalie Bob Wilson was out injured with a cartilage injury, so Geoff Barnett was playing. I'd no idea what he was like as a keeper, but he had more hair than Wilson.

'Leeds! Leeds! Leeds! Leeds! Leeds! Leeds! Leeds!'

I didn't give a damn where I was in the stadium or who was around us. The louder the better, the louder the prouder.

'Oh when the Whites, go marching in, Oh when the Whites go marching in, I wanna be in that number, Oh when the Whites go marching in!'

'David, David Harvey, tra la la la la, la la la laa.'

'Oh Eddie Eddie, Eddie Eddie Eddie Eddie Eddie Gray!'

'Super Jack! Super Jack!'

'Billy, Billy Bremner, Billy Bremner is our king.'

The Cup final referee is David Smith. He's being paid fifteen guineas for his afternoon's work. Captains Frank McClintock and Billy Bremner share friendly chat and jokes with the ref in the centre circle before the coin toss. I'm not sure who wins the toss but the teams keep the same ends and Arsenal kick off. And away we go, the Centenary FA Cup final 1972, Leeds United versus Arsenal.

Within five seconds there's a foul, by Allan Clarke on Alan Ball. Norman Hunter always said that the first one's a 'freebie' but this was more an accident than anything else, I reckon. Clarke's foul is a trivial one but it sparks worries that the game's going to be another war rather than an entertaining final. And less than two minutes later Bob McNab chops Peter Lorimer down near the halfway line. That *is* a nasty challenge; McNab missed the ball completely, but gave Lorimer a right crack close to his right ankle. McNab gets booked for it. Fortunately, the match turns out to be just a fast-paced and keenly fought game between two well-matched teams. Confrontations occur all through the match but there's little malice involved at any stage.

Eddie Gray has so far been well shackled by Arsenal, or fouled as a last-ditch effort to stop him when he's had the ball. It's clear that the Gunners are scared of him, though he hasn't had much chance so far to dance. Allan Clarke has been marked tightly too but he looks super fit and is striving very hard to get the better of their very good defence. In midfield, Ball has been much more involved than Billy and Johnny Giles and has tackled Eddie Gray a few times already, though there hasn't been much threat from Ball attacking-wise. For us, Peter Lorimer has never stopped and looks dangerous on the right wing: Bob McNab has a hard afternoon in front of him, especially after being booked so early on.

In defence, Norman Hunter has so far had the better of John Radford while Jack Charlton has beaten Charlie George to every single thing coming their way, by land or air. To be fair to the Arsenal strikers, they haven't been fed one decent pass yet, while Clarkey and Jonesy are always prowling and marauding in attack, like they're big cats hunting. Except Frank McLintock looks pretty unbeatable, I have to say, and Simpson is no slouch alongside him. McLintock reminds me of Bobby Moore, strangely enough.

Twenty minutes or so in, Charlie George gets the ball in our half and quickly passes it. Then Norman sort of runs into him and concedes a free kick, fifteen yards outside the Leeds penalty area. Alan Ball and Charlie George stand over the ball, preparing, or pretending to prepare, to take the kick, discussing quietly their plan. But McLintock is jogging up into the fray and so Ball passes the ball short and square to him. McLintock shoots and connects well, his shot arrows in waist-high through a crowd of players, curving at the last instant as it's about to hit the target. The swerve deceives David Harvey in nets and he moves wrongly to his right, then suddenly corrects himself to dive forward and slightly left to grab the ball. It's a good shot and an even better save, which Harvey does well to keep hold of and not fumble.

By the twenty-fifth minute, Frank McLintock has beaten Clarke to the ball again and Norman has done the same with Charlie George as well. I've noticed that McLintock likes to support the Arsenal attack, on the wing at times, while for us Eddie Gray and Peter Lorimer switch flanks quite regularly. And we're on the attack again – it's a proper end-to-end match is this – Paul Madeley at full-back strides forward and links up well with Billy on the left wing. Madeley dashes to the by-line and manages to get a low but weakly hit cross into the area past Arsenal's defenders. It rolls gently across the area in front of goal but there are no Leeds players close enough to take advantage of the opportunity, so it goes begging and Arsenal clear their lines.

Half an hour's gone and, bar a couple of good touches, John Giles is not having a good game at all, he's hardly been at the races and I'm worried big time. He looks tired and is possibly limping while any passes he makes seem to be hard work. And he's given the ball away more than any other Leeds player. Normally you can count the number of mistakes Giles makes in a month of games on one hand – today he's already lost possession two or three times. He might be injured, no he *is* injured. Mick Bates should be brought on to give him a rest. There's Monday night's game to think of as well after all.

I've noticed other things too, like the fact that the Arsenal full-backs Pat Rice and Bob McNab especially like to go to ground quickly, diving in to slide-tackle or nip Leeds players' ankles from behind. Right from my school days, Mr Hatfield always said the best defenders stay on their feet as much as possible – diving in often gives the attacker the crucial, split-second advantage. Our defenders were a great example of how to defend the best way, and it's the same with Bobby Moore and even Frank McLintock. There's such thing in football as being *too* eager and I think today the Arsenal full-backs are being exactly that.

Our back five have hardly done a thing wrong in this half, and Paul M has supported the attack even more than Paul R. Madeley looks so composed, so quick and strong, I wouldn't be surprised if he got a goal, even from left-back. The midfields have just about cancelled each other out, though Ball seems to have got more tackles in and made more ground than anyone.

Mick Jones has been quiet until just after the half-hour mark when Lorimer puts in a good cross, which Jonah jumps marginally too soon for. He wins it in the air but heads it well over the crossbar. Soon after it's back up at our end – Jack, running towards his own goal but under pressure from Charlie George, concedes a corner kick. The kick is lofted in and I have to admit it's a pearler, a pinpoint pass to Alan Ball waiting on the edge of the area. He volleys it, clean as a whistle, low and on target. It's the best effort of the game so far but, luckily for us, Paul Reaney is on the goal-line and manages to stretch out his right boot and just manage to clear the ball away.

Right back down to the other end of the pitch and we're on the attack now. The more tired players get, the more open the play is, and the more scoring opportunities occur. Tiredness is even more likely when it's a hot day, like today, even though it's rained and is still cloudy.

Allan Clarke has run from near the half-way line with the ball. He reaches the edge of the area and a breakthrough looks possible, even with three Arsenal defenders trying to stop him. Finally he's half tackled and the ball rolls to Mick Jones, who swings his left foot at it. It's not the best of connections but he has hit a good, grass-cutting shot towards goal, which beats Barnett but unfortunately beats the goal as well, skimming the outside of Barnett's left hand post, and goes out for a goal-kick.

A few seconds later, near the half-way line, Norman Hunter is booked for a high and late tackle on Alan Ball, who needs treatment from the physio. Norman has probably committed the most fouls so far in the match, but that was nowhere near as malicious as Bob McNab's on Lorimer in the second minute.

We get a free kick eight yards outside the Arsenal penalty area after Allan Clarke is fouled. Leeds fans shout 'Lorimer, Lorimer!' and the BBC's David Coleman mentions that he has reputedly the hardest shot in football, measured at over seventy miles per hour, but it's John Giles who's standing over the football, 'Lash' is a few feet away. Arsenal form a wall to try and block any Leeds shot and Coleman comments that there is 'some pushing'. Tempers are definitely getting frayed – specifically Arsenal striker Charlie George's – but it's not *pushing* going on in the wall exactly, it's Charlie George trying to get at Allan Clarke, who has just regressed briefly to his playground days, reaching round his back to sneakily yank George's long hair.

John Giles wastes the free kick, weakly skewing the ball as he tries to lay it off square. He definitely isn't the fantastic architect and schemer we know and love today, his pencil's blunt and he's not having a good one. The kick is easy meat for Arsenal, with a defender rushing out from the wall to intercept the pass, but somehow the ball goes loose again and bounces to Lorimer a yard or two away. He sends a fizzing snapshot in on goal, which bounces awkwardly in front of Barnett, who's very nearly caught unawares, but he parries it out, just, for a Leeds corner kick.

'Leeds! Leeds! Leeds! Leeds!' But the corner amounts to nothing. Soon after, there's another Leeds attack after Bob McNab slices a clearance straight up into the air. With Lorimer's amazing volleying skills, even though the ball is nearer the corner flag than it is the goal, Arsenal have suddenly got problems. From a tight angle he whacks the ball in the direction of the goal and six-yard box. Typically, Allan Clarke has sniffed a chance and is waiting to pounce, but the ball dips at the last second. He twists his body and sort of crouches to get his head to it. Not a powerful header, but strong enough to be on target and beat Geoff Barnett and … brush the crossbar and land safely for Arsenal.

It's half-time. The Don rushes down the side of the pitch to get back to the tunnel and the dressing room. I'm thinking maybe he's spotted an Arsenal weakness that he needs to explain to the lads urgently. It's been very tight, keenly contested, and whilst Leeds have had marginally the better of the chances, Arsenal have possibly had more possession and their central midfield has had a better time of it than ours. The defences have both done really well, with McLintock their best and big Jack well on top for us. There were even chants of 'Charlton for England' late on. You'd never think he was thirty-seven, he looks as fit as anyone, and better.

Second half, the teams switch ends, and it's our turn to kick off. Nothing much has changed as far as I can tell – no substitutions or tactical changes, it's very much 'as you were'.

Billy Bremner was about to commence an attacking run with the ball but Charlie George clumsily brought him down. Billy sprang up off the deck ready to have a tangle but then realized it hadn't been a deliberate foul (George being near enough half a foot taller might have had something to do with it as well). Making friends, Billy puts his arm round Charlie with the referee warning the Gunner that no more fouls will be accepted. Billy's trying to help Charlie keep out of trouble, but there's no point, the big long-haired lug isn't listening and is arguing with the referee instead. So the ref books him.

Arsenal are playing well – they're strong and fit and capable of beating most teams, but what they lack in particular I reckon, compared to us at least, is pace and flair on the wings. We've got Eddie Gray and Peter Lorimer, though it has to be said that Arsenal's defenders have contained them pretty well so far.

There's about fifty minutes gone and it's all so even, difficult to pick a winner. Left-back Bob McNab got forward well and ended up getting on the end of a cross in our penalty area, but he wasted a good move, heading into the side-netting. He should have nodded square to near the penalty spot where their strikers would have had a good chance of scoring. It's a let off for us, no denying it, though I'm still confident we'll win.

Around the fiftieth minute mark, Allan Clarke loses out to Frank McLintock in their half again, getting his foot to the ball and prodding it clear before Clarke can control and shield it. The ball runs to Alan Ball in the centre circle, inches from the half-way line. He scurries forward twenty yards and then taps the ball to Charlie George. Ball carries on running, expecting a one–two return from George, but it doesn't arrive – Jack Charlton has easily dispossessed George and he casually taps the ball into the stride of

227

Paul Madeley a few feet away on our left side, still in our half of the pitch. Madeley runs diagonally with the ball, his graceful pace taking him over ten yards in no time before he strokes a fifteen-yard pass with the outside of his right boot to Peter Lorimer in the centre circle. There's no one near him so he has time to suss out his options and who to pass to. He canters with the ball for ten yards and decides to knock it with the outside of his right boot and again diagonally, to Mick Jones midway in the Arsenal half on the right flank.

Jones seems to idle and dawdle with the ball at his feet, making very little progress as Bob McNab blocks his way, waiting to win the ball off him with another biting tackle. But really, Jones is testing him, gauging the situation, seeing what McNab will do, seeing if he can catch him off guard. He'd do well to catch McNab off guard normally, but Jones suddenly bursts into rapid action, running with the ball and controlling it with his right foot, into the penalty area. McNab is no slowcoach and can match Jones for pace. But he makes a mistake. Instead of staying on his feet and keeping up with Jones' run, he decides to try and win the ball outright with an attempted slide tackle. He doesn't connect enough with the ball though, only scuffing it and nudging it just a few inches. The football remains in Jones' stride. And even though McNab springs back up from the floor to just about catch up with Jones, we have the advantage. *And* the ball bounces just nicely for Jones as it nears the dead ball line. McNab gets another stretching, sliding last-ditch challenge in but it's too late, Mick Jones has already hit a dangerous cross in towards the Arsenal penalty spot. He was quite fortunate that the bounce went in his favour, and McNab told him so, in no uncertain terms. Well, bollocks to Bob McNab is what I say, he should have stayed on his feet.

Two defenders rush out hoping to block whatever attempt on goal the onrushing Clarke makes. 'Sniffer' Clarke, probably the best all-round striker in English football if you ask me, seeing the ball drop more sharply than expected, decides to head rather than kick it. And he throws himself at it, slamming a brilliant bullet header into Barnett's left side of the net. The keeper got nowhere near it, I doubt any one could have got near it, it's a bloody superb finish. Clarke, 1–0! Allan Clarke, 1–0!

For a few seconds it's almost deafening, dizzying pandemonium where we are and wherever I look, with Leeds fans shouting, jumping about, swaying, hugging, falling, getting back up again (even in the seated bits), waving their, our, colours in celebration.

Blue, yellow, white. White, blue, yellow. Yellow, white, blue. Everywhere I look.

'We shall not, we shall not be moved, it's like a team that's gonna win the FA Cup ... and we shall not be moved!'

'Oh when the Whites, go marching in ... oh when the Whites go marching in, I wanna be in that number, oh when the Whites go marching in!'

'Super Leeds! Super Leeds! Super Leeds!'

I didn't see how many of our white shirts ran to congratulate and celebrate with arms-aloft Allan Clarke but it might have been all of them. I'm pretty sure the green shirt of David Harvey stayed put in his goal, but you never know ...

And then we supporters get involved again, we get in on the action, hoping to help the Leeds players, hoping to keep them focused and intent on keeping a clean sheet. Do that and we've won the FA Cup for the first time ever. Up and out it comes, from the throats and mouths of countless supporters, stronger, deeper, louder, harder than possibly ever before – 'Leeds! Leeds! Leeds! Leeds! Leeds!' on and on, pumping, pulsing, almost like it's a repeated war cry, a savage, spine-tingling, exhilarating war cry. All the while the Arsenal supporters stay completely still and, I would guess, completely silent too.

Things are calming down now; there's still ages to go in the match. I don't even see the ball returned to the centre-circle or Arsenal kick off the game again. There's no stopping Leeds fans singing now, and the longer we sing, the stronger the chance our hopes will become reality.

'And you'll never walk alone ...'

'Super Leeds! Super Leeds! Super Leeds! Super Leeds!'

Peter Lorimer's been fouled. We have a free kick in a threatening position. The free kick amounts to nothing and play moves on. Near the touchline on our right wing, Alan Ball is frustrated at not being able to prize possession from Leeds. He hacks Billy Bremner from behind, giving Billy's left leg one hefty crack. Billy hits the deck and is definitely hurt, though he may well be playing for time too, in order to have a little breather. Ball has walked away but rushes back and tries to drag Bremner to his feet. He's letting his frustration get the better of him and he could be in trouble with the referee if he doesn't watch out. Billy notices that Ball is more than likely going to get a booking so he gets to his feet, grabs and shakes Ball's hand, hoping to dissuade the referee from booking Ball. It works and Ball is a lucky fella.

And then someone shouts from the sidelines 'Let's keep sanity!' and it doesn't half sound like The Don's voice to me.

Mick Jones gets barged down between two Arsenal defenders on the edge of their area. It's not serious but it looks like he's took a knock to the head, so Les Cocker gives him some treatment on the pitch with water and a sponge. Jonah's okay, he's a true footballing warrior and used to all the knocks. He'll need to be. He walks into the penalty area, awaiting the free kick. Allan Clarke takes it, squaring the ball to Peter Lorimer who, not surprisingly, gives it a mighty whack. It flies in towards goal, three, four foot off the ground to smack a player instead of the goal net. A Leeds player in fact, and it's one Mick Jones! Fortunately it hasn't whacked his family jewels but a few inches higher, in his rib cage, so he's okay.

Alan Ball and George Graham are still working hard in midfield but rather than making real progress they're more just cancelling out Billy Bremner and Johnny Giles. I'm sure Giles could do with a rest and be substituted by Mick Bates, he still doesn't look right.

A few yards outside the left corner of our penalty area, Ball passes to Peter Simpson, who evades a Bremner challenge and gives the ball to George Graham. He quickly switches it back to Ball again who takes a couple of scampering steps before hitting a right-foot shot, low and hard. It's going wide though, until, that is, it takes a deflection and angles gently on the grass to Charlie George. He never needs to think twice about taking a pot shot on goal. Swivelling, he hits a great shot on the turn with his right foot, which beats David Harvey in goal easily, only for it to thud against the crossbar. The rebound lands to Simpson but it's bouncing too high and too quickly and as soon as he's hit it he knows straight away that he's fluffed it, skying it over Harvey's bar. It was only a half chance in truth, but still, it was a chance.

George's shot could be Arsenal's last serious effort on Leeds' goal. They're pushing forward a lot and hitting a load of crosses in but big Jack seems to win every single one of them, it's blooming great. And while the Gunners attack, they leave gaps behind them, meaning that we have more chances to exploit the space. We had a three-on-two situation but Clarke cocked it up by slicing a left-foot shot high and wide, and then Eddie Gray brought a good tip-over save from Barnett a few seconds later.

Ray Kennedy replaces John Radford but there's no sign of The Don making a substitution for us. I don't like it, John Giles is almost anonymous by now, through no fault of his own: fresh legs wouldn't do us any harm especially when it's a class player like Mick Bates we're talking about.

In the eighty-second minute Eddie is put clear through on goal after a clever little pass from Peter Lorimer. Eddie could pass it to Clarke on his left who's free but instead he shoots at goal and it's weak as soapy water and straight at Geoff Barnett. In the eighty-fifth minute Lorimer shoots from the corner of the area and hits the outside of their post. It was probably never going in, but still, while the ball's at Arsenal's end of the pitch it means they can't equalize.

The ninetieth-minute mark arrives and there can't be much to add on either. Norman Hunter intercepts a sloppy Simpson pass midway in our half and reaches Johnny Giles. He returns it to Norman, who jabs a pass out to Mick Jones on the right wing again, not far away from the Arsenal area. He only needs to keep possession of the ball – just keep it and stop Arsenal from getting it – then the FA Cup is ours. And Jonah is aware of this, he knows the game is nearly over, he's heard the shouts from the Leeds bench, he may have even seen the electric scoreboard clock. But maybe he wants to banish any possible suggestions that Leeds United like to waste time deliberately, that they are negative and too professional, whatever that means, and that they're happy with a 1–0 victory. Or maybe he senses a chance to score a second and definitely seal the tie. And so Mick Jones races with the ball at his feet towards the corner of the Arsenal penalty area.

He eludes Frank McLintock by nudging the ball past him, and now he's through on goal just about, though wide of their left goal post. Barnett rushes out and dives towards Jones' feet, hoping to snatch the ball away from him. He succeeds, just, the momentum of his frame causing Jones to fall over him, backside first. Jones lands awkwardly, his left arm is twisted and tucked under his body weight. It's crushed as he hits the turf, yelping at the terrible pain.

Barnett shouts an insult at him, believing Jones is feigning injury. In the whole of Mick Jones' football career, and probably before it too, he has *never* feigned injury. Barnett throws the ball out to a team-mate to commence another Arsenal attack. Peter Lorimer has noticed that Jones is in a bad way, but there is nothing he can do to help.

A minute later Leeds have soaked up the weak Arsenal attack and have kept possession of the ball, in our half. And then the referee blows his whistle for full time.

Jack Charlton has his arms aloft, he's smiling big time, it's the only major domestic trophy he hasn't won before. Though Clarkey got the goal and Jones set it up brilliantly, big Jack is my man of the match, he's been near perfect. He hugs Alan Ball in a gesture of commiseration. Captain Billy Bremner, with arms bent at the elbows and fists clenched, is also delighted as he shakes hands with as many players as he can. John Giles celebrates with Mick Bates, chatting excitedly with him and sharing the moment. Mick Bates, who hasn't played and still has his tracksuit jacket on, just looks thrilled to be there, he has no qualms about not appearing in the match and looks as pleased as any of the eleven victors. Norman Hunter joins them and the three men hug. But the scene close to Arsenal's goal posts is a completely different story.

Les Cocker, with his small black Stylo Matchmakers holdall to hand, crouches by the prone, distressed Mick Jones. It's horrible to watch, even though you can't see for certain what Jonah's injury is. He's lying there in agony, his face as white as his shirt, and he's whispering to Les Cocker. I don't know what his words are but it's like he's saying his last words and breathing his last breath before he finally passes away.

More and more people are buzzing around Jonesy now – photographers, cameramen, Dr Adams, Wembley stretcher-bearers. Les Cocker barks at people to stand back and give them room and air to breathe.

On television David Coleman mentions Mick Jones could be suffering from a dislocated shoulder but he'll learn later that it's his left elbow that's been done in. Bobby Charlton is briefly interviewed by Coleman and mentions what an achievement it is for his thirty-seven-year-old brother Jack to be winning the Cup, and in such a great side.

The camera is on Jack again, still walking around the pitch, taking it all in, absorbing the occasion, unable to stop himself grinning proudly. But then he is informed by a press photographer that something serious is afoot with Mick Jones, so he runs back across the even more crowded pitch towards the Arsenal goal to find out what's going on. He gets there and, realizing it's a nasty injury, he kneels down to comfort Jones while Les Cocker tries bandaging and securing Mick's left arm down to his side.

Clad in a dark grey pin-striped suit, our Dr Adams is helping out. And Don Revie is there now too. The Doc and Les want to take Mick Jones for treatment straight away but Mick Jones, even though he's in excruciating pain, is adamant he wants to get his medal and meet the Queen. The Don asks Mick how he's feeling, again. Revie knows how important the FA Cup final is to a player, any player, and so gives Jones his permission.

The new FA Cup winners begin to climb the steps to collect their prizes. Bremner reaches the top of the steps to where the trophy and medals presentation takes place, where the FA Cup stands on its ledge, directly beneath Queen Elizabeth and the other guests. Billy, quite like Bobby Moore in 1966, wipes his right hand on his shirt to rid it of sweat and grime, to make himself presentable for the monarch. Immediately behind him is Jack Charlton, eager to meet the VIPs, anxious to smarten his straggly, thinning hair.

Her Majesty and Our Captain shake hands and she warmly congratulates him. Ted Heath and Jack Charlton act like good old friends and Billy, with the dark blue 4 on his back to the watching world, takes a few seconds to compose himself and make sure too that everything is in order. And then, grasping the two solid handles swathed in pure white silk ribbons, he turns around and lifts the beautiful trophy high in the air, as it glints and dazzles and captivates, to declare to the world – and, amidst a mighty roar from the stadium crowd, most importantly to the supporters of his team – that Leeds United are the 1972 FA Cup winners, in its hundredth year.

There is probably no need, but David Coleman guides the television audience through the Leeds players as they each are presented with their small boxed awards. 'Jack Charlton receives the Winner's medal and also the plinth. Johnny Giles, the architect of so much of the Leeds play. Paul Reaney, who missed the final

two years ago, who kicked off the line today. Paul Madeley ...
Norman Hunter ... Eddie Gray ... David Harvey, who showed
Don Revie to be right in picking him. Peter Lorimer and Allan
Clarke the goal scorer, and finally the substitute Mick Bates.'

Bates has the longest audience with the Queen as she asks him
about Mick Jones' condition whilst handing over two medals.
Over on the pitch, Mick Jones walks with Dr Adams in front of the
goal posts with photographers buzzing all over, rushing in front
and around them, turning towards them, walking backwards and
trying to get good shots. Meanwhile, the Arsenal team collect their
Losers' medals from the Queen. A few seconds later the referee
and his linesmen collect their own individual awards, too. Below
them, at ground level, Dr Adams and Mick Jones now stand
waiting, not entirely sure of what to do or what they are *allowed* to
do. Mick Bates joins them.

Dr Adams desperately does not want to accompany Mick Jones
up those steps, he insists he has not contributed to Cup Final day
and has not earned the privilege of meeting royalty. Eventually,
Norman Hunter rushes up in response to Adams' urgent appeals
for one of the Leeds players to help Jones. Climbing the steps,
leaning over the adjacent waist-high wall, well-wishing Leeds fans
stroke Jones' head, gently pat him or applaud and cheer him. His
wife Glenis amongst them, understandably tearful and upset.

'And in fact Mick Bates has got Jones's medal by the look of it,
but Jones will go into football history here at the Centenary Final.
Being helped by Norman Hunter to go up and be officially
presented with his medal by Her Majesty the Queen.'

Mick Jones later revealed that he nearly collapsed three times in
those few minutes.

While the Leeds team minus one pose for photographs, Mick
Jones is placed on a stretcher and covered with a grey blanket.
Once he's being taken care of in the Wembley treatment room, it
will need four doctors to hold him down and re-set his elbow.

The Don stands with Billy, holding the Cup between them for
the cameras. Those Leeds-crammed Wembley terraces are a
shimmering ocean of white, blue and yellow scarves and banners,
as the players wave and salute them, while the fans shower them
with songs and cheers of adulation.

There wasn't to be a great deal of time for celebration, though, as Monday was to decide the Championship, at Wolves. We only needed a draw to win the Double, but Liverpool were in the running for the title still and were to play Arsenal on Monday too.

| 1 | Derby | Played 42, | Points 58 |
| 2 | Leeds | Played 41, | Points 57 |
| 3 | Man City | Played 42, | Points 57 |
| 4 | Liverpool | Played 41, | Points 56 |

Like I said, we only needed a draw. We had a better goal average than Derby and Liverpool needed to win by a good margin, as long as we lost. The media reckoned it would be straightforward for Leeds not only to draw but to get a win and the two points, even so close to a knackering Cup final two days prior. I wasn't so sure: the Leeds players were very tired. Wolves' weren't. Obviously, Mick Jones was out, while Allan Clarke and Paul Madeley needed painkilling injections to play and Eddie Gray had his thigh problem again. His leg had to be strapped up from knee to groin. Also, Wolves were widely expected to lose, which was pretty good motivation on its own for them to do the opposite. And they were tenth place before the match – if they didn't lose they would leapfrog Sheffield United and go up a place. Leeds might have been unbeaten at Elland Road, but they'd lost eight out of twenty away League games already. In total we'd scored seventy-two goals, but only eighteen of them were away from home. There were mad, bad rumours about Wolves players being bribed by Leeds representatives too. What a load of shit. We'd heard similar in the sixties as well, and if I remember rightly, we never won a match that we'd been accused of trying to rig. Funny, that.

On the morning of the match, Wolves manager Bill McGarry got his squad together on the Molineux pitch. He spoke to his players about rumours of possible bribery attempts, warning them that they must play to beat Leeds, play till they dropped and play as if their Wolverhampton futures depended on it. Anyone not giving their all for Wolverhampton could leave the club, simple as that. The integrity of the club and its good name rested on the perfor-

235

mance – they could be ruined if it was suspected that bribes took place involving any Wolves players.

Yes, I was biased, but honestly and truly, I just couldn't believe for one second that anyone from Leeds tried to fix that match before or during it. And anyway, if Leeds really had ever tried to fix matches and bribe players then they were seriously shit at it.

Mick Bates replaced Mick Jones, slotting into central midfield, while Billy moved up into the attack alongside Allan Clarke. Terry Yorath was named as substitute.

'I thought we should have had three clear penalties. It was definitely handball twice. It's just too much. When you get decisions like that going against you, what can you do? But I was proud of the team even in defeat. I don't know where they got the energy from in the second half.'

Wolves played well, really well, especially their keeper Parkes, but even most of the media seemed in agreement with the Don that Leeds had been badly done to.

Liverpool, who could only draw 0–0 at Arsenal, must have been kicking themselves. The title had been waiting for them, but Derby somehow managed to win it.

I wouldn't have minded staying in to watch *Star Trek* but I had to work, to help set up and then clear up afterwards. They were expecting a busy night. The plan was that there was a civic reception in town for the players and then they'd ride on an open-top bus back to Elland Road to parade the FA Cup around the pitch to all the fans. The Queens Hotel in Leeds City Square was the focal point again. The bus would start there, then go along Wellington Street, Gelderd Road, Lowfields Lane and Road and then on to Elland Road and into the West Stand car park.

The next day the procession and all the celebrations were in the *Yorkshire Post* and made it to *Look North* on BBC and *Calendar* on Yorkshire TV. None of them mentioned the trouble. Nothing much happened to spoil the party in City Square. Okay, some supporters got a bit boisterous, climbing on bus shelters and up the various nearby statues, but none of them meant harm, they just wanted to get a better view. As far as I know, all the trouble occurred in and around the stadium.

On the bus top deck, Jack Charlton's smoking and he doesn't care who sees, the players hang over the sides waving, smiling, catching scarves and hats that fans throw to them. Poor Terry Cooper's at the back, seated, looking left out a bit, as ashen faced as Jonesy had on Saturday. Jonesy's there too, looking quite relaxed, with his left arm in a white sling. There were 1,500 fans in City Square, the reports said, and 35,000 at Elland Road. God knows how many more had stood on the pavements to cheer the bus home into Beeston.

I have never understood some Leeds fans. Why the hell they wanted to cause trouble tonight of all nights was beyond me. On normal match days *you would not believe* the number of empty wallets and purses we have to fish out of the Elland Road toilets – both the Gents' and the Ladies'. But pickpockets are one thing, fighting and vandalism at your own stadium is just stupid, if you ask me.

The radio announcer was cranking up the atmosphere as the team and their prize approached, the supporters were getting more excited, singing songs non-stop, and seeming to name every player who'd played in The Don's Leeds teams. And then they entered the arena, on the cinder track surrounding the pitch, with Terry Cooper in a wheelchair, God bless him.

'Here they are, ladies and gentlemen, the one and only 1972 and centenary year FA Cup winners – super Leeds United!' The roar and the applause from the supporters all over the ground shook the rafters and nearly raised the roof, I swear, even though it wasn't a capacity crowd. Trouble was, some of the fans got a bit too excited and decided to join the players. The *Evening Post* said about a thousand had tried to get on the pitch as the players paraded the Cup. I don't think it was that many, but who knows? They were warned to get off the pitch or Don Revie would take the team and the Cup off. The threat worked for a while, but some obviously thought they had a right to get closer to their Leeds heroes than the rest of us. There were shop and office windows all around Elland Road that were broken that night, including offices within the stadium. It was barmy, and it caused a lot more unnecessary sodding work for us overworked and underpaid ground staff and casuals.

# Chapter 13

## 13–1

1974, in the Queens Hotel, Eamonn Andrews continues to address the audience, telling them of the prizes won by the 'Super Leeds' team during the thirteen years so far of Don Revie's management ... 'the Football League and Fairs Cup, the League title and FA Cup in 1972 ...' Footage of Allan Clarke's winning goal and then the Queen presenting the trophy, with commentator Brian Moore announcing '...and the Cup goes to Billy Bremner and Leeds United,' is played, to great cheers from the guests.

Although Don Revie smiles proudly, it is clear he prefers for his players, his boys, to receive the praise and credit. The television camera focuses on Billy Bremner, sitting in the audience with his Leeds team-mates and coaches, all suitably attired for the occasion. And Bremner gets up from his chair, mistakenly thinking it's his cue to go on stage. Realizing his error, he sits back down, embarrassed. Next to him, Peter Lorimer smiles at the gaffe from the notoriously forgetful team captain.

July 1972. Player details.

**Gary Sprake**, born April 1945, now aged 27 – unhappy at missing Cup final.

**David Harvey**, born February 1948, aged 24.

**Paul Reaney**, born December 1944, aged 27.

**Terry Cooper**, born July 1944, aged 28 – out injured with broken leg.

**Nigel Davey**, born June 1946, aged 26 – also out with a broken leg.

**Jack Charlton**, born May 1935, aged 37 – looking to be a manager.

**John Faulkner**, born March 1948, aged 24 – has struggled with injuries.

**Norman Hunter**, born October 1943, nearly 29.

**Paul Madeley**, born September 1944, nearly 28.

**Billy Bremner**, born December 1942, nearly 30 – a concern.

**John Giles**, born January 1940, aged 32 – the main concern.

**Mick Bates**, born September 1947, aged 25.

**Peter Lorimer**, born December 1946, nearly 26.

**Eddie Gray**, born January 1948 – nearly 24, injuries have restricted him badly.

**Allan Clarke**, born July 1946, aged 26.

**Mick Jones**, born April 1945, aged 27 – his knees aren't good, and he is presently recovering from dislocated elbow.

**Joe Jordan**, born December 1951, nearly 21.

**Terry Yorath**, born March 1950, aged 22.

**Trevor Cherry**, signed from Huddersfield £100,000 – born February 1948, age 24.

**Frank Gray**, born October 1954, aged 18. He's not Eddie but has plenty to offer.

**Roy Ellam**, bought for £35,000 with Cherry – born January 1943, aged 29.

Soon after embarking on his management career, Revie had discussed the merits of not just his Leeds squad but professional footballers in general, remarking that the best years 'are between twenty-five to twenty-eight'. By 1972, eleven years later, the matter was becoming more pertinent with every day.

Player fitness problems and weaknesses increase as the weeks and games go by, and of course age played a part too. The older the player, generally the less use to the team he was. Revie was the man blessed with the responsibility of deciding the Leeds men's futures, whether to extend or, bluntly speaking, cut short the careers of lads he had helped bring up as his own. It was a responsibility he feared, and the feeling grew as the end of certain players' contracts approached.

Leeds were expected to tear out of the traps, determined to put the record straight and passionately intent on giving their opponents a sound beating. But in the 1972–73 season, Don Revie's team seemed strangely subdued, almost unmotivated, as if their appetite existed only for the big games.

On August 12, the new season began badly for Leeds in a tough tie at Chelsea in front of over 51,000 at Stamford Bridge. The scoreline read Chelsea 4, Leeds 0 but it did not tell anywhere near the full story. To begin with, the United eleven had lined up without Norman Hunter and Allan Clarke, both suspended, plus the injured Jack Charlton and Terry Cooper, who was still hindered by the broken leg injury of April. Two new signings came in for the injured duo – Roy Ellam at centre-half for Charlton and Trevor Cherry in for left-back Cooper. Both came from Huddersfield Town. Ellam was a respected centre-half, especially good in the air, while Cherry was good with both feet, renowned for his hard tackling and versatility in defence.

Around ten minutes before the half-hour mark and the scoreline still 0–0, Leeds keeper David Harvey was knocked unconscious and Mick Jones hurt with a twisted ankle, within two minutes of each other. Both needed to be carried off. Terry Yorath came on for Jones while Peter Lorimer replaced Harvey in goal. Down to ten men, a makeshift goalkeeper in the Leeds nets, and with most of the match remaining, the result was just about a foregone conclusion. A Peter Osgood goal put Chelsea 1–0 up by half-time, and they added three more goals before the final whistle.

The upheaval endured by the team in the Chelsea match would prove strangely indicative for the whole season, with not one Leeds player ever present, and only Lorimer and Harvey playing in more than forty League games. The team would also have to make do without Terry Cooper for the entire campaign, his recovery from a broken leg was taking longer than expected and complicated by a lack of calcium in his body. Meanwhile, Jack Charlton had been offered a two-year extended contract at Leeds, but not just in a playing capacity – the club wanted him to help on the scouting and coaching side too, as well as 'spying' on future Leeds opponents. Charlton felt he still had plenty to offer the team, and so turned the offer down.

By the end of September 1972 Leeds were not even in the top six. They had played eleven games, won five, drawn one and already lost three. The defeats were at Chelsea, 2–3 at Newcastle, and 1–2 at home to Liverpool. And the victories, even though there were five of them, had not been achieved in typical Leeds fashion. Their form so far had been patchy. So far, the stop–start season, with the enforced interruptions and changes to the line-up, had spoiled any real chance of consistency.

League Division One table (top), September 30 1972:

| | | | |
|---|---|---|---|
| 1 | Liverpool | Played 11, | Points 16 |
| 2 | Arsenal | Played 12, | Points 16 |
| 3 | Everton | Played 11, | Points 15 |
| 4 | Spurs | Played 11, | Points 14 |
| 5 | Wolves | Played 11, | Points 14 |
| 6 | Chelsea | Played 11, | Points 13 |
| 7 | Leeds | Played 11, | Points 13 |

On September 17, in a *Sunday People* newspaper article, insinuations were made that several Wolverhampton players had been offered bribes to 'throw' the Championship decider of last season against Leeds. None of the players approached had accepted the offer, the article stated. Later, the then-Leeds chairman Percy Woodward (to be succeeded by Manny Cussins soon after) said that his club had nothing to do with this attempt to 'buy' the game, but there would be a full investigation anyway. Football League president Len Shipman also promised there would be an inquiry. Two days later another alleged attempted bribery case came to light, with Manchester City's Francis Lee disclosing in a newspaper article that he had been approached before one match against a team fighting relegation, and asked to help fix the result.

The same week, in response to the Wolverhampton allegations, Revie declared that he would not be quizzing his own players on the matter. 'My players have nothing to hide. There is no need for me to speak to them on this matter. The issue will be discussed at our board meeting on Thursday. We shall decide then on the possibility of taking legal action.'

Falling match attendances were a worry too, although it was a national problem and not just restricted to West Yorkshire. Smaller crowds signified smaller gate receipts, naturally the most worrying thing for football club directors and chairmen. Various voices gave various opinions on why attendances were in decline: too many games, too high prices, too little value for money, a lack of entertainment, too much hooliganism and crowd trouble, violence on the pitch, soccer on TV too much, as well as the national side's decline.

### 13–2

Another one for my bedroom wall, the Footie Honours list for 1971–72. Half decent it was too. No, half great in fact, but I was fed up of halves.

**Division One winners**: Derby. Ripped off runners up: Leeds.
**FA Cup winners**: Leeds. Runners up: Arsenal.
**League Cup winners**: Stoke. Runners up: Chelsea
**European Cup winners**: Ajax. Runners up: Inter Milan.
**European Cup Winners' Cup winners**: Rangers. Runners up: Dynamo Moscow.
**UEFA Cup winners**: Spurs. Runners up: Wolves.
**Football Player of the Year**: Gordon Banks, Stoke.
**European Footballer of the Year**: Franz Beckenbauer, Bayern Munich.
**Leeds crowd average, home games**: 35,636.

For the 1972–73 season, as well as buying Trevor Cherry and Roy Ellam from Huddersfield, there were other new or newish faces coming into the first team squad. Mick Bates would be almost a regular this season, and he fully deserved it. Terry Yorath, Joe Jordan and Eddie Gray's younger brother Frank would appear quite a lot, too. Frank was handy and had a sweet left foot on him but he wasn't anything like Eddie, they were very different sorts of player. We signed a blond beanpole Jock too, who had so much hair it made his head look outsized – Gordon McQueen, a centre-half from St Mirren, for £30,000. He was recommended by Scottish talent scout John Barr, and Les Cocker had played in the same Accrington Stanley side as McQueen's dad, who was in nets. Small world.

From what I saw of Gordon McQueen in the reserves, I thought he had the lot to replace and maybe even outdo Jack Charlton. He was quick, tough, had good ball control for such a big fella, and he looked like he'd easily beat everyone in the air. I once saw him walking up and down the corridor outside the players' changing rooms, juggling a ball. Somehow, every step he took he'd flick the ball from that foot to his other, a bit like really good pinball machine players do with that ball and the flippers. I was no chump when it came to keeping a football up, but this was wizardry, and from such a big lad as well. We were lucky to have got him, because he'd had trials at Rangers and at Liverpool, but here's where he wanted to come. Jack was preparing for his retirement, it was obvious – it was a surprise he had any time for playing soccer, what with all his sideline businesses and hobbies. He'd run that souvenir stall on Elland Road some time back, opposite the main gates, and since then he'd opened proper sports shops around Leeds, while the club itself opened a new sports and souvenirs shop early in the new season.

Jimmy Mann and Chris Galvin were on the fringe of the first team again, while young ones Billy McGhie, Gary Liddell and Peter Hampton would get a look in every now and then. I'm not sure what the score with Chris Galvin was, he looked to me like he could definitely make a go of it as a winger, especially when Eddie was struggling for fitness, but it never seemed to happen. When your ambition is to replace one of *the* Leeds stars you can't afford one slip up, ever.

In comparison to last season, certain players definitely didn't seem as up for it as before. Some team changes had to be made due to injuries and suspensions but I just didn't believe they explained why the team wasn't as lively or committed. Some of the team just didn't look that bothered any more, as if winning the FA Cup was their last hurrah sort of thing. Maybe that was it, maybe some of them were bored of winning. Or maybe Don Revie's secret worries about contracts and stuff weren't that secret after all and were somehow affecting player morale.

I sort of knew about boredom, with the St Anthony's side. There's only so far you can go until you get to thinking it's all a bit stale and humdrum, and you need new challenges. You didn't get new challenges in Sunday football, you were lucky if you got new pitch markings. And after the muscle tear in my calf, I'd put on a bloody load of weight again. I couldn't shift it, even when I was training a load of times every week. My body seemed to have accepted that my 'career' had gone as far as it could, and so it was going to enjoy itself by piling on the pounds. I still nearly always played well for a really good St Ant's team but I couldn't take it as seriously as I should have, usually having a few too many pints the nights before games as well. Most of our games were walkovers, we were that tight and well organized, and there wasn't much pressure on me. If I'd been Passy I'd have probably dropped my arse to the sub's bench, giving it a good kick (my arse, not the bench) at the same time, because it was probably all I deserved.

It took ages for Leeds to get going properly this season, and we went out quite early in the League Cup to Liverpool, plus we looked like we'd caught a cold in the European Cup Winners' Cup, even though it was our first crack at the trophy. We'd scraped through the first round against some Turkish team, Ankaragucu, 2–1 on aggregate, and then made hard work of beating Carl Zeiss Jena of Austria 2–0. Half the time the Leeds players couldn't seem to get out of first gear. And yet, in spite of all my worrying and whingeing about our less-than-great form, by the end of November we had twenty-six points from nineteen games and were second, with Liverpool top and Arsenal third. And our next League game was at Arsenal.

Elland Road crowds were slightly down compared to previous seasons, but that was supposedly happening all over Britain. The thing is, with the team not playing as well as in previous seasons, plus strikes and money worries and all that crap hitting people's pockets and peace of mind, I think the Leeds attendances – averaging well over 30,000 – proved how loyal the real and true supporters were, not how apathetic the stay-away ones were. I know The Don and the directors forever frothed at the mouth about low crowds, but when times really do get hard for normal folk, we should all be grateful there are so *many* Leeds fans turning up, not so *few*.

## 13–3

October 1972 proved to be a better month for Leeds. Since losing 2–1 at home to Liverpool at the end of September, they had won three League games and drawn one, including a 5–0 thumping of Derby and a solid 2–1 win at Everton. The month also spelt the end of one particular footballing era.

Following a car accident and the resultant loss of sight in his right eye, Stoke City and England goalkeeper Gordon Banks announced his retirement. He would stay on as a coach at the Victoria Ground but his playing days had been cruelly cut short due to the crash. *Match of the Day* showed him receiving a magnificent send off by supporters of both teams at the Liverpool versus Stoke League match. On November 2, Leeds United's unsettled goalkeeper Gary Sprake submitted a transfer request, stating a need for regular first team matches as his reason.

On December 2 1972 at Highbury, third-placed Arsenal beat the team in second position, Leeds, 2–1, in a blood and thunder game at Highbury. Two penalties, one for each side, and a Radford cross apparently palmed into his own net by David Harvey, decided the result. Referee Clive Thomas booked five Leeds players, plus Alan Ball of Arsenal, and as a result manager Revie later issued a statement advising that in future he would fine any Leeds player who argued with a referee. Only captain Billy Bremner would be allowed to approach the referee and ask courteously for an explanation on any decisions. And, as in continental football,

Bremner would wear an armband to indicate he was the team captain.

League Division One table (top), December 2 1972:

| 1 | Liverpool | Played 20, | Points 30 |
| 2 | Arsenal | Played 21, | Points 27 |
| 3 | Leeds Utd | Played 20, | Points 26 |
| 4 | Spurs | Played 20, | Points 23 |
| 5 | Chelsea | Played 20, | Points 22 |
| 6 | Ipswich | Played 19, | Points 22 |

That defeat to Arsenal was Leeds' fourth in the League so far. Not a too-alarming figure, bearing in mind that pacesetters Liverpool had lost three games in the same period, but the Reds were a stronger and more resilient side than of recent years.

Leeds followed up the Arsenal defeat with a 1–0 home win over West Ham, a 4–0 win against Birmingham City and a creditable 1–1 draw at Old Trafford on Tommy Docherty's debut as Manchester United manager, on December 23. Allan Clarke's equalizer was an early Christmas cracker for the many travelling Leeds fans after Ted MacDougall had scored for the home team in the first half.

At home to Newcastle on Boxing Day, Leeds had a Joe Jordan goal to thank for settling the hard-fought match in front of over 45,000 spectators. Their seven points gained in December was no mean figure by any standards, but the problem was Liverpool clocked up ten points in the same period, albeit from one game more.

January 1973 saw Leeds go unbeaten throughout, though four of their six games happened to be against the same opposition: Norwich City. Home wins over Tottenham, 2–1, and Stoke City, 1–0, plus a 2–1 away win at First Division newcomers Norwich, gave them six points from the three League games, but two FA Cup third round replays against Norwich meant Leeds were steadily falling behind in Division One games played. They already knew more than any other team about toiling in end-of-season fixture pile-ups, and weren't hoping for a recurrence.

The two teams drew 1–1 in their first FA Cup third round tie at Norwich; the Elland Road replay produced the same result. The tie was finally settled at Villa Park on Monday January 29, with a crowd of over 33,000. In the previous Cup games goalkeeper Kevin Keelan had been in superlative form for Norwich, but on this occasion the yellow and green defence was finally run ragged. An Allan Clarke hat trick in the first twenty minutes, followed by a Mick Jones strike and a Peter Lorimer thumper in the second half, made it Leeds 5, Norwich 0.

After February victories over Plymouth Argyle and then West Bromwich Albion, Leeds steadily progressed through to the quarter-finals of the FA Cup. The draw had so far been kind to them, with both ties at Elland Road.

February 1973 was not a good month for Leeds' title aspirations though, with a 2–0 defeat at Leicester City on February 10 and a home 1–1 draw with Chelsea a week later, with Liverpool staying perched at the top of Division One.

On March 3, Leeds travelled to Derby and scraped a 3–2 win. The following Saturday, another good 2–1 win over Everton gave them the double over the Merseysiders, and on the Wednesday inbetween they again stamped their European pedigree with a 5–0 Cup Winners' Cup quarter-final home win over Rapid Bucharest. A week later they sealed the tie with a 3–1 win in snow-covered Romania. It was back to Derby's gluey Baseball Ground in the FA Cup on the Saturday. The tie, between Derby in all blue and Leeds in all red, was predicted to be a classic match. It turned out not to be, but Leeds fans will not have been complaining.

One goal settled the match, scored in the first half of a keenly contested, tight affair. It came on the half-hour mark for Leeds, from the one and only Peter Lorimer, a sweet volley after a Mick Jones flick-on. However, the goal was quite fortuitous, as Allan Clarke stood in an offside position as the shot hit the net. After consulting with his linesman, though, the referee adjudged Clarke as not interfering with play. It prompted the often-asked question

– if a player is on the pitch, how is he not interfering with play (especially if he is in the penalty area)? Despite Derby's grievances about the goal, Leeds had been the better side overall in the match and deserved to win.

A 0–0 draw with Wolves, 1–1 with West Bromwich Albion, and a 1–0 defeat at Manchester City meant that by the beginning of April third-placed Leeds had played thirty-four games and earned forty-six points while table-toppers Liverpool had played thirty-six games and won fifty-three points. The two sides were due to meet at Anfield on April 23, St George's Day, in what might well be yet another title-decider involving the two sides.

The month of April was, for Leeds, a customary make or break time, regardless of which competition they were involved in. April 1973 was no exception, with Wolverhampton Wanderers their FA Cup semi-final opposition and, over two legs, Yugoslavian team Hajduk Split the opposing side in the Cup Winners' Cup semi-finals. They also had seven League games, the fifth of which was that trip to Liverpool. In all, a total of ten games within twenty-eight days for Leeds: no rest for the successful, or the wicked, it would seem.

A rare goal from Paul Reaney won the Whites the two points at the Sky Blues of Coventry City on April 2, to keep Leeds within tripping distance of Liverpool. But then came a disappointing 1–1 draw at West Ham and a disastrous 1–0 home defeat to Manchester United four days after. Three days later, at home to Crystal Palace on April 21, first-half goals from Bremner, Lorimer and Frank Gray on his full League debut, and a late sniff from Allan Clarke, earned them an impressive 4–0 win. The title dream was still alive for Leeds, though only 31,000 and a few score seemed to want to share it with them. Two days later, on the Monday evening, it was first versus third, the Reds versus the Whites, Liverpool versus Leeds, while second-placed Arsenal travelled to Hampshire to face Southampton.

The first forty-five minutes had been very even, and Liverpool and Leeds were drawing 0–0 by half-time, but within two minutes of the restart Peter Cormack had put the Reds ahead with an expertly taken low volley. Late in the game, a comedy of errors witnessed David Harvey drop the ball twice, the second landing very nicely for Kevin Keegan to take advantage and finish the match. 2–0 to Liverpool, and with main title rivals Arsenal – the only team to beat Liverpool at Anfield this season – only managing a draw at Southampton, bar mathematical improbabilities and a drastic and incredible loss of form by Bill Shankly's team, Liverpool were Division One champions.

13–4

And to think that there were people who actually wondered why Leeds fans adored Billy Bremner! Okay, he argued with referees a lot and he snapped and he snarled at opponents if ever they fouled him or had a go at him – his flame-coloured hair proved he was hot-headed – but he always gave as good as he got *and* he scored important goals for us. His disciplinary record wasn't good and he definitely was suspended too many times, but when he played he never, ever gave in. He lived and breathed the Keep Fighting spirit and I truly believe there was no better captain in football, anywhere, ever. He *was* Leeds United. With Billy it was never just football we were watching, it was war in the name of sport.

This was our fifth FA Cup semi-final in seven, eight years, and we'd only lost one of them. But this year's semi-final was against Wolves, who'd nicked a 0–0 draw in the League at our place a couple of weeks before to help spoil our title chances.

Getting to the 1973 final certainly wasn't going to be easy, especially as Wolves were doing well and weren't far below us in the table. On the face of it, we were doing well too – third in the League, semi-finalists (so far) in Europe, current FA Cup holders and one match away from the final again – but I honestly knew better, even if I was in the minority. Quality wise, we'd had a poor season in my book, and hadn't played well in far too many games to mention.

Billy scored the winning goal in two of our previous FA Cup semi-finals, in 1965 against Man U and 1970 against Man U again. Our Wolves semi-final at Maine Road was nearly as close as those two, though it was the Whites doing most of the attacking in this one, against desperate defending from the Old Golds of Wolves. It was a nervy, dead close game, and it didn't take an expert to predict one goal would settle it. And that's exactly what happened: one goal settled it. One goal to us. And when Leeds win an FA Cup semi-final by the one goal, who scores it? Billy Bremner, that's who, this time with a cracking left-foot half-volley from near the penalty spot.

It wasn't all good news though – Jack Charlton had to go off with a hamstring injury, which was a blow, to him and to us, remembering how well he'd done in last year's final. I couldn't see him playing many more games for Leeds: he was nearly thirty-eight, for God's sake.

The Wednesday after the Wolves match was the first leg of the other semi-final we were in, the European Cup Winners' Cup, at our place. We'd been drawn against Hajduk Split of Yugoslavia. Yugoslavian sides were always hard to beat, they reckoned, and these were no different. The first leg was a tough match and it had plenty of needle in it, mainly from the Yugoslavs. Allan Clarke was being kicked left, right and centre all night by the player marking him – Boljat I think his name was, however you pronounced it – yet the referee did sweet FA about it. The backs of Clarke's legs will have been lots of different colours after the match, he got whacked that many times. But at least he was the one to smack in the winning goal for us. The trouble was, soon after scoring the goal, he was fouled by Boljat yet again. And badly – Clarke's legs were scythed away from under him this time. Allan Clarke shouldn't have done it, he shouldn't have reacted, but he did, enough was enough, and he retaliated by kicking Boljat right in the bollocks and got sent off for it. He received a ban for two European matches as a result.

We went into the second leg with a 1–0 lead, so only needed a draw to go through. Except the match was only two days after the Liverpool defeat. Those Leeds players who weren't injured were already very tired. Liverpool away on the Monday, Hajduk Split away on the Wednesday, how could they feel anything else but worn out? There wasn't a footballer on earth who wouldn't be done in after that. For Leeds, April 1973 was another one of those tons-of-games-in-sod-all-space-of-time months, with so many important matches (ten) in so short a period (twenty-eight days).

The Don called Leeds' performance away at Hajduk Split their equal-finest European display, up there with the 1968 match at

251

Ferencvaros. That was during happier days for Gary Sprake, when he'd played like a superhero, keeping a clean sheet and winning us the Fairs Cup. We wouldn't have done it without him, everyone said it. Now, with David Harvey in goal, we drew 0– 0 and made it to the final, to play AC Milan. But Billy Bremner got booked in the second leg in Split so he'd miss the final as well.

In the run-up to the FA Cup final against Sunderland, we weren't exactly on top form it has to be said, losing 3–1 at Southampton and then 2–1 at Birmingham, on April 28 and 30. It was pretty obvious that The Don had told the players to go easy in both games, though, as there was nothing really riding on the results, and we didn't want any more injuries, of course. We finished a decent third in the League, behind Arsenal and Liverpool, who totally deserved to win the title.

May 5 1973, FA Cup Final. Leeds United versus Sunderland. I'd hardly heard of any of the Sunderland players before. Of course, I knew who their manager was, Bob Stokoe. But the players were unknowns, just about. *After* the Cup final, it was a different story.

The choice in my house: watch it on BBC1 or ITV? No contest really, I couldn't stand the adverts, they just interrupted and got in the way of whatever you were watching, so it was always the BBC for me. Besides, I could watch the highlights of the match on Sunday afternoon on ITV.

Both teams looked dead smart, us in our white zip-up tracksuit tops, white shorts, white socks and brilliant blue and white sock tags. The Sunderland players had on red tracksuit tops over their red and white striped shirts, and black shorts and black socks.

David Coleman tells us that Trevor Cherry is the only team-list change from the 1972 final (at left-back) with Paul Madeley moving to centre-half in place of Jack Charlton. And Cherry is the only non-international in the Leeds side, and that includes our Welsh substitute Terry Yorath. Meanwhile, Sunderland have only one player, Ritchie Pitt (number 6), who has played at Wembley before, and that was as a schoolboy. Meanwhile, Billy Bremner at five foot five and Bobby Kerr at five foot four are the smallest captains to appear in a FA Cup final. The referee is Ken Burns.

The skippers meet and shake hands in the centre circle but it's hardly friendly. Kerr wins the referee's coin toss and decides the teams will change ends.

In Wembley Stadium there are 45,000 spectators seated and 55,000 standing. The rain drizzles down and it is therefore quite cool on the pitch, with the playing surface looking top-notch lush and green but very slippery.

The match gets underway, three o'clock on the dot. It's a yellow ball, which looks like the normal white gone sour. Within two minutes the first foul of the afternoon's committed, Pitt chopping Allan Clarke down, midway in the Sunderland half. It's a bad challenge; Clarke needs treatment from Les Cocker while Referee Burns gives Ritchie Pitt a firm talking to. Johnny Giles is set to take the free kick, with Peter Lorimer hanging around ominously.

Giles passes it square to Lorimer, who connects well and cracks it, but it whizzes low a few yards wide of Jim Montgomery's right post.

It's been described as underdog versus giant, David versus Goliath, but when it all boils down to it, it's just eleven men versus eleven men on an energy-sapping pitch, with the small-fry Sunderland players looking fresher and more energetic than Leeds. Without a doubt, Sunderland have had more time to prepare for the big day than Leeds, and the most worrying thing is, they look more determined than us as well.

It's fast and frenetic, there's hardly any time on the ball for the players in possession, and every time a man gets it, a challenge comes snapping in almost straight away, with the wet grass making the ball hard to control and cocking up a lot of the passing. Gilesy looks out of sorts and he's given the ball away more times already than he would normally.

Having said all that, David Harvey's not had a save of note to make, while Jim Montgomery has had just one cross to deal with, when being challenged by Mick Jones.

Their ginger twenty-year-old Micky Horswill shoots just wide of Harvey's right post. It wasn't the strongest of shots, but had it been on target, Harvey, with no number on his green shirt, might well have been in trouble.

Although the quality of the match isn't as high as people hoped, it is exciting and end-to-end stuff. Twenty minutes gone so far, according to the electric scoreboard clock, and there's nothing in it. There is no letup, no challenge shied from, no responsibility shirked, every single player on each side is trying his hardest, giving it his all. But Sunderland have more to give, they're not as tired as our lads.

And then Bobby Kerr wins the ball in the Leeds half on the right flank and punts a hopeful high ball into the Leeds penalty area. It's too close to David Harvey, standing on his goal-line between the posts. But Sunderland's Billy Hughes is prowling near him, watching the ball as it drops, and watching Harvey as well, waiting for a mistake. Hughes is hanging around like a bad smell, too close for comfort, so when the ball drops in just inches below our crossbar, Harvey has no choice but to tip the ball over. Sunderland have a corner, their first of the match, while we've had two so far.

More red and white stripes move up into attack, including Vic Halom and the bruiser centre-halves Dave Watson and Pitt. Both those big sods pose a real aerial threat against us, especially as we've no great header of the ball in defence today.

Billy Hughes takes the corner kick, and he's aiming for Watson. It's a long and high cross, which floats over the penalty spot and lands near the edge of our area. Dave Watson is great in the air but Hughes' corner kick misses him and everyone else's heads and the ball just seems to hit Watson's left shin and then bobble away from him before he can control it. It bounces forward, waist-high in the direction of our goal, in front of Sunderland's Ian Porterfield, standing side-on to the net. He controls it on his thigh and then swivels to whack a half-volley on goal. He's set it up so invitingly that the ball just begs to be thumped as hard as possible, it's one of those shots that is so well hit that you don't even feel anything as it rockets off your boot. Just like the best golf shots, it just happens, it's pure, it's smooth, it's natural almost. I hate it, but it's a great goal, hitting the roof of our net.

Thirty-two minutes gone, Leeds 0 Sunderland 1, and I want to puke. The television screen shows all the Sunderland players and supporters going crazy.

Half-time.

The second half. The lads have come out clearly more attack minded. Allan Clarke jumps for the ball as a cross comes in, but he collides with and fouls Jim Montgomery, who has caught the ball but then dropped it. Trevor Cherry nets but the goal isn't given.

Billy Bremner darts into the Sunderland area with the ball. He shapes to hit it with his left foot, but then cuts in, deceiving the defender who dives in and seems to catch Bremner and swipe his feet away. Billy hits the deck with a dramatic fall, but it is too dramatic for the referee's liking and he waves play on, saying that no contact was made. Me, I think it's a foul, there might not have been that much contact but there definitely was *some* contact. Billy Bremner couldn't have physically jumped backwards in that position, there had to be some sort of impact to knock his feet out of the way. I don't care if he did overdo it or if he took bloody acting lessons in his spare time, it was a definite, clear infringement. A foul is a foul regardless of the reaction to it: Leeds should have had a penalty. Jesus, Francis Lee gets penalties in his own half he dives that much. Billy didn't dive and wasn't acting.

Sixty-five minutes gone and it's all pretty much the same as the first half, every ball fought for, every player grafting non-stop, no chickening out or shirking of duties. How Sunderland are in the Second Division is beyond me. Leeds are trying to cut loose a bit and there's good build-up play occurring, we're definitely dominating the play now even though there's still very little time on the ball. Terry Yorath comes on for Eddie Gray. Eddie's been out of sorts and not really involved throughout. He looks injured to me, even though I don't think he was limping or anything. No disrespect intended to 'Yogi', but he's not likely to create any sparks for us in attack like Eddie can. He can't half tackle, though.

Mick Jones receives the ball on the edge of the Sunderland penalty box but he's being tightly marked and so can't turn with the ball as he'd lose it, so he lays it out wide to Paul Reaney on the right flank. Reaney crosses, long into the area. It's a great pass and the ball is dropping just a yard or so in front of the on-running Trevor Cherry. He dives full-length to try and reach it with his head. And he manages to, connecting with the right side of his head and the ball spears towards goal. It's a really good effort and looks like it will deceive Jim Montgomery but somehow he twists his body to dive left instead of right, parrying the ball out. And it rebounds straight to Peter Lorimer, standing on the six-yard line. He hits it decently, though it's not a one of his trademark lashes really. It's on target and looks like the equalizer. Until Montgomery somehow lifts himself off the ground to dive backwards and left and he bloody well reaches the shot and pushes the ball up into the air – and it hits the crossbar. Next to Lorimer is Mick Jones and he raises his arms in celebration, thinking we've scored, that Montgomery couldn't have possibly saved it. Jones' joy seems to convince Peter Lorimer that he's scored even though he has seen with his own eyes that his shot didn't go in. Trevor Cherry, who dive-headed the first attempt on goal, is still lying on the bloody ground, and as the ball ricochets off the bar it bounces gently towards and by Cherry and he can only wave his right sodding calf at it as the chance trickles away. What drama, what tension, and what a holy pain in the arse!

Five minutes left and the sun comes out at last, as if the heavens are smiling in approval on the Sunderland team as they close in on the win.

Leeds, pressing forward desperately to get the equalizer, are tiring and leaving gaps at the back, which Sunderland try to exploit. Nerves seem to get the better of them though and they waste two decent chances of nabbing a second goal. Regardless, Jim Montgomery's brilliant performance is really what's stopped us getting the goal back: he should have had a red cape on, the bugger. And then the referee blows the final whistle and Sunderland have won, supposedly against all the odds, but that team has battled so well there is no way they belong in Division Two and, even though it makes me sick as a dog to say it, they deserve to win the Cup. There's hardly any difference in class judging by today.

Years later I'd be able to watch the match without feeling too bad or sickened, and give credit where it's due to Sunderland, but on that May 1973 afternoon, sitting on my own in the front room, I hate Sunderland, and I hate red and white stripes even more.

Our last League game of the season was the Wednesday after Wembley, at home to Arsenal. I must admit, I was expecting a decent but not spectacular match, but we absolutely slaughtered them, it was like the players were desperate to prove something or even exorcise the ghost of the Saturday past. We won 6–1, against the second-best team in the League.

Not that it made me feel the slightest bit better about the rumours that were increasing the closer we got to the Cup Winners' Cup final in Greece. Was it true that Don Revie was leaving Leeds for Everton? I asked John and Ces. Neither of them replied, they didn't bloody well need to. John just raised his eyebrows and gave a sad 'Sometimes life disappoints you' sort of smile, and Ces wouldn't even look at me, as if he was bitterly upset and lost for words.

Okay, so attendances were never as high as we'd all hoped they would be, but those supporters who turned up at Elland Road week in, week out always backed the team and the management to the hilt. How the hell could Don Revie feel under-appreciated, like people were saying? This season hadn't been the best, but still, most of us knew that we were Super Leeds thanks mainly to The Don, and Harry Reynolds of course, twelve or so years back. Nope, if Don Revie was to leave Leeds, the club he had grown up as a manager with, then he'd need better reasons than what we were being asked to believe.

Everton were looking to replace Harry Catterick, who'd had to retire for health reasons after having a heart attack in January 1972. The club was loaded, money wasn't a problem, so they assumed Don Revie would be tempted to accept the job offer and be able to take over quickly and easily. Everton were half right with their assumptions. Tuesday May 15 1973, the day before the AC Milan game, Don Revie was planning on having breakfast at the home of John Moores, the Everton chairman. Moores' home was called Freshfields and Revie, driving in his unmistakable yellow Mercedes, called upon a passer-by for directions to it. That passer-by went yapping to the press afterwards and soon it was in print.

'Don Revie lost in search for Freshfields!' It was all coming out now, no one knew what to believe. Some reports said Everton were offering Revie a £50,000 signing-on fee and an eight-year contract worth £250,000 before tax. Others were saying that money *was* an issue, the major issue – not how much Everton had of it but more to do with government employment rules, the Pay Board and the tax office – it was supposedly common knowledge that companies weren't allowed to pay more wages to new people hired to replace employees who'd done the same jobs previously.

Not surprisingly, I suppose, he took plenty of stick from various quarters for his 'lousy timing' and for neglecting team preparations for the final, but to be fair to him, the players did know of his intentions to leave and he'd told them to make this a match to remember as it was probably his last as Leeds manager. And he'd told Norman Hunter that if he took the Everton job he would make him his first signing.

## 13–5

BBC images appear on screen, of charming monuments and a busy, pretty harbour awash with sunshine and swish white yacht sails. Barry Davies announces: 'Tonight on BBC1 at ten-forty, the final of the European Cup Winners' Cup competition, Leeds United versus AC Milan, played in Thessaloniki in north-east Greece.'

Most Greeks at the United–Milan match are said to be 'Leeds daft', and a crowd of 45,000 is expected in the new Kaftatzoglio Stadium. It's a big occasion for football – it's a huge occasion for the people of Greece. They hope to impress the world of football with the friendly reception and fine hospitality and sports facilities. The Greek match referee and his two linesmen are probably anxious to please as well.

Barry Davies confirms the team line-ups as the names appear on screen at the same time, each team's players numbered from one to eleven, plus the substitutes at twelve.    AC Milan: Vecchi, Sabadini, Zignoli, Anquilletti, Turone, Rosato, Sogliano, Benetti, Bigon, Rivera, Chiarugi. Sub: Dolci.

 Leeds United: Harvey, Reaney, Cherry, Bates, Yorath, Hunter, Lorimer, Jordan, Jones, F. Gray, Madeley. Sub: McQueen.

The weather has changed dramatically from the earlier scenes, and Davies sounds as if he is there under duress, a sports commentator forced to report on unpleasant events that don't belong in football or on television.

Viewers are informed that AC Milan could be the first team to win the Cup Winners' Cup twice, and that they are probably their country's League Champions for this season, too, one point ahead with one game to go.

'Whether this was or this wasn't the last match Leeds United played under the managership of Don Revie, only time will tell,' comes Davies' rather unimpressed comment. 'An enthusiastic welcome and a pretty wild night to greet the two teams as they come into the Kaftatzoglio Stadium. It's threatening to rain, there's quite a strong wind and we've had claps of thunder and the odd flash or two of lightning ...'

The teams enter the arena, walking on the running track, while a nearby brass band plays lively music. Two men in traditional Greek costume walk in front of the two side-by-side single-file teams. One leads AC Milan, carrying the Italian national flag, swaying in the breeze, and his compatriot carries the Union flag aloft in front of the Leeds team. The two lines of footballers bear the national flag of Greece between them, like a huge stretcher.

'Leeds United on the right in their all-white strip, being captained tonight by Paul Reaney.'

Reaney is captain due to Bremner being suspended, along with striker Allan Clarke, and injuries to Johnny Giles and Eddie Gray and of course Terry Cooper have caused them to miss the match too. Also, Jack Charlton had recently retired from playing. Conversely, this will be Frank Gray's full Leeds debut in Europe.

'The referee in the centre, Christos Michas of Athens. And the two linesmen both come from Salonika.'

It is raining quite heavily, proven not so much by the television cameras but by the frequent, bothersome tip-taps of sizeable raindrops dripping on to the commentary box roof.

'Leeds United battling for a trophy which has been won four times by English clubs ... Leeds United in the all-white strip defending the goal to our left. AC Milan in their black and red stripes and white shorts ...'

In comparison to Milan's shirts, and set against the murky surroundings, despite the floodlighting, Leeds' white shirts stand out brilliantly, almost glowing in the dark.

Slippery on the surface due to the elements, the pitch nevertheless looks perfect, a lush green carpet. The opening couple of minutes of the game are keenly contested, played at a quick pace with both teams aiming to play attacking football.

In the second minute, near the half-way line, the referee adjudges Paul Madeley to have fouled his opposite number as they challenged in the air to win Vecchi's incoming goal-kick. Not one player on the pitch claimed a foul had been committed, the referee is the only person present to have seen a supposed infringement. Already, protesting whistles sound from the crowd, but fortunately, for Leeds at least, nothing comes of the free kick.

Seconds later, Norman Hunter receives the ball and switches the play from the left side to the right with a lofted pass, midway in the Leeds half, to Peter Lorimer, with the time to bring the ball under control before choosing his pass, a low diagonal arrow to the feet of Mick Bates in the centre circle. Bates begins to run with the ball, only to be challenged by the outstretched leg of Sabadini, Milan's number 2. Sabadini fails to reach the football but he does foul Bates by catching the Leeds number 4's trailing foot. Bates tumbles to the floor. Perhaps not deliberately, but Sabadini, nonetheless, has fouled Bates, and the referee, less than five yards away, cannot fail to see it.

But 'No free kick given,' states Barry Davies, and the referee waves play on, as if there has been no infringement. Shocked, Bates gets to his feet and protests to Referee Michas, who ignores him. And Milan's Benetti escapes with the ball into the Leeds half.

Paul Madeley challenges Benetti for the ball but is pushed away by the Italian, illegally. Another foul by Milan against Leeds, another foul dubiously missed by the referee.

Barry Davies: 'Benetti finding Bigon, trying to set himself for the shot ...' but Paul Madeley is still in pursuit, and he is too fast and too strong for Bigon, easily overtaking him, causing the Italian to lose control of the ball without being touched, close to the D of the Leeds penalty box. Curiously, the referee has now seen a foul.

'And the free kick given against Madeley,' declares Davies. 'Well that's the second decision given, one after the other. The first the decision *not* given, then the one given. Both of them going against Leeds ...'

Terry Yorath, aghast already at the poor refereeing, remonstrates furiously with the match official while Paul Reaney claps his hands, as if imploring the referee to improve his performance, which has been grossly inadequate even with so little time passed.

Leeds players hastily form a defensive wall between where the alleged foul took place and David Harvey's goal.

'David Harvey covering the near post ...'

The free kick is over and done with in short time and the Leeds defence has had little time to organize their wall efficiently. What's more, its component defenders seemed to break ranks just as Chiarugi's direct shot was fired in. Leeds have defended poorly against Chiarugi's well-struck shot, which pierces the wall and spears through a crowd of players to smack the base of David Harvey's left-hand post. And it ricochets into the net. It is bad luck on Harvey's part as he saw the ball late and it took at least one deflection on the way, taking it a crucial inch or so away from his desperate attempt to finger-tip it out.

'Three minutes of the match gone and AC Milan in the lead.'

From the kick off, Leeds give the ball away almost straight away. AC Milan are on the offensive again, progressing dangerously down Leeds' left wing. It's an indication of what a fast, tough and skilful side they can be when they want purely to play football, with no need of dubious refereeing decisions to support them.

'Milan really dictating things at the moment. Sogliano is in the middle ...' A dangerous cross whips into the Leeds area. 'There he is!' But it's just past the far post and is a goal-kick for Leeds. 'Sogliano got up well, he wasn't picked up as he made the run on the near post.' It could easily have been 2–0. 'And Paul Reaney's got a lot to do to lift this Leeds team at the moment ... It's always easy to say that one goal counts for a lot but in Leeds' present situation it does count for an awful lot.'

Leeds fight back though, and get into more of a rhythm now, taking the game to their opponents. A Mick Bates free kick near the Milan left corner flag is passed short to Peter Lorimer. He places a good cross into the goal mouth, straight to Norman Hunter, who has a free header on goal but can only direct the ball straight at the goalkeeper.

As the rain continues to fall, and the number of black umbrellas continues to increase, chants of 'Leeds! Leeds! Leeds! Leeds!' sound from crowd, trying to lift and spur on the men in white. A few yards outside the Milan penalty area, centrally, Lorimer receives the ball again. He has a good, clear sight of goal ahead of him, and he is never a man in need of thinking twice about taking a pot shot. He hits it, on target, low and, of course, hard. In goal, Vecchi scrambles on his line and blocks it but he can't keep the ball in his grasp. It rolls a few inches away before he snatches it back securely, and just before Paul Reaney and then Trevor Cherry get there. Reaney jumps harmlessly over Vecchi but Cherry, a half second later, arrives in the hope of taking advantage of any handling errors. He does not get the ball or even touch it, nor does he make any contact with the goalkeeper. Unwisely though, instead of running back to his position, he stays put to stand over Vecchi, perhaps in hope of intimidating him. It doesn't work, as the calm Vecchi remains on the ground with the football safe and sound in his hands. Cherry's actions, however, have seemingly incensed three other Milan players – numbers 2 Sabadini, 5 Turone and 4 Anquilletti. Suddenly, Turone is the ringleader, cursing Cherry and then kicking him hard on the back of his right ankle, with the referee merely feet away. And then Anquilletti and Sabadini hassle Cherry, threatening him, trying to get him to react as well as incriminate him, waiting for the slightest encouragement to inflict a sly strike or two of their own on him. They tell the referee that Cherry has committed a bad foul. He hasn't. As Cherry begins to walk away, Mr Michas calls him back, to give him a stern talking-to, as well as Anquilletti, who pleads absolute, unblemished innocence.

A few minutes later, blatant cheating incidents occur in the Milan penalty area. Match commentator Barry Davies needs to watch a replay of the shameful events for them to sink in - 'Lorimer doing the protesting bit with the referee … and he's been booked for it … Jordan, who made the break and Rosato nearly fouled him then … Jones, getting pushed and shoved all over the place. He tries to turn. Is he tripped?'

Oh yes, he is definitely tripped, and gouged, and kicked, and dragged, and barged. Mick Jones endured at least three fouls while in possession of the ball for ten or so seconds, and the referee was there, right on the spot and perfectly positioned, to witness the series of Milan misdemeanours.

'Well he certainly looks as though he was that time …' Davies says, answering his own question.

But to the incredulity of players and spectators, referee Mr Michas decrees that not one single foul has been committed within a whole chain of assaults on Mick Jones. And so, soon after, retaliating against the scandal of the refereeing, Terry Yorath inflicts a horrendous, shinbone-jarring foul on Sogliano near the half-way line. His violent reaction is understandable but inexcusable, and he is lucky the referee really did miss it.

Joe Jordan receives the ball at his feet on the edge of the Milan box. He turns with it quickly, deceiving his marker Anquilletti who stretches a leg out to kick the ball or the man but succeeds in missing both, but he doesn't miss the chance of tugging Jordan's shirt to stop him getting far. The referee does miss that sneaky little foul though. Nonetheless, Jordan has earned himself a chance to shoot on goal. He does so, and had it been on target then Milan would have been in trouble, but he skews the shot yards wide. It's a disappointingly poor effort from the young Scot, after such promising play.

Shortly after, a towering and strong Jordan header brings a fine save from Milan's keeper. The corner kick leads up to a left-foot stinger from Lorimer – yes, his left foot – only to see another acrobatic save prevent the equalizer. Seconds later, and a low drive from Norman Hunter outside the area is again well saved, while Frank Gray has a dangerous cross-cum-shot narrowly miss the goal, also.

Early in the second half, the pitch is even wetter and greasier. Leeds take the initiative and attack from the off. Mick Bates slips and misses an opportunity to shoot in the Milan area: he is beaten by the rainwater, of all things. The next minute, Trevor Cherry stumbles in the Leeds half to leave a gap for Milan's Bigon to hit a sharp shot, which flies beyond the despairing Terry Yorath but brings about an excellent stop from David Harvey.

The chants of 'Leeds! Leeds! Leeds!' grow in frequency and loudness, the vast majority of the crowd urging the English side to win the final. Peter Lorimer has the ball at his feet on the right wing, he jinks and swerves with it, and gracefully slinks and curves through two Italian defenders to strike a rasping shot towards goal. But it fizzes a disappointing few yards wide and doesn't trouble Vecchi.

Not one of the Leeds officials at the side of the pitch is enjoying the occasion. The older Leeds men have other issues on their minds too, personal, more important issues, especially as word has already reached them that the outcome of the tie has been pre-determined. In other words, the match is fixed – Leeds will not be allowed to win. Someone from the media and close to UEFA has advised Leeds officials that the name engraved as 'Winners 1973' on the Cup Winners' Cup would be an Italian team's. And as if that wasn't enough, the confusion over manager Don Revie's career intentions was affecting the Leeds backroom team: Revie's backroom team, the men who had been with him from the very start of his managerial career, all those years ago, who are now unsure of their Leeds futures and their careers in football altogether. If Don Revie leaves the club, what happens to them? Even Maurice Lindley, normally the most relaxed and easygoing of Leeds men, looks unhappy.

Seated on the bench, Revie grinds his chewing gum ardently, but he is tired, irritated, bemused. For all manner of reasons, his mind is annoyingly cluttered. Next to him, Dr Adams has his hands to his face, as if he can't bear to watch any more.

Bespectacled Bob English, too, expects nothing but bad from the night. Syd Owen stares at the pitch, in a daze, like he is in shellshock. Agitated, nervous Cyril Partridge is furiously chewing too – his fingernails – and disliking intensely this whole sorry affair, hating being there. In front of them, seated on a cushion, Les Cocker can hardly keep still, like he is playing in the match himself. The players out on that pitch are his immediate responsibility, everything else can wait, even his job prospects.

The strong and lanky Gordon McQueen has entered the fray in place of Frank Gray, and makes an impact almost straight away. A free kick, taken by Norman Hunter, finds McQueen's head and he connects with the ball firmly and on target. It is so nearly the equalizer, but Vecchi contrives to push it out and away for a corner. The corner kick is safely cleared by Milan but Leeds continue to attack and are awarded another free kick near the Italian penalty area. Peter Lorimer places the ball on the ground.

'Lorimer prepares to have another crack ...' but something has happened in the Milan penalty area. Terry Yorath appears to have been struck, in the face, by a Milan player. Leeds captain Reaney and striker Jordan try to inform the referee that Yorath has been punched. Yorath sits up, rubs his face, shakes his head while referee Michas brushes off the protests and physically pushes Paul Reaney away. The referee is more aggravated than the badly done to Leeds players.

Lorimer takes the free kick and it's a hard, low and accurate shot, but straight at the keeper, who saves comfortably. Seconds later, back in the Leeds half, as they successfully defend a Milan move, Jordan runs with the ball on the left wing but is tripped by Sabadini in a pointless and spiteful foul. Terry Yorath clips Sabadini's foot to return the favour and Norman Hunter dashes in too to remonstrate with the Italian player. The referee books Sabadini.

Gordon McQueen makes a marauding run into the Milan half, his long strides swallowing up the yards. He looks a fine prospect to replace the great Jack Charlton. McQueen coolly passes the ball to his right, to Paul Reaney on the wing. The captain traps the ball and then tries crossing it into the area – the ball's flight is blocked within five yards, inside the Milan penalty area, by a defender's outstretched arm. It did seem, too, as though the defender had deliberately handled the ball and a penalty to Leeds should therefore be awarded. The referee, however, indicates it's just a corner. Mick Jones, normally a quiet man who rarely complains to match officials, regardless of the rough treatment dished out to him, rushes up to Mr Michas, animatedly demanding he do the honourable thing and give the penalty kick. But the referee ignores all the protests, from the players and the numerous spectators. The Leeds corner kick floats in and Mick Jones is accidentally floored for his troubles.

'But Leeds have got to keep their heads in this situation, it's becoming a physical battle.'

A deflected Mick Bates pass veers across the Milan area, with Jones in close pursuit of it. But his progress is halted abruptly yet again, as an Italian defender hauls him down to the ground, unfairly. The ball goes out of play and Jones stands up, already expecting the referee to give anything but the penalty-kick. Still, Jones throws his arms up in exasperation and questions the Michas, standing just a couple of feet away. Again the referee pays him no heed and turns his back.

It is not all Leeds attacking: in the eighty-fifth minute, goal-keeper David Harvey stretches and just manages to push a Milan shot wide. Straight back down to the other end of the pitch, Jones controls the ball well, close to the Milan area. He taps the ball to Lorimer inside the box, near the dead-ball line. Lorimer runs at the defender Zignoli, knocks the ball by him and is then brought down by the despairing defender's sliding challenge. Although Lorimer's fall is dramatic, there is little doubt that it is yet another foul on Leeds in the Milan area and that a penalty should ensue.

As the end of the match approaches, Norman Hunter tries to commence another Leeds attack. He beats number 11 Chiarugi to the ball but then feels a stab to his lower left leg – Chiarugi has kicked Hunter with a malicious jab. He turns back to run at Chiarugi and push him. Chiarugi theatrically sprawls away to the floor, as if hit by a knockout punch. He wasn't, he wasn't even pushed so forcefully. And then, from a few yards away, Milan's Sogliano races towards Hunter and aims a high kick at him.

Seemingly overreaching himself, though, he falls comically flat on his back on the ground. Mick Bates, one of the mildest of men in football, immediately stands over him, incensed and fists clenched at the ready. Fortunately, Joe Jordan intervenes and steers Bates away from the hotspot. Officials from Milan, Leeds and UEFA enter the stage, trying to get involved, but after a while relative calm is restored and Referee Michas decides to send Hunter and Sogliano off.

A minute or so of uneventful football then takes place while the bemused Barry Davies, with disgust in his tone, remarks 'The two players who were sent off have just shaken hands.'

The final whistle is blown and AC Milan have 'won' the 1973 European Cup Winners' Cup. Any cheers for the Italian side are vociferously drowned out by booing, jeering and whistling from the crowd.

The AC Milan players walk up the stand steps to the platform to be presented with the trophy, the dignitaries and UEFA officials seemingly gushing with praise, but with scant applause or cheering from the paying public.

The closing shots show the brilliant white of the Leeds team together on the stadium running track, making their way back to the changing rooms. The defeated, in the eyes of the crowd, are the victorious. The pride of the fallen is wounded, but not mortally so. A bittersweet end to a bitter, bitter season.

Revie had declined Everton's offer to become their manager, or so went the official version of events at least. His reputation certainly did not profit from the 'will he, won't he?' saga, but in the main a wave of relief swept through the city of Leeds when the news broke. But rumours that he would ditch the club still had substance.

Following the AC Milan defeat, Revie stayed on in Greece for a family holiday. Reports of him finding a new employer – in Greece now – surfaced and would not go away, leaving Leeds fans just as worried as before. And, it would seem, even chairman Manny Cussins was unaware of the present Leeds manager's intentions.

During his visit, Revie had been a guest on the yacht of Nikos Goulandris, the president of Olympiakos FC, while the president of the Greek Football Association was also hopeful of luring Revie to manage the Greece national team, for a salary rumoured to be £20,000, tax free, a year. Panathanaikos were also said to be interested and willing to pay Revie £28,000.

One morning early in June 1973 came news that Leeds fans had hoped for. Revie had telephoned the club's secretary Keith Archer, from his hotel room in Greece, and stated that he wanted to remain as Leeds' manager.

Although it was not officially confirmed, he was expected to stay on as the manager until 1979–80. He would be fifty-two by then, the age at which he had vowed he would retire.

# Chapter 14

## 14–1

More surprise guests arrive, and the *This Is Your Life* host introduces former players from the Middlesbrough Swifts team, in which Don Revie had played as a teenager. Revie meets and greets them all, one by one, exchanging pleasantries, shaking their hands, expressing his pleasure to see them all again.

Andrews: 'That was Don's team of over thirty years ago. Your team of today is, as we know, here tonight. And skipper Billy Bremner ... Billy, you have another surprise for him, haven't you?'

Bremner enters the tiny stage area to loud applause. Andrews holds the microphone out for the Leeds captain to speak into. 'Well we have a surprise for him Eamonn, but the memory like I've got ...' he chuckles, 'I've left it down in the safe down the stairs!'

Andrews toys with him. 'The next best thing you can do, as you're a real Scot, is tell us what it is.' More merriment.

'Well we thought like, tonight, there were so many honours going on the boss that we felt that we couldn't be left out, for all he's done for us. So we bought him something that we think will be worthwhile to him. It's a little gold cup and on it it's got "To the Boss, the greatest in the world, from the players at Elland Road."'

Although Revie is more relaxed now, once the initial shock of the surprise party has passed, he still looks uncomfortable and rather embarrassed. Eamonn Andrews, however, intends to enjoy himself as well as make the occasion as entertaining as possible for all the viewers. And he has more interesting and famous guests lined up.

The signature tune arises once again. 'Fellow managers are here to pay tribute too … Your old friend and great rival Bill Shankly …'

Andrews: 'Now Bill, you're the manager of Liverpool and right now your teams are battling it out for the First Division title. You and Don are great mates.'

The famous Shankly growl, capable of sandpapering wood panelling within twelve yards, responds: 'Yes, we're the greatest of enemies,' to loud laughter. 'Again we're battling it out … ay … When the … ay … media talk about flair and skill and things like that, but Leeds United and Liverpool have got more flair and skill and guts than any other team and they're a credit to England.' Now cheers from the audience. 'Don … ay … is a household name throughout the world in football, and I mean, you can't take his achievements away from him.'

'How would you sum him up, Bill?'

'Well … ay … he goes down in history as one of the greatest managers of all time.'

'What better than that? Thank you Bill Shankly.'

Shankly shakes hands with Revie again, and then kisses Elsie Revie on the cheek before returning to his seat. He raises a hand in gratitude to the audience.

Andrews: 'Don, you turned to one man for advice. That man was then Britain's most famous manager.'

Sir Matt Busby emerges through the curtain, met by another rousing reception from the appreciative audience.

As the applause fades, Eamonn Andrews speaks to him, 'What advice did you give Don?'

Busby is thin, gaunt even, but when he speaks, his strong Scottish voice contradicts his age and build. 'Well actually I started off by saying, if you're going to be a successful manager you're going to have to have a successful team. That was number one …' As he speaks, Revie looks up at him, solemnly and respectfully.

'Can I tell you what Don's first question was? "Can you enlighten me Matt, about the snags in the game?" And I thought to myself, that's a very good, quick thinker – he wants to know the snags before he meets them … I got the tremendous impression that here was a man bursting to build, bursting to succeed and bursting to build a great side. And this, the world knows, Don Revie has done.'

The 1972–73 season had seen discipline in football generally decline, and Leeds' record was not at all good, termed 'above average misconduct' with Trevor Cherry and Norman Hunter the worst offenders. In July 1973, manager Revie and chairman Cussins were summoned to a Football Association disciplinary hearing at Lancaster Gate, London where they were adjudged to have brought football into disrepute for 'permitting players to violate the laws of the game'. The club was given a £3000 suspended fine. If the team's record had not improved by the new season's end, they would have to pay. It was a hefty punishment, though not hefty enough for some outspoken critics of the situation. After the meeting, Leeds called a press confe- rence in which Revie promised that the players' behaviour would improve. The club also hired a public relations manager, Peter Fay, to improve its image. A forlorn hope, in some quarters.

In early August, in customarily forthright fashion, Brian Clough wrote of his disgust at the FA's leniency shown to Leeds. 'The men who run soccer have missed the most marvellous chance of cleaning up the game in one swoop.' He added that he believed Leeds should have been kicked out of Division One and that Revie deserved a personal fine for his part in the club's disciplinary record. Revie ignored the jibes. Meanwhile, the President of the Football League, Len Shipman, called for the return of corporal punishment, specifically public birching for football hooligans who were increasingly harmful to the game.

Desperate to motivate and win back the affections of his players and personnel, and fans, Revie decided on a new strategy for the team. 'We're going to win the title and we're not going to lose a single game' he declared to the Leeds squad. He had said similar to them a few years before but the challenge, not surprisingly, had been too steep a one, especially as Leeds had then tried to win, and lost, every competition possible. This time around, Revie approached the situation differently, primarily because the situation itself was different now. For one thing, this time around he was only interested in winning the League Championship title. And winning it well.

He was aware too of the need of fresh ways to motivate the players, due to some of them having been dismissed by the media as too old or too injury prone for the team to be a force again, even though most of the side were younger than thirty. Combine those player weaknesses, said the sceptics, with Revie's obvious unrest at Leeds and there you had the proof that Leeds were on the wane, on the brink. The Sunderland Cup final defeat delivered conclusive evidence that he and Leeds were finished. The negative press articles went up on the dressing room wall for the players to see, while copies of the less-than-flattering television pieces were recorded and replayed to them.

It was believed that Revie blamed himself for the Sunderland defeat, having restricted the players from playing attractive, attacking football all season. This time around, he was intent on putting it right: 'From now on they have freedom of expression.'

## 14–2

### The Honours 1972–73

**Division One winners**: Liverpool. Runners up: Arsenal. Third: Leeds.
**FA Cup winners**: Sunderland. Runners up: Leeds.
**League Cup winners**: Spurs. Runners up: Norwich City.
**European Cup winners**: Ajax. Runners up: Juventus.
**European Cup Winners' Cup winners**: AC Milan. Robbed, ripped-off runners up: Leeds.
**UEFA Cup winners**: Liverpool. Runners up: Borussia Monchengladbach.
**Football Player of the Year**: Pat Jennings, Tottenham.
**European Footballer of the Year:** Johan Cruyff, Ajax.
**Crowd average, home games**: 35,831.

Honours? That was taking the piss and not very mildly either, thank you not very much. There wasn't any honour coming this way last season. We'd been embarrassed, dishonoured, humiliated even, by Sunderland at Wembley and ripped off ultra-dishonourably against Milan in Salonika, plus we'd had to endure the prospect of Don Revie leaving for Everton or Greece or bloody Timbuktu for all we knew. 'Honour' wasn't a word you could associate with Leeds United last season.

That corrupt cash-clutching Greek referee who'd cheated us out of the Cup Winners' Cup was banned from refereeing ever again *plus* he was jailed for match fixing, I heard. I hope he thought it was all worth it.

So that meant a tiny bit of justice had been done but it still didn't give us our rightful trophy or motivate UEFA into thinking about what could be done to stop it.

I'm not sure whether the world knew at first of Don Revie's target of going unbeaten in the League, but we all knew about it at Elland Road, once the players had been informed of course. When it looked like he really was leaving, in May, I couldn't believe it. I'd even wake up in the middle of the night thinking 'He won't go, he just won't,' I was that sappish. Eventually, though, I *expected* him to leave Leeds, and sooner rather than later, in spite of mentions that he had a contract to stay with the club until round about 1980.

I knew someone who *definitely* would be moving on in the next few years – me, and all the other poor buggers living in the Hoxton streets. The council wrote to us to say that we were all, at some stage or other, going to be shipped out of our homes and re-housed. Our houses were to be knocked down and replaced by much nicer new ones not too far away. Oh, ta very much, do we kiss your backsides now or once we've been turfed out?

Leeds were spending money on building too: their spending on the stadium was up to nearly a million pounds, due to revamping the south end, the Scratching Shed, of the stadium, plus putting up three absolutely massive floodlights. But the main thing that the fans love to see is big money being spent on the team, and that didn't seem to be happening, not really. It was obvious to most supporters that the Leeds first team squad needed strengthening, sooner rather than later. There were some great youngsters coming up through the ranks, but not enough of them. McQueen looked good enough to replace Jack, but where were the next-generation of Billy Bremners and Johnny Gileses?

## 14–3

Match 1. Saturday August 25 1973. Leeds 3, Everton 1 on the opening day of the new English League season. A vociferous crowd of nearly 40,000, a warm sunny afternoon and a rousing performance from the Whites, with Billy Bremner running the show against an unlucky Everton. Unlucky because they had encountered a Leeds team revving up and raring to go. And with this being Bremner's testimonial year, the captain was desperate to show the supporters what they and the club meant to him.

Match 2. August 28. Arsenal 1, Leeds 2. Arsenal dominated the first half and took a second-minute lead through Blockley, but Leeds responded in kind after the break, with early goals from Madeley and Lorimer.

Match 3. September 1. Tottenham Hotspur 0, Leeds 3. 'I know Chivers can be brilliant but Norman Hunter has already given me plenty of information about him,' said Gordon McQueen, the young centre-half who was already making his mark as Jack Charlton's replacement. This match was effectively over as a contest after just thirty minutes. The first goal came on four minutes when a Lorimer free kick from the right was met by the smallest man on the pitch, Bremner, unmarked at the near post, who nodded it into the net to Pat Jennings' left. Ten minutes later, from open play, Lorimer hit a perfect through-ball for Bremner to run on to and steer home, in off the post. The third Leeds goal comes from another defence-splitting cross, which Clarke takes advantage of after a Jones-miscued header plus hesitancy in the Spurs rearguard. On a darker note, Clarke was carried off in the second half with a leg injury.

Match 4. September 5. Leeds 4, Wolves 1. Two goals from Lorimer, one a third-minute penalty, and one each from Bremner and Jones, before a crowd of 39,946, saw Leeds coast home. Wolves' Derek Dougan had made it 2–1 near half-time.

Match 5. September 9. Leeds 3, Birmingham 0. Rumours circulated that Terry Cooper's career was over due to the broken leg suffered in 1972, so, as if to quell such talk, Revie arranged for Cooper to present prizes to certain reserve and junior players before kick off. Although he had not played a first team match for over a season, the England left-back looked fit, healthy and cheerful. Award recipients included Frank Gray, Billy McGhie, Glan Letheran, Gary Liddell, Peter Hampton, plus Byron Stevenson, Derek Loadwick, Keith Parkinson and David McNiven. Ahead of the match, Revie's programme notes mentioned these and other lads, such as Bobby Shields, Neil Parker and Billy McGinley: 'These are all boys you're going to hear a lot of in the not-too-distant future.' Leeds made short work of Birmingham with a hat trick from Lorimer past City keeper Paul Cooper, two in the first half – one a penalty – and a trademark rocket deciding it.

Match 6. September 11. Wolves 0, Leeds 2. The hosts put up a much more resolute display but were undone by the classic 'hammer and blade' partnership of Jones, scoring on eleven minutes, and Clarke, scoring near the half-hour mark, in a majestic Leeds display. This was Leeds' sixth League win in a row, equalling the club record.

Match 7. September 15. Southampton 1, Leeds 2. Two more typical strikes from Clarke, one in each half, took the points, while O'Neill pulled one back for the Saints at the death.

Match 8. September 22. Still unbeaten, but the winning sequence is ended in this thriller: Leeds 0, Manchester United 0. Bad news too, with Eddie Gray suffering another bad injury.

Match 9. September 29. Norwich City 0, Leeds 1. Carrow Road is never an easy place to visit, but another gritty display and a well-taken goal from Giles saw Leeds depart Norfolk with two more points in the bag. Sir Alf Ramsey had called Giles 'the complete footballer' and his excellent strike showed a corresponding touch of class.

In October, Birmingham City manager Freddie Goodwin tabled a £100,000 bid for former team-mate Gary Sprake and Leeds accepted the bid. Sprake, who had played just one first team match the previous term, felt out in the cold and his resentment was not helped by not yet being offered a testimonial season for his ten-plus years' service to the club. In fairness to Leeds, Sprake would not have been the first in line for a benefit year. The club held a farewell party for him, and Revie commented 'I have looked on Gary like a son,' and would often wax lyrical about two incredible Sprake saves against Ferencvaros and Liverpool respectively, describing them as the best he had ever witnessed. Business is business though, and Leeds signed keeper David Stewart from Ayr United for £30,000 the day after Sprake left.

Match 10. October 6. Leeds 1, Stoke 1. Another point dropped at home, though Leeds remained firmly positioned at the top of Division One with eighteen points out of a possible twenty. A forty-first-minute Jones strike is cancelled out by Stoke defender Denis Smith in the last minute of the match. Burnley occupy second spot, three points behind the Peacocks.

Match 11. October 13. Leicester 2, Leeds 2. The hosts give Leeds a fright in a pulsating battle, leading 2–0 after only twenty minutes through Frank Worthington and Alan Birchenall, but well-taken Jones and Bremner strikes square matters by half-time.

Match 12. October 20. Leeds 1, Liverpool 0. In the thirty-third minute another Lorimer cross expertly put away by Jones wins the two points against the current champions, in front of nearly 45,000. No one is enjoying their game more, or playing better, than Jones, who looks quicker and keener than ever before, while Liverpool haven't found their form yet. Unfortunately, Giles was hurt in the warm-up, aggravating a long-term calf injury, which will restrict his first team appearances this season.

Match 13. October 27. Manchester City 0, Leeds 1. No unlucky number thirteen for Leeds as a rare Mick Bates strike fifteen minutes from time deservedly grabs both points in an excellent-all-round Leeds performance. Lorimer earned Leeds a corner. He took it, only for City to head it clear, but straight to Bates, who whipped a super right-foot volley straight back in, hard and low, to the corner of the net.

Match 14. November 3. Leeds 4, West Ham 1. Bates, in for Giles, gets the first goal with a left-footed snapshot in a crowded penalty area. Jones prods home the second after another supply from Lorimer, and Jones' second is a deft lob over the advancing West Ham keeper. Bates caps a splendid performance by setting up the fourth goal with a perfectly placed cross for Clarke to bury with a powerful header into the top corner. Ted MacDougall scored a late consolation goal for the visitors.

Match 15. November 10. Burnley 0, Leeds 0. A tough match and no love lost between the clubs off the pitch, due to 'disrespectful' behaviour in the transfer market from outspoken Burnley chairman Bob Lord and manager Jimmy Adamson towards Don Revie and the Leeds directors.

Match 16. November 17. Leeds 3, Coventry 0. Leeds at their devastating best again, even without Giles, Jones and Gray. Bates is in fine form again, involved in all three Leeds goals, from Clarke, Jordan and Bremner.

Match 17. November 24. Derby 0, Leeds 0. Managed now by Dave Mackay, following Brian Clough and Peter Taylor's shock depar-ture, presently eighth in the table, a draw at the Baseball Ground is no mean feat and keeps Leeds in top spot.

Match 18. December 1. Leeds 2, Queens Park Rangers 2. Although QPR were a creditable seventh, it's a disappointing result for

Leeds, who had Jones and Bremner to thank for the one point. Leeds need just one more undefeated game to equal Liverpool's record, but Revie said, 'We concentrate on one game at a time.'

Division 1 table (top), December 1 1973:

| 1 | Leeds | Played 18, | Points 30 |
| 2 | Liverpool | Played 18, | Points 24 |
| 3 | Newcastle | Played 17, | Points 22 |

Match 19. December 8. Ipswich 0, Leeds 3. All the goals came in the second half of a generally one-sided affair, the first a looping Terry Yorath shot from the edge of the box, which sneaks in just under the crossbar. Yorath sets up the second too – a fine right-foot cross to Jones, who heads it home. The third is a wonderful virtuoso effort from Clarke, dribbling the ball from thirty yards out on the right wing, beating all before him and then finishing with a left-footed arrow. Ipswich manager Bobby Robson describes the Leeds performance as the finest team display he has ever seen and says that he wants Leeds to win the League as they have more panache than Liverpool.

Match 20. December 15. Chelsea 1, Leeds 2. A superb win, with Leeds overhauling Liverpool's record of unbeaten games from the start of a season. Indeed, the scoreline barely skims the surface of Leeds' superiority and even the partisan Chelsea crowd applauds the quality of the northerners' win. Sir Richard Attenborough, a Blues director, made a special point of personally congratulating the team on such a fine victory. Nonetheless, Revie had suspicions that the Leeds team's performances were becoming less fluent, maybe even blasé. Peter Osgood had equalized Jordan's forty-fourth-minute strike before Jones sealed the tie in the sixty-eighth minute with a superb half-volley from a Jordan knock-down. Many had predicted the match would be Leeds' first League loss.

By now they had been knocked out of the League Cup by Ipswich and, more surprisingly, the UEFA Cup by Portuguese side Vitoria Setubal. Revie, though, was concerned only about the

Championship, and his selection of Roy Ellam, Jimmy Mann, Peter Hampton and Frank Gray for the away leg in some way proved that.

Match 21. December 22. Leeds 1, Norwich 0. Before the kick off, 34,747 see Billy Bremner presented with a silver salver for his five hundredth League game for Leeds. Terry Yorath notched up the all-important goal in the fifty-sixth minute. The team display was far from the best but the win keeps them on course, with fifteen wins and six draws so far.

Division 1 table (top), December 22 1973:

| 1 | Leeds | Played 21, | Points 36 |
|---|-------|-----------|-----------|
| 2 | Liverpool | Played 21, | Points 29 |
| 3 | Burnley | Played 20, | Points 26 |

Match 22. December 26. Newcastle 0, Leeds 1. Over 54,400 crammed into St James' Park to watch the Boxing Day battle, most of them hoping and many expecting Leeds' unbeaten run to be ended. It wasn't to be, as Madeley gets his second of the season with a belter from twenty-five yards late in the first half.

Match 23. December 29 1973. Birmingham 1, Leeds 1. A hard but not a nasty game with five bookings, City belied their lowly status in the table by giving Leeds a real fright at St Andrews in front of another 50,000-plus crowd. Leeds is the team everyone purportedly loves to hate, but they are so many times the main attraction too. Bob Latchford scored City's goal on twenty-one minutes, but a late pounce by Jordan salvages a point for the visitors.

Match 24. January 1 1974. Leeds 1, Tottenham 1. A holiday crowd of 46,000 watches Jones net for Leeds on twenty-one minutes to help ensure their fantastic sequence continues, and beats Sheffield United's Division One record of 1899–1900. Spurs' winger Chris McGrath had levelled the scores in the seventy-seventh minute. Martin Peters was a constant threat to the Leeds defence and looked the likeliest match winner on show.

An impressive 43,000-strong crowd watches the FA Cup third round replay at Elland Road between Leeds and Wolves, with a Jones goal sealing the Wednesday afternoon tie after the 1–1 draw at Molineux on the Saturday before.

Match 25. January 12. Leeds 2, Southampton 1. Back to the quest for the title, with goals from Jones and Jordan winning the points against a hard-working Saints side, who replied with a late Mick Channon strike.

Match 26. January 19. Everton 0, Leeds 0. Another plus-55,000 crowd at Goodison sees a tight game, which eighth-placed Everton probably should have won, though there were few goal-scoring chances.

Match 27. February 2. Leeds 1, Chelsea 1. A cold and wet afternoon was brightened by United's welcome inclusion at left wing of Terry Cooper, making his first full League start for nearly two years. He had played well in Saturday's 4–1 FA Cup fourth round win at Peterborough and his experience was a major boost given the absence of Gray. Chelsea stood too close for comfort to the relegation zone and Dave Sexton's men put up a valiant fight. They could justifiably feel disappointed to take only one point from the match. They had taken the lead just before half-time with a header from Bill Garner and fended off the majority of Leeds attacks with relative ease. It took a defender to grab the equalizer for Leeds, with left-back Trevor Cherry diving in to head home on sixty-eight minutes.

Match 28. February 5. Leeds 3, Arsenal 1. Arsenal, who were having a mediocre season anyway, were outplayed in an improved Leeds display, despite Alan Ball's goal separating the sides at half-time. A Simpson own-goal plus two goals from the excellent Joe Jordan brought Leeds a relatively comfortable win.

Match 29. February 9. Manchester United 0, Leeds 2. A huge Old Trafford crowd of over 60,000 saw the second-bottom hosts put up a gritty fight against the table-toppers, emerging with much credit but no points. Goals from Jones and Jordan – on in place of Reaney for a matter of minutes – after great probing work by Madeley and Hunter respectively sorted the men from the boys and left the Reds at the foot of Division One. Now Leeds could relax a little and look forward to their FA Cup fifth round tie at Bristol City next Saturday.

Across the city of Manchester, Leeds were lining up a move for City right winger–forward Mike Summerbee. However, for reasons unstated, the transfer fell through and Summerbee stayed with Manchester City.

## 14–5

I saw Bill Shankly at the ground for the Tuesday afternoon replay against Bristol City, he was sitting in the Directors' Box. Even though he was about my height, he stood out in a crowd. Always did, in any crowd, just like Don Revie. Anyway, I bet Shanks left the ground in good spirits after the Cup replay, seeing as somehow we managed to lose to Second Division Bristol City and went out, with our FA Cup tail well and truly flopping between our legs again. Not that Bristol were lucky, because they weren't: they beat us fair and square and by rights probably should have beaten us at Ashton Gate in the first place. Billy had popped up with the equalizer in that one, when we hadn't really deserved it.

From absolutely loving the FA Cup just a couple of years before, I now hated the sight of it and wanted nothing to do with the competition any more. I wished we'd stop entering the sodding thing, because I knew, I just knew, we'd never win it again, ever. Had we retained it in 73 I reckon we could have gone on winning it, but we didn't and that's the point – I believed that fate would stop us from now on. There was one saving grace to the Cup matches this term – at least Terry Cooper got a run out and was looking like his old self again, a silver lining (with white boots on) if ever there was one.

We were drawn against Hibernian in the UEFA Cup second round, the first leg here in late October. Everyone at the club knew Europe was a low priority this season, and low crowds proved it.

Don Revie had said all along that the League Championship was the target and nothing else, even the FA Cup, would get in the way. The League was *the* proof you were the best team, not some or other cup competition. It ended 0–0, which was about the fair result. To be totally honest, I don't remember one thing of note about the game itself, though three or four of the reserves got to play. The away leg was 0–0 again after ninety minutes so had to go to thirty minutes' extra time. And even then it stayed at 0–0, so it would be penalties to decide it. When the penalty kicks were being taken, Don Revie and Les Cocker were on the pitch talking to their players. This, apparently, was against the rules even though the referee didn't seem bothered. But the next day, two Hibs directors flew over to Zurich to officially protest to UEFA about Leeds' 'illegal coaching'. I could just imagine the vital, intensive, match-winning coaching given to the Leeds players. 'Right lads, gently put the ball on the penalty spot, take a few paces back and wait for the referee to blow his whistle. When he does – listen son, because this bit is very important – you run up to the ball and you kick it and you make sure it goes in the net past that bloke in the goalkeeper jersey who's trying to stop it.'

Anyway, we won the penalties, obviously: those directors wouldn't have gone to all that trouble to complain if they'd won. In the next round we were drawn against some Portuguese lot called Vitoria Setubal. It was blatantly obvious we weren't bothered about getting through, even though we beat them 1–0 at home in the first leg. With less than 15,000 watching. Over there, we lost 3–1, and the Leeds players played golf in the afternoon of the match, more concerned about who won that than the football.

The Bristol City defeat was a sign that we weren't infallible and that no team could be dismissed, they could all nick a win against us. The manager and the players took the FA Cup seriously and so did 47,128 supporters (what a crowd for a Tuesday afternoon) so Bristol deserved a ton of credit for beating us and I hoped they'd go on to win it. But they didn't.

The following Saturday we were at Stoke in the League and two goals up after only eighteen minutes, so it looked like a 'normal service has been resumed' situation. But Mike Pejic pulled a goal back and it didn't take long before they equalized, Hudson hitting it around the thirtieth minute. Once they'd drawn level, their tails were up. The second half was a right battle but Stoke were on top and it wasn't a total shock when they scored again. Denis Smith got the third goal about twenty minutes from time. That was it, the winning goal, 3–2 to Stoke. Our brilliant run was over, and people were reacting like we'd lost a cup final or even been relegated, it was weird. I was upset, but it was only one match, we were still top by a mile, so what was there to worry about?

Well, it didn't matter whether I was worried or not, it was how the manager and the players were feeling that was important. The problem was, they *were* worried, and all of a sudden it looked like they'd lost their confidence, judging by most of the games after the Stoke defeat. First there was Leicester at our place, on February 26. I mean, fair do's, Leicester were sixth in the table so obviously no pushovers, but still, we should have been beating teams like that easily enough. We were one up at half-time from a Peter Lorimer penalty, but we were still edgy, so whenever a move broke down or a shot didn't go in, the players looked less sure of themselves, while the supporters, 30,000 of them, got more and more impatient even though we were winning. Leicester had a good spirit about them, they reminded me of Leeds in the mid-60s when we were new to Division One. Keith Weller in midfield was having a very tidy game and it was him who equalized late on. I heard that Leeds had been checking out Weller and might put in a bid for him – he'd fit in well, in my opinion. He had good skill, looked quick and could hit the ball sweetly.

He was interviewed after the match and said that the Leeds supporters had nothing to worry about; the League title was virtually Leeds' already. Nice of him to say, but you don't talk like that while Liverpool are anywhere nearby, for chuff's sake. We were still top with forty-nine points from thirty-one games, whilst Liverpool were second with forty-two points from thirty games. Derby were third, but nowhere near points-wise. As long as we didn't lose any more games I thought we'd be alright. Draws aren't so bad providing we win the home games. The big nagging doubt though was the fact that we had to play Liverpool at their place yet – the number of times the League title is decided at

Anfield late in the season is bizarre. There was some good news for Leeds though, as Liverpool looked to be heading for a fixture backlog due to still being in the FA Cup, and they had done better than us in the League Cup too. Not that that took much doing, like.

## 14–5

On March 2, while Leeds were drawing 1–1 at home with a plucky Newcastle side, Liverpool were beating Burnley 1–0 at Anfield, and so kept alive their hopes of retaining the League title. Six points separated the top two, with Liverpool having a game in hand on Leeds. If either team were to slip up in the closing stages of the title race, then the money was mainly on Leeds.

Seven days later, as Liverpool were visiting Bristol City in the FA Cup quarter-finals, Leeds were hosting one of the season's underachievers, Manchester City. A Peter Lorimer thirtieth-minute penalty put Leeds ahead but they were unable to extend their lead. Despite the penalty award being a controversial one, Leeds were good value for the win, and their inability to score a second wasn't for want of effort. A collective sigh of relief was breathed around Elland Road when the final whistle was blown.

The match to possibly decide the 1973–74 First Division title outcome was between the two high-quality heavyweights of the English game, on March 16 at Anfield: Liverpool versus Leeds. Lose or even draw and Liverpool could probably wave farewell to the Championship trophy. With a fervent crowd of 56,003 there, the home side had most of the possession in the match and put Leeds under almost relentless pressure, though Leeds did have their bright moments. It needed just one goal, in the eighty-second minute, to divide the sides. Steve Heighway's winner, exploiting confusion in the Whites' penalty area, meant that Leeds' lead in the table stood at six points while Liverpool still held two games in hand.

League Division One table, March 16 1974:

| 1 | Leeds Utd | Played 34, | Points 52 |
| 2 | Liverpool | Played 32, | Points 46 |

On March 23 Leeds were at home to Burnley while Liverpool were visiting Wolverhampton Wanderers. Burnley took advantage of a sluggish all-round Leeds display and inept defending, and won 4–1. Worse for Leeds was Liverpool's 1–0 victory at Wolves, thanks to a first-half Brian Hall goal.

Division 1 table (top), March 23 1974:

| 1 | Leeds | Played 35, | Points 52 |
| 2 | Liverpool | Played 33, | Points 48 |

Were they to win their games in hand, Liverpool could now equal Leeds on points, though the Whites had a better goal average, and providing there were no more heavy defeats, the outlook was not too bleak just yet.

For the match at West Ham on March 30, Revie made a surprise alteration to the Leeds line-up by dropping Peter Lorimer and replacing him with less-than-fully fit John Giles. The change looked to be working for the better as Leeds took the lead on thirty-two minutes through Allan Clarke. A few minutes later and Clarke had an apparently fair goal ruled out for offside – and he earned himself a booking for arguing. In the second half, West Ham bucked up their ideas and goals from Clyde Best, 'Pop' Robson and Trevor Brooking meant another depressing defeat for the Peacocks. Liverpool could now overhaul them.

Revie had been optimistic after the West Ham defeat, and his side next put in a decent performance to see off third-placed Derby 2–0. There was no let up in the race for the crown though, with Liverpool beating QPR 2–1 at Anfield on the same afternoon. Leeds, though, could rest for six days now as their next match was away at Coventry on Saturday April 13. Liverpool, meanwhile, were away to Ipswich Town on that date, plus they were away to Sheffield United on the Monday April 8 and to Manchester City on Good Friday, April 12, hours before the Ipswich game. The Blades beat them 1–0. And Good Friday brought more good news Leeds' way, as Liverpool could only draw with Manchester City, 1–1 at Maine Road. And the day after that, Ipswich took a point against the Reds with the same scoreline, while Leeds drew at Coventry, 0–0. Leeds could and possibly should have won it but in the end were thankful to come away with a share of the points, as Coventry had begun to dominate the later stages.

The Division 1 table (top), April 13 1974:

1  Leeds       Played 38,    Points 55
2  Liverpool   Played 37,    Points 52

The advantage was back with Leeds but the jitters seemed to return in the Coventry match, and their 0–0 draw with Sheffield United on the Bank Holiday Monday was an edgy performance. The very next day the teams met again, at Bramall Lane, and the first forty-five minutes passed uneventfully, while at Anfield Liverpool were in front against Manchester City by an incredible 4–0 scoreline. The title race was again hanging in the balance, with disaster looming for Leeds as the odds swung markedly back Liverpool's way. Yet a Leeds strongpoint, possibly their strongest, was resilience in the face of adversity. 'Keep Fighting' was their dictum, and a Don Revie team might be often down but rarely were they out until the end. The Liverpool–Manchester City score stayed at 4–0, while two Peter Lorimer goals, the second a penalty, reignited the Whites' spirits.

Their next game was at home to the division's top scorers, third-placed Ipswich, while Liverpool had a derby match with Everton, traditionally the toughest of ties.

The Leeds–Ipswich game was a tense but exciting affair, watched by 44,015 tense and excitable spectators. Goals from Lorimer and Bremner put Leeds two up and helped the Leeds crowd relax, but Brian Talbot soon pulled a goal back to make it 2–1 at half-time. In the second half matters soon worsened for Leeds as Bryan Hamilton hit the equalizer in the fifty-fourth minute – they desperately needed a spark to win the two points, regardless of what was happening at Anfield. The spark arrived in the form of Allan Clarke, detecting a chance and putting it away coolly and expertly to win the match 3–2. Even better news for the Leeds fans was the Merseyside derby producing no goals: another point dropped by Liverpool.

Division 1 table (top), April 20 1974:

1  Leeds        Played 41,    Points 60
2  Liverpool    Played 39,    Points 55

Andrews: 'Now Bill, you're the manager of Liverpool and right now your teams are battling it out for the First Division title. You and Don are great mates.'

'Yes, we're the greatest of enemies.'

On Tuesday April 24 1974, millions tuned into ITV's pre-recorded *This Is Your Life* show, with Leeds boss Don Revie the unsuspecting recipient of all the, frankly unwanted, attention. Many of those viewers might well have switched on the radio soon afterwards to listen for news of a Division One football match taking place at Liverpool's Anfield stadium.

On May 3 1971, Arsenal's Ray Kennedy had scored the solitary goal in a match against Tottenham, three minutes from time, to seal that year's League title for Arsenal and dump Leeds into second place. On April 24 1974, Arsenal's Ray Kennedy – who would sign for Liverpool in the summer – again had a vital say in determining the Championship trophy's destination, by scoring the only goal of the Liverpool–Arsenal game. The 1–0 defeat left Liverpool stranded in second place and wrapped up this year's title for Leeds. For all the stress and anxiety they had endured in recent weeks, from times of ecstasy to virtual agony, Leeds' winning of the League came without them actually kicking a football.

Commenting on a 'great week for Don Revie', Les Cocker said, 'The Championship, *This Is Your Life* and he even beat Val Doonican at golf!'

Liverpool, who had never given up the chase despite Leeds' fantastic early unbeaten run through to late February, deserved great credit for their efforts. Manager Bill Shankly was bitterly disappointed at the weak finale to the title race but he showed graciousness in defeat. 'My congratulations. I know Leeds care about everyone, from the cleaning ladies right through, and that's how it should be.'

And with a May 4 FA Cup final victory over Newcastle, Liverpool's disappointment was soon erased.

Leeds' final League game of the season was at QPR on Saturday April 27. The Loftus Road club rolled out a red carpet to congratulate their visitors on the title win, and Rangers' players presented Leeds' with a bottle of champagne each. A second-half Allan Clarke strike won Leeds the points.

## 14–6

Leeds United, champions, again! But the good feelings didn't last long. A week after we'd bagged the title and Don Revie had been on *This Is Your Life*, Sir Alf Ramsey got booted out of the England job. The writing had been on the wall for ages for him but the FA had made him sweat like the thoughtless gits they were. And once his leaving was confirmed, then there was more writing on the wall, but for us.

There was really only one man suitable and good enough to replace Ramsey, and that was Don Revie. I reckoned it was just a matter of whether he actually wanted the job or not. I prayed he didn't but suspected he did, even though he'd said he would rather stay to have a crack at next season's European Cup. The fears came true: Don Revie admitted he wanted to be the new England manager. I felt hurt, really hurt, and that's no exaggeration, and I was stewing inside about it all. So, not long before he was set to leave, I let him know – he was the man who mattered to me the most.

One specific June morning, I had the ultra-important job of sweeping the Home and Visiting Team dressing rooms, plus the tunnel area. I'd just about finished the corridor when Don Revie came sauntering by, towards the reception area door. I felt a bit awkward and not sure what to say or do.

So I just said 'Hello' to him at first. And he said the same back, but with hardly a glance my way. I wanted to say 'Please don't leave Leeds' to him but couldn't muster myself to do it, it would have humiliated me. I did, though, manage to say 'No one wants you to leave, Mister Revie …' and it took him aback a bit I think. And then, because he'd stopped, I said, 'You *are* the club, you are The Don of Leeds United.'

He turned around and said, 'I'm a bit busy at the moment but I won't forget you said that. Thanks John.' And off he walked, up the corridor and through the door to the reception area.

But then the door opened again and he popped his head round, with a shy smile on his face. 'I've a lot on my mind … I meant to say Jim. Sorry.'

I told him it was alright, and he disappeared again. I suddenly had a good feeling inside that everything was going to turn out alright, too. The crap you believe when you're in your twenties.

July 4 1974 arrived. I'll never forget it. It was announced that Don Revie was leaving Leeds to take over as England manager. The television cameras were there at Elland Road as Ted Croker from the FA arrived at the ground to sort it out with the Leeds board. I'm there on film, as Croker walks towards the glass doors of the club reception. Many a time I've wondered what would have happened if I'd told him to piss off and leave The Don and Leeds United alone, whether it would have done any good. I wish I'd had the nerve to find out.

Various comments and opinions were expressed as to why Don Revie left, most of them wrong, I reckon. Don Revie was accused of running out on the club like a coward, scared of his responsibilities, especially with regards to the players' and coaches' contracts. Some said that the team and manager were past it, that he was getting out before being 'found out', even though we were League Champions and up for the European Cup next season. And some said he went just for the money, even though England didn't pay that well.

It was all a lot simpler, I was sure of it. It was the England job. The England job! The *top* job. No self-respecting Englishman could turn the chance down. No one was better suited for it than Don Revie, even though Jimmy Bloomfield of Leicester, QPR's

Gordon Jago and Coventry's Gordon Milne were supposedly short-listed for it. I'm sure loudmouths Malcolm Allison and Brian Clough would have loved a crack at it, too. But Don Revie was better than them all.

At one stage I did think he could be leaving the club in the lurch, due to the seven or eight player contracts needing sorting out, but it turns out he tried to help Leeds by recommending the man he thought best to succeed him – Johnny Giles. He was very clever, highly respected and trusted at the club – he'd do things the right way, like Don Revie had always tried to do. I suppose it always looked like Don's 'favourite son' Billy Bremner was being groomed to be the manager, but Billy had more games left in him than Giles, he was about a year younger and he'd always been luckier with injuries. It was obvious he wanted the job, but a fantastic captain wouldn't necessarily make a fantastic manager. But I read a Percy Woodward quote in the paper: 'It's not for the manager who is leaving to invite his successor.' Alarm bells in my head started ringing.

The week after Don left, Bill Shankly left Liverpool and Bill Nicholson would soon pack it all in at Tottenham. Shankly didn't retire, he was just wanting a break, as his wife was worried about his health. Being a top football boss was very stressful work.

Shortly after, Leeds 'welcomed' the new manager they'd appointed to succeed Don Revie OBE. The oddest, maddest, most stupid, idiotic appointment made in football, ever, by directors who seemed to have taken leave of their bloody senses. I really, *really* wish they hadn't bothered.

Early in September, Harry Reynolds died, outside the Leeds boardroom, soon before a Leeds reserves match. God bless him. Had he had a choice, I bet he won't have minded dying there, at Elland Road. None of this would be what it is without Harry Reynolds. The *city* wouldn't be what it is without him, I mean it. Harry and Don in 1961, thirteen years ago. Thirteen: unlucky for some, but definitely not for us, not for Leeds.

# Bibliography

Bagchi, Rob and Rogerson, Paul, *The Unforgiven: The Story of Don Revie's Leeds United* (Aurum, 2009)

Bale, Bernard, *Bremner! The Legend of Billy Bremner* (Andre Deutsch, 1999)

Ball, Peter and Shaw, Phil, *The Book of Football Quotations* (Hutchinson, 1996)

Best, George, *Hard Tackles and Dirty Baths: The Inside Story of Football's Golden Era* (Ebury, 2005)

Charles, John, *King John* (Headline, 2003)

Charlton, Jack and Byrne, Peter, *Jack Charlton: The Autobiography* (Corgi, 1997)

Clough, Brian, *Brian Clough: The Autobiography* (Corgi, 1995)

——, *Cloughie: Walking on Water* (Headline, 2005)

Friedman, Graeme, *Madiba's Boys: The Stories of Lucas Radebe and Mark Fish* (Comerfield & Miller, 2001)

Giles, Johnny, *Forward with Leeds* (S Paul, 1970)

Gray, Eddie, *Marching On Together: My Life at Leeds United* (Coronet, 2002)

Holt, Oliver, *If You're Second You are Nothing: Ferguson and Shankly* (Macmillan, 2006)

Hunter, Norman, *Biting Talk: My Autobiography* (Hodder, 2005)

Jarred, Martin and Macdonald, Malcolm, *Leeds United: A Complete Record* (Breedon, 1996)

Jordan, Joe, *Behind the Dream* (Hodder & Stoughton, 2005)

Keith, John, *The Essential Shankly* (Robson, 2001)

*Leeds United Book of Football* (Souvenir Press, 1969)

*Leeds United Book of Football: No. 2* (Souvenir Press, 1970)

Lorimer, Peter and Rostron, Phil, *Peter Lorimer: Leeds and Scotland Hero* (Mainstream, 2002)

Lovejoy, Joe, *Bestie: A Portrait of a Legend* (Pan, 1999)

Morgan, John and Joy, David, *A Celebration of Leeds* (Great Northern, 2006)

Mourant, Andrew, *Don Revie: Portrait of a Footballing Enigma* (Mainstream, 1990)

*News of the World Football Annual* (News of the World, 1961–74)

Peace, David, *The Damned United* (Faber and Faber, 2007)

Revie, Don, *Soccer's Happy Wanderer* (Museum Press, 1955)

Saffer, David, *Bobby Collins* (NPI, 2004)

——, *Boys of '72: Leeds United's FA Cup Glory* (The History Press, 2006)

——, *Leeds Legends* (NPI, 2002)

——, *Leeds United's 'Rolls Royce': The Paul Madeley Story* (Tempus, 2003)

——, *The Life and Times of Mick Jones* (History Press, 2002)

——, *Match of My Life – Leeds: Fourteen Stars Relive their Greatest Victories* (Know the Score, 2006)

——, *Sniffer: The Life and Times of Allan Clarke* (NPI, 2001)

Sprake, Stuart and Johnson, Tim, *Careless Hands: The Forgotten Truth of Gary Sprake* (Tempus, 2007)

Stott, Richard, *Dogs and Lampposts* (John Blake, 2007)

Thornton, David, *Great Leeds Stories* (Fort, 2005)

——, *Leeds: The Story of a City* (Fort, 2003)

Thornton, Eric, *Leeds United and Don Revie* (Robert Hale, 1970)

Yorath, Terry and Lloyd, Grahame, *Hard Man, Hard Knocks* (Celluloid, 2004)

*Yorkshire Evening Post* newspapers

*Leeds Leeds Leeds* magazine

Leeds United match programmes, 1973–74 season

## Websites

www.bob7071.co.uk

www.leedsfans.org.uk

www.leedsutd-mad.co.uk

www.leedsunitedmemorabilia.co.uk

www.leedsunited.com

www.lufctalk.com

www.mightyleeds.co.uk

www.onemickjones.com

www.ozwhitelufc.net.au

www.soccerbase.com

www.waccoe.com

http://homepage.ntlworld.com/carousel/ITVfootball68-83.html

# Acknowledgements

There are certain people no longer alive who, naturally, I haven't been able to personally thank. Some are men who I honestly believe had more influence in the growth of Leeds than is probably recognized. They most certainly inspired this story.

Included in that are John Charles and Billy Bremner, two of the best football players of *any* generation, and Harry Reynolds, the ex-chairman and 'founder' of the reincarnated Leeds United. There is, too, a man about whom most folk probably haven't heard, but who is prominent within the story: Ces Burroughs. I didn't know him very well at all, I was only a kid, but he was a good friend to my dad while they were on the Elland Road ground staff, and he helped with the development of some of the great Leeds players during the 1960s, too. The same goes for John Reynolds, a fantastic bloke who thankfully is still alive and well! John has helped me many times over.

And as I started on this particular trek, David Peace's *The Damned United* came out. Now it wouldn't be completely fair to say that that story had much to do with *Dirty Leeds*, but I am proud to admit that David was always very quick to offer guidance and advice whenever I asked for it. To begin with, I was actually considering writing a story involving not only Don Revie as Leeds manager but also his four successors. Fortunately, David helped me concentrate and to focus on Don Revie alone. If the 'five managers' idea had happened, I daren't think what Jill Morris, the editor's, reaction would have been, bearing in mind that this book had 'lost' around 400 pages by the final edit! Thanks, Jill, for all your very hard work, and Stu Wheatman, of course, for having the courage too to believe in this book.

Above all, it is Don Revie OBE I have to thank. It doesn't really matter whether I'm a born and bred Leeds fan or not, as I've tried and I hope succeeded in being objective in writing *Dirty Leeds*: the important aspects for me were always that not only did we have a fantastic football team and coaching staff receiving only mere fractions of the praise and respect they deserved, but a great man and manager in Don Revie, who received so much unkind, unjust and unproven criticism along the way. This book is for him and for those men and women who really knew him. I hope I've done it all justice.

There are a number of organizations and individuals I would like to thank: Beeston Historical Society, Beeston Library (Jane Smith and co), the British Film Institute, BBC Radio Leeds, Paul Eubanks, Facebook, Leeds Central Library, Leeds United AFC, *Match of the Day*, the National Museum of Football, Joseph Ross (for the cover photo), (South Leeds) Health for All, The Standards, Waterstone's Leeds and the Yorkshire Film Archive.

Special acknowledgements and thanks also go to: Chris and Adele Archer, Dorothy and Keith Archer, Kester Aspden, Graham Barnes, Sue Batchelor, Craig Bradley, Vicky and Ian Bradshaw, Jack Bray, Pete Cluderay, Dave Cocker, Mick Cotter, Teresa Courtney and family, and the Hurleys, Gary Edwards, James Ellis, Jack and Norma Emery, Sam and Sophie Emery, Sam Gibbard, Graham Endeacott, Gayle Graham, Carole Gutherson and Borders Birstall, Julian and Sarah Hardcastle and family, Tony Hill, Peter Holme/Gordon Small, Phil Hodgson, Harry Hogg, Ben Hunt, Alwyn Hutchinson, Rachel Irwin, Neil Jeffries, Steve 'Johna' Johnson, Gary Kaye, Nick King, Peter Lorimer, Johnny Lorrimer, Fraser Marr, Lance McCrickard, Hugh Neill, Kevin, Lynda and Amy O'Rourke, Tom Palmer, Brian Passmore and family, David Peace, Dean Plews, Adam Pope, Brian Revis, John Reynolds, Steve Riley, Deborah and Peter Robinson, Jason Thornton, and Margaret and Peter Veitch.

Robert Endeacott, August 2009

## About the Author

Robert Endeacott was born and bred in Leeds and still lives in the south of the city. Slowly realizing that the rat race was too quick and smelly for his liking, he got out of 'normal' work to try his hand at writing books. *Dirty Leeds* is his third novel, the others being *No More Heroes* and *One Northern Soul*.

READ MORE FROM TONTO BOOKS:

**The Road to Hell**
Sheila Quigley
*Hardback, £18.99, 9781907183034, available November 2009*

DI Lorraine Hunt is back in the next instalment of Sheila Quigley's gritty crime dramas set in Houghton-le-Spring.

When a woman's body is found mutilated in a field outside of Houghton-le-Spring, it's more than just another case for DI Hunt. Not only does the body show evidence of violation and human bites, it transpires that Hunt knows the victim. But she also knows that this is an exact replica of a crime that occurred more than fifteen years ago, on an evening that changed her and her friends' lives forever.

With flashbacks to Lorraine's past, *The Road to Hell* is a charged, fast-paced page turner with appeal to Quigley fans old and new.

For information and details on all Tonto Books past, present and future, please visit the website www.tontobooks.co.uk

## READ MORE FROM TONTO BOOKS:

**Slimmer Charlie**
Charlie Walduck
*Paperback, £8.99, 9780955632686, available October 2009*

Growing up in Barrow-in-Furness, painfully shy as a child and oversensitive for as long as he can remember, Charlie Walduck was drawn to food as an escape. He went from being an obese child to weighing nearly fifty stones by the time he was in his mid-thirties. Working as a bingo caller in Manchester, the catalyst for change came when one day he was up on stage and the chair he was sitting on collapsed. The shame of that moment sent him to rock bottom.

It was at this time that his best friend took Charlie's life in her own hands by penning a letter to Fern Britton on *This Morning*, asking for help. With the nation watching and with the immeasurable support of the programme's GP, Dr Chris Steele, Charlie began his weight loss quest, eventually losing thirty stones in less than two years.

*Slimmer Charlie* follows Charlie's weight loss journey in his own words, recalling with insight his struggles with food and the associated problems of low self-esteem, lack of confidence and shyness. With vivid recollections of growing up in a working-class family in the north of England, this is as much a memoir as a self-help guide.

For information and details on all Tonto Books past, present and future, please visit the website www.tontobooks.co.uk

READ MORE FROM TONTO BOOKS:

**Shakespeare and Love**
Raymond Scott with Mike Kelly
*Paperback, £7.99, 9780955632693, available April 2010*

The Shakespeare First Folio is one of the most revered books in the English language and worth millions. One is owned by billionaire John Paul Getty; another was in the hands of Raymond Scott, who lived with his mum in their modest Tyneside home until his arrest.

When he tried to sell the folio to fund the good life with his young Cuban dancer fiancée, Raymond sparked an international investigation involving the FBI, Interpol and the British police. Did he steal it from Durham University ten years ago, or was he just an innocent middleman for the real owner, a former bodyguard to Fidel Castro?

*Shakespeare and Love* lifts the lid on this real-life crime mystery, told by the man at the centre of the extraordinary tale – Raymond Scott himself. As he says: 'There are two Raymond Scotts – one who lives quietly at home with his mother, the other who people think is some Raffles-type international thief.'

For information and details on all Tonto Books past, present and future, please visit the website www.tontobooks.co.uk

READ MORE FROM TONTO BOOKS:

**Sin Cities: Adventures of a Sex Reporter**
Ashley Hames
*Paperback, £7.99, 9780955632600, available now*

With a weakness for women, good times and binge drinking it seemed inevitable that Ashley Hames would turn cult hero with *Sin Cities*, blazing a toxic trail through a minefield of debauchery and fantasy across the globe.

As clown prince of L!VE TV, he happily changed his name by deed poll to News Bunny and produced such lowbrow classics as *Topless Darts*. A few months down the line his career had him hoisted up on meat hooks, tortured, clamped and generally trampled on in the name of entertainment. It was only when the cameras stopped rolling that it got messy.

In this book, Ashley investigates the sexual habits of some of the most extraordinary people on the planet – from the bizarre to the unimaginable – and somehow helps it all make perfect sense.

For information and details on all Tonto Books past, present and future, please visit the website www.tontobooks.co.uk

**The Non-Beardy Beer Book: An Alternative Guide to the UK's Favourite Beers, Lagers and Ciders**
*Paperback, £7.99, 9780955632648, available now*

An alternative to beardy and boring real ale guides, *The Non-Beardy Beer Book* is a humorous and no-nonsense guide to booze Britain's favourite drinks, featuring irreverent reviews of a hundred of the UK's bestselling brands of beer, lager and cider, plus bluffer's guides to the most popular wines, alcopops, spirits and cocktails, lovingly put together by a panel of completely independent (possibly inebriated) reviewers.

An essential companion for any trip to the pub, club, supermarket or off-licence, this king of beer guides refreshes the parts other books cannot reach.

READ MORE FROM TONTO BOOKS:

**9987**
A novel by Nik Jones
*Paperback, £7.99, 9780955632662, available now*

To him, the shop is everything; always neat and tidy, safe and reliable. The rental DVDs carefully categorized, alphabetized and memorized. But when one valued member starts to leave bloodstains on the fresh new carpet, handing back porn still sticky with gore and paying in blood-smeared banknotes, his careful existence is compromised and uncomfortable.

Then the girl arrives, with her pale skin, green eyes and fresh scarlet slashed beneath her thin cotton blouse. He wants to rescue and protect her. He wants to be with her. Forever.

Tragic and dark, *9987* is a story about a wholly jagged and at times disturbing, uncaring world where only three things are constant: fantasy, loneliness and love. A tale of a crime that only one person seems to care about.

READ MORE FROM TONTO BOOKS:

**Being Normal**
A collection by Stephen Shieber
*Paperback, £7.99, 9780955632631, available now*

A confident, poignant collection filtered with debauchery, melancholy and black humour, Being Normal is an examination of loneliness, rejection and of living in and against contemporary society.

Stephen Shieber brings together the glory of everyday nothingness and elevates it to great drama; where loveless marriage, teen angst, childhood misadventure, lonely Christmases and family dysfunction are the norm.

Each character in this stunning debut provides a very different slant on the notion of mundane – a book for anyone who has ever found themselves on the outside, dancing to the beat of their own drum.

*'There is an incredible freshness and optimism about Shieber's stories that is very rare in writing today. He's like a wonderful new biscuit you've never tried before. Open it up, have a bite, then take the packet home and devour it.'*

Laura Hird

For information and details on all Tonto Books past, present and future, please visit the website www.tontobooks.co.uk

READMORE FROM TONTO BOOKS:

**Stephen Miller: Paralympian – My Autobiography**
*Paperback, £9.99, 9780955632617, available now*

Stephen Miller is one of Britain's most successful athletes.
Record-breaking Stephen, who has cerebral palsy, is also a writer
and poet. Stephen's inspirational autobiography tells of his
struggles and triumphs, and is told with refreshing honesty and
infectious humour.

*'I know how hard it is to compete at the highest level. It takes
dedication, courage and self-belief, and Stephen has those
qualities in abundance. His story is truly unique and inspiring'*

Kevin Keegan, Foreword

For information and details on all Tonto Books past, present and
future, please visit the website www.tontobooks.co.uk